WARWICK SCHOOL

Form Prize for Upper 5L

Awarded to **James Coathup**

July 2010

Headmaster

SKILLS · FOR · FLIGHT

Principles of Flight

Airframe Limitations – **Theory of Flight** – **Aeroplane Performance**

5

OXFORD
AVIATION TRAINING

This book has been produced by Oxford Aviation Training.

Production Team

Subject Specialists - Principles of Flight:
Les Fellows, Jon Hedges, Laurie Knight

Subject Specialist - Aeroplane Performance:
Steve Francis

Contributors:
Rhodri Davies, Steve Partridge, Glyn Rees, Lesley Smith, Roger Smith

Created and Compiled by:
James Kenny

Assisted by:
Andrea Goddard, Hailey Masterson, Monica Messaggi de Souza, Samuel Tierney

Design Team:
Mohammed Afzal-Khan, Andrea Goddard, Chris Hill, Jon Kalicki, James Kenny,
Hailey Masterson, Monica Messaggi de Souza, Samuel Tierney

Editor:
Les Fellows

Cover Design by: Chris Hill
Cover Photo by: Mike Jorgensen

First Published by: Oxford Aviation Training, Oxford, England, 2007
Printed in Singapore by: KHL Printing Co. Pte Ltd

Contact Details:
OATmedia
Oxford Aviation Training
Oxford Airport
Kidlington
Oxford
OX5 1QX
England
Tel: +44 (0)1865 844290
Email: **info@oatmedia.com**

Innovative learning solutions for

www.oatmedia.com   ISBN 978-0-9555177-4-7   www.oxfordaviation.net

<u>GENERAL</u>

<u>PRINCIPLES OF FLIGHT</u>

FOREWORD TO THE FIRST EDITION.

INTRODUCTION.

Whether you are planning to fly microlights, space shuttles, gliders, combat aircraft, airliners or light aircraft, it is essential that you have a firm grasp of the theoretical knowledge which underpins practical piloting skills. This Oxford Aviation Training "Skills for Flight" series of text books covers the fundamental theory with which all pilots must come to grips from the very beginning of their pilot training, and which must remain with them throughout their flying career, if they are to be masters of the art and science of flight.

JOINT AVIATION AUTHORITIES PILOTS' LICENCES.

Joint Aviation Authorities (JAA) pilot licences were first introduced in Europe in 1999. By 2006, almost every JAA member state, including all the major countries of Europe, had adopted this new, pan-European licensing system at Air Transport Pilot's Licence, Commercial Pilot's Licence and Private Pilot's Licence levels, and many other countries, world-wide, had expressed interest in aligning their training with the JAA pilot training syllabi.

These syllabi, and the regulations governing the award and the renewal of licences, are defined by the JAA's licensing agency, 'Joint Aviation Requirements - Flight Crew Licensing', (JAR-FCL). JAR-FCL training syllabi are published in a document known as 'JAR-FCL 1.'

The United Kingdom Civil Aviation Authority (UK CAA) is one of the founder authorities within the JAA. The UK CAA has been administering examinations and skills tests for the issue of JAA licences since the year 2000, on behalf of JAR-FCL.

The Private Pilot's Licence (PPL), then, issued by the UK CAA, is a JAA licence which is accepted as proof of a pilot's qualifications throughout all JAA member states.

Currently, the JAA member states are: *United Kingdom, Denmark, Iceland, Switzerland, France, Sweden, Netherlands, Belgium, Romania, Spain, Finland, Ireland, Malta, Norway, Czech Republic, Slovenia, Germany, Portugal, Greece, Italy, Turkey, Croatia, Poland, Austria, Estonia, Lithuania, Cyprus, Hungary, Luxembourg, Monaco, Slovakia.*

As a licence which is also fully compliant with the licensing recommendations of the International Civil Aviation Organisation (ICAO), the JAA PPL is also valid in most other parts of the world.

The JAA PPL in the UK has replaced the full UK PPL, formerly issued solely under the authority of the UK CAA.

Issue of the JAA PPL is dependent on the student pilot having completed the requisite training and passed the appropriate theoretical knowledge and practical flying skills tests detailed in 'JAR-FCL 1'. In the UK, the CAA is responsible for ensuring that these requirements are met before any licence is issued.

EUROPEAN AVIATION SAFETY AGENCY.

With the establishment of the European Aviation Safety Agency (EASA), it is envisaged that JAA flight crew licensing and examining competency will be absorbed into the EASA organisation. It is possible that, when this change has taken place, the PPL may even change its title again, with the words "EASA" replacing "JAA". However, we do not yet know this for certain. In the UK, such a step would require the British Government to review and, where necessary, revise the Civil Aviation Act. But, whatever the future of the title of the PPL, the JAA pilot's licence syllabi are unlikely to change fundamentally, in the short term. So, for the moment, the JAA Licence remains, and any change in nomenclature is likely to be just that: a change in name only.

OXFORD AVIATION TRAINING AND OATMEDIA.

Oxford Aviation Training (OAT) is one of the world's leading professional pilot schools. It has been in operation for over forty years and has trained more than 15 000 professional pilots for over 80 airlines, world-wide.

OAT was the first pilot school in the United Kingdom to be granted approval to train for the JAA ATPL. OAT led and coordinated the joint-European effort to produce the JAR-FCL ATPL Learning Objectives which are now published by the JAA, itself, as a guide to the theoretical knowledge requirements of ATPL training.

OAT's experience in European licensing, at all levels, and in the use of advanced training technologies, led OAT's training material production unit, OATmedia, to conceive, create and produce multimedia, computer-based training for ATPL students preparing for JAA theoretical knowledge examinations by distance learning. Subsequently, OATmedia extended its range of computer-based training CD-ROMs to cover PPL and post-PPL studies.

This present series of text books is designed to complement OATmedia's successful PPL CD-ROMs in helping student pilots prepare for the theoretical knowledge examinations of the JAA PPL and beyond, as well as to provide students with the aviation knowledge they require to become safe and competent pilots.

The OAT expertise embodied in this series of books means that students working towards the JAA PPL have access to top-quality, up-to-date, study material at an affordable cost. Those students who aspire to becoming professional pilots will find that this series of PPL books takes them some way beyond PPL towards the knowledge required for professional pilot licences.

THE JAA PRIVATE PILOT'S LICENCE (AEROPLANES).

The following information on the Joint Aviation Authorities Private Pilot's Licence (Aeroplanes); (JAA PPL(A)) is for your guidance only. Full details of flying training, theoretical knowledge training and the corresponding tests and examinations are contained in the JAA document: **JAR–FCL 1, SUBPART C – PRIVATE PILOT LICENCE (Aeroplanes) – PPL(A).**

The privileges of the JAA PPL (A) allow you to fly as pilot-in-command, or co-pilot, of any aircraft for which an appropriate rating is held, but not for remuneration, or on revenue-earning flights.

For United Kingdom based students, full details of JAA PPL (A) training and examinations can be found in the CAA publication, **Licensing Administration Standards Operating Requirements Safety (LASORS),** copies of which can be accessed through the CAA's Flight Crew Licensing website.

Flying Training.
The JAA PPL (A) can be gained by completing a course of a minimum of 45 hours flying training with a training organisation registered with the appropriate National Aviation Authority (the Civil Aviation Authority, in the case of the United Kingdom).

Flying instruction must normally include:

- **25 hours** dual Instruction on aeroplanes.

- **10 hours** supervised solo flight time on aeroplanes, which must include **5 hours** solo cross-country flight time, including one cross-country flight of at least 150 nautical miles (270km), during which full-stop landings at two different aerodromes, different from the aerodrome of departure, are to be made.

The required flying-instructional time may be reduced by a maximum of 10 hours for those students with appropriate flying experience on other types of aircraft.

The flying test (Skills Test), comprising navigation and general skills tests, is to be taken within 6 months of completing flying instruction. All sections of the Skills Test must be taken within a period of 6 months. A successfully completed Skills Test has a period of validity of 12 months for the purposes of licence issue.

Theoretical Knowledge Examinations.
The procedures for the conduct of the JAA PPL (A) theoretical knowledge examinations will be determined by the National Aviation Authority of the state concerned, (the Civil Aviation Authority, in the case of the United Kingdom).

The JAA theoretical knowledge examination must comprise the following 9 subjects: *Air Law, Aircraft General Knowledge, Flight Performance and Planning, Human Performance and Limitations, Meteorology, Navigation, Operational Procedures, Principles of Flight, Communication.*

A single examination paper may cover several subjects.

The combination of subjects and the examination paper titles, as administered by the UK CAA, are, at present:

1. Air Law and Operational Procedures.
2. Human Performance and Limitations.
3. Navigation & Radio Aids.
4. Meteorology.
5. Aircraft (General) & Principles of Flight.
6. Flight Performance and Planning.
7. JAR-FCL Communications (PPL) (i.e. Radiotelephony Communications).

The majority of the questions are multiple choice. In the United Kingdom, examinations are normally conducted by the Flying Training Organisation or Registered Facility at which a student pilot carries out his training.

The pass mark in all subjects is 75%.

For the purpose of the issue of a JAA PPL(A), a pass in the theoretical knowledge examinations will be accepted during the 24 month period immediately following the date of successfully completing all of the theoretical knowledge examinations.

Medical Requirements.
An applicant for a JAR-FCL PPL(A) must hold a valid JAR-FCL Class 1 or Class 2 Medical Certificate.

THE UNITED KINGDOM NATIONAL PRIVATE PILOT'S LICENCE (AEROPLANES).

One of the aims of the United Kingdom National Private Pilot's Licence (UK NPPL) is to make it easier for the recreational flyer to obtain a PPL than it would be if the requirements of the standard JAA-PPL had to be met. The regulations governing medical fitness are also different between the UK NPPL and the JAA PPL.

Full details of the regulations governing the training for, issue of, and privileges of the UK NPPL may be found by consulting LASORS and the Air Navigation Order. Most UK flying club websites also give details of this licence.

Basically, the holder of a UK NPPL is restricted to flight in a simple, UK-registered, single piston-engine aeroplane (including motor gliders and microlights) whose Maximum Authorized Take-off Weight does not exceed 2000 kg. Flight is normally permitted in UK airspace only, by day, and in accordance with the Visual Flight Rules.

Flying Training.
Currently, 32 hours of flying training is required for the issue of a UK NPPL (A), of which 22 hours are to be dual instruction, and 10 hours to be supervised solo flying time.

There are separate general and navigation skills tests.

Theoretical Knowledge Examinations.
The UK NPPL theoretical knowledge syllabus and ground examinations are the same as for the JAA PPL (A). This series of books, therefore, is also suitable for student pilots preparing for the UK NPPL.

THE UNITED KINGDOM FLIGHT RADIOTELEPHONY OPERATOR'S LICENCE.

Although there is a written paper on Radiotelephony Communications in the JAA PPL theoretical knowledge examinations, pilots in the United Kingdom, and in most other countries, who wish to operate airborne radio equipment will need to take a separate practical test for the award of a Flight Radiotelephony Operators Licence (FRTOL). For United Kingdom based students, full details of the FRTOL are contained in LASORS.

NOTES ON CONTENT AND TEXT.

Technical Content.
The technical content of this OAT series of pilot training text books aims to reach the standard required by the theoretical knowledge syllabus of the JAA Private Pilot's Licence (Aeroplanes), (JAA PPL(A)). This is the minimum standard that has been aimed at. The subject content of several of the volumes in the series exceeds PPL standard. However, all questions and their answers, as well as the margin notes, are aimed specifically at the JAA PPL (A) ground examinations.

An indication of the technical level covered by each text book is given on the rear cover and in individual subject prefaces. The books deal predominantly with single piston-engine aeroplane operations.

Questions and Answers.
Questions appear at the end of each chapter in order that readers may test themselves on the individual subtopics of the main subject(s) covered by each book. The questions are of the same format as the questions asked in the JAA PPL (A) theoretical knowledge examinations, as administered by the UK CAA. All questions are multiple-choice, containing four answer options, one of which is the correct answer, with the remaining three options being incorrect "distracters".

Students Working for a Non-JAA PPL.
JAA licence training syllabi follow the basic structure of ICAO-recommended training, so even if the national PPL you are working towards is not issued by a JAA member state, this series of text books should provide virtually all the training material you need. Theoretical knowledge examinations for the JAA PPL are, however, administered nationally, so there will always be country-specific aspects to JAA PPL examinations. 'Air Law' is the most obvious subject where country-specific content is likely to remain; the other subject is 'Navigation', where charts will most probably depict the terrain of the country concerned.

As mentioned elsewhere in this Foreword, this series of books is also suitable for student pilots preparing for the United Kingdom National Private Pilot's Licence (UK NPPL). The theoretical examination syllabus and examinations for the UK NPPL are currently identical to those for the JAA PPL.

Student Helicopter Pilots.
Of the seven book in this series, the following are suitable for student helicopters pilots working towards the JAA PPL (H), the UK NPPL (H) or the equivalent national licence:

Volume 1: 'Air Law & Operational Procedures'; Volume 2: 'Human Performance'; Volume 3: 'Navigation & Radio Aids'; Volume 4: 'Meteorology', and Volume 7: 'Radiotelephony'.

The OATmedia Website.
If any errors of content are identified in these books, or if there are any JAA PPL (A) theoretical knowledge syllabus changes, Oxford Aviation Training's aim is to record those changes on the product support pages of the OATmedia website, at: www.oatmedia.com

Grammatical Note.

It is standard grammatical convention in the English language, as well as in most other languages of Indo-European origin, that a single person of unspecified gender should be referred to by the appropriate form of the masculine singular pronoun, *he*, *him*, or *his*. This convention has been used throughout this series of books in order to avoid the pitfalls of usage that have crept into some modern works which contain frequent and distracting repetitions of *he or she*, *him or her*, *etc*, or where the ungrammatical use of *they*, and related pronouns, is resorted to. In accordance with the teachings of English grammar, the use, in this series of books, of a masculine pronoun to refer to a single person of unspecified gender does not imply that the person is of the male sex.

Margin Notes.

You will notice that margin notes appear on some pages in these books, identified by one of two icons:

a key 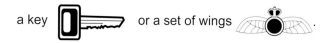 or a set of wings .

The key icon identifies a note which the authors judge to be a key point in the understanding of a subject; the wings identify what the authors judge to be a point of airmanship.

The UK Theoretical Knowledge Examination Papers.

The UK CAA sets examination papers to test JAA PPL (A) theoretical knowledge either as single-subject papers or as papers in which two subjects are combined.

Two examination papers currently cover two subjects each:

- **Aircraft (General) & Principles of Flight**: The 'Aircraft (General) & Principles of Flight' examination paper, as its title suggests, covers 'Principles of Flight' and those subjects which deal with the aeroplane as a machine, 'Airframes', 'Engines', 'Propellers' and 'Instrumentation', which JAR-FCL groups under the title 'Aircraft General Knowledge'.

- **Flight Performance & Planning:** The examination paper entitled 'Flight Performance & Planning' covers both 'Aeroplane Performance, and 'Mass & Balance'.

When preparing for the two examinations named above, using this Oxford series of text books, you will need **Volume 5, 'Principles of Flight'**, which includes 'Aeroplane Performance', and **Volume 6, 'Aeroplanes'**, which includes 'Mass & Balance' as well as 'Airframes', 'Engines', 'Propellers', and 'Instrumentation'. So to prepare for the 'Aircraft (General) & Principles of Flight' examination, you need to take the **'Aeroplanes'** infomation from **Volume 6** and the **'Principles of Flight'** information from **Volume 5**. When you are preparing for the 'Flight Performance & Planning' examination you need to take the **'Aeroplane Performance'** information from **Volume 5** and the **'Mass & Balance'** information from **Volume 6**.

It has been necessary to arrange the books in this way for reasons of space and subject logic. The titles of the rest of the volumes in the series correspond with the titles of the examinations. The situation is summed up for you in the table on the following page:

JAA Theoretical Examination Papers	Corresponding Oxford Book Title
Air Law and Operational Procedures	Volume 1: Air Law
Human Performance and Limitations	Volume 2: Human Performance
Navigation and Radio Aids	Volume 3: Navigation
Meteorology	Volume 4: Meteorology
Aircraft (General) and Principles of Flight	Volume 5: Principles of Flight Volume 6: Aeroplanes
Flight Performance and Planning	Volume 5: Aeroplane Performance Volume 6: Mass and Balance
JAR-FCL Communications (PPL)	Volume 7: Radiotelephony

Regulatory Changes.

Finally, so that you may stay abreast of any changes in the flying and ground training requirements pertaining to pilot licences which may be introduced by your national aviation authority, be sure to consult, from time to time, the relevant publications issued by the authority. In the United Kingdom, the Civil Aviation Publication, LASORS, is worth looking at regularly. It is currently accessible, on-line, on the CAA website at **www.caa.co.uk**.

Oxford,
England

April 2007

TO THE PILOT.

This book comprises two main sections: 'Principles of Flight' and 'Aeroplane Performance'.

For those who fly, a thorough knowledge of the Principles of Flight – also referred to as Aerodynamics - is essential if they are fully to appreciate the flight characteristics of their aircraft, and become safe and proficient pilots.

One of the main aims of the Principles of Flight section of the book, therefore, is to provide both student and qualified pilots with study material which will enable them to learn as effectively and enjoyably as possible the scientific principles upon which flight itself depends, and to acquire an understanding of the nature of the physical forces in play when an aeroplane is being manoeuvred.

Complementary to the study of the Principles of Flight, in terms of acquiring an understanding of the way an aeroplane flies, is the study of Aeroplane Performance, which is the subject of the second section of this book. The Subject of Aeroplane Performance deals with all the main phases of flight: take-off, climb, cruise, descent and landing. In Aeroplane Performance, it is not only aerodynamic factors but also engine power and thrust considerations, along with atmospheric conditions, which must be borne in mind in order to explain an aeroplane's overall performance.

As a pilot, you must at all times have a clear perspective on your aircraft's capabilities. A knowledge of Aeroplane Performance is crucial to your understanding of the performance potential of your aircraft and, what is more important from the flight safety point of view, its performance limitations. It is essential for you to know how well, or how badly, your aircraft performs in the various phases of flight: what take-off distance it requires, how well it will climb, how far it will fly, how long it can remain airborne, and so on.

While we have attempted, in this book, to relate the subjects of Principles of Flight and Aeroplane Performance to the practical aspects of piloting, it is a further primary aim of the book to prepare the student pilot for the PPL theoretical knowledge examinations. Appropriate emphasis, therefore, has been given to the pure theory of the two subjects which is demanded by the PPL ground examinations.

The depth and scope of the treatment of both subjects are such that this book should also provide a sound introduction to the subjects of Principles of Flight and Aeroplane Performance for those students who are preparing for examinations at professional pilot level.

Finally, be aware that, at PPL level, the United Kingdom Civil Aviation Authority (UK CAA) examines the subject of Principles of Flight along with the subject of Aircraft Systems in one paper, currently entitled Aircraft (General) and Principles of Flight, while Aeroplane Performance and Mass & Balance are examined by the UK CAA in a separate paper called Flight Performance & Planning. Volumes 5 and 6 of this series of books, entitled respectively 'Principles of Flight' and 'Aeroplanes', will prepare you for both examinations.

COMPONENT PARTS OF
THE AEROPLANE

THE PIPER PA28 WARRIOR.

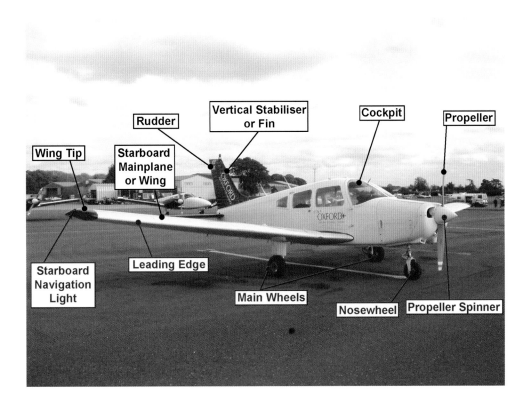

THE MAULE M-7.

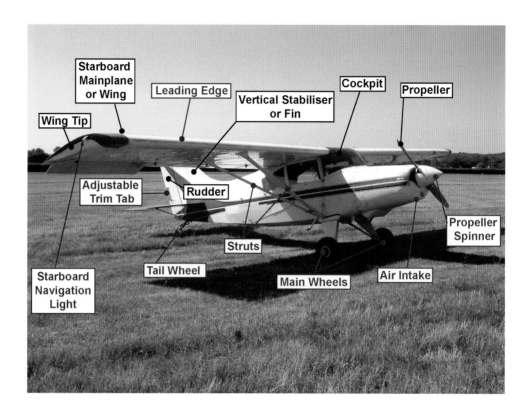

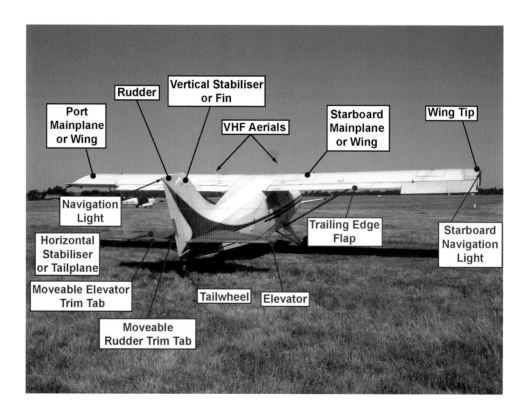

CHAPTER 1
PHYSICAL DEFINITIONS

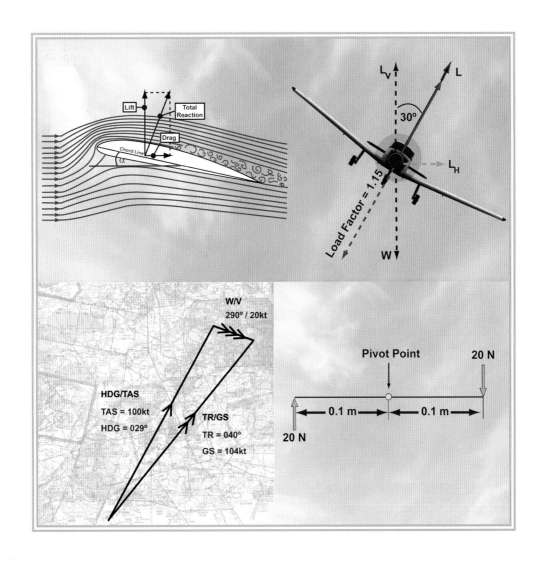

PRINCIPLES OF FLIGHT AND THE LAWS OF NATURE.

For our purposes, as pilots, **Principles of Flight** may be defined as the study of the forces generated by, and acting on, an aircraft in motion.

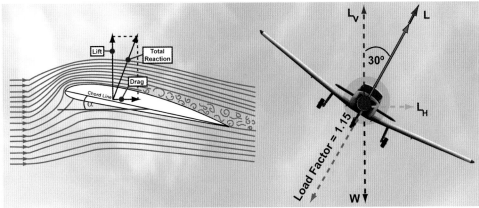

Figure 1.1 Principles of Flight is a branch of applied science.

Principles of Flight is, essentially, a branch of **applied science**. Though you will not need to have studied **science** to learn enough about **Principles of Flight** to pass the PPL theoretical knowledge examination, if you wish to master the subject of **Principles of Flight** thoroughly, you need to possess a basic knowledge of another **applied science**, the **science of Physics**.

Physics is another name for **natural science**; that is, **the science which explains the way matter and energy interact in nature**. The **Physics** which governs the everyday phenomena and occurrences with which we are all familiar, including the phenomenon of flight, deals with such things as **motion**, **mass**, **momentum**, **force**, **work**, **energy** etc.

If you have understood **Physics** or **Combined Science** at school or college, you will have enough knowledge of **Physics** to follow the subject matter of this book.

But, in case you have never taken **Physics** at school, or do not remember much about the subject, we summarise in this chapter certain **physical definitions** and fundamental **laws of Physics** which are referred to in our treatment of the **Principles of Flight**. The **definitions** and **laws** are not listed alphabetically, but rather in logical groups of interconnected concepts. Bear these **physical fundamentals** in mind as you work through this book, and refer to this section, as and when you wish.

If you would like to learn more about the **physical fundamentals** that we summarise here, any school text book on **Physics** should provide what you are looking for. Alternatively, you may wish to work through the self - teach, interactive CD-ROM, **Essential Physics 2**, conceived and produced by **OATmedia** as pre-course study material for student professional pilots. Details of that material can be found on the **OATmedia** website at www.oatmedia.com.

Figure 1.2 Essential Physics 2 is a self-teach, interactive CD-ROM dealing with Forces, Motion, Energy and Astronomy.

BASIC SCIENTIFIC DEFINITIONS AND LAWS.

BODY: a 3-dimensional object, possessing mass.

MASS: the amount of matter in a body. The standard unit of **mass** is the **kilogram (kg)**.

WEIGHT: Weight is the **force** acting on a **body** of a given **mass** by virtue of the presence of that body in a gravitational field. The standard unit of **weight** is the **Newton (N)**. The **force** of **weight** acting on a body will impart an acceleration to the body towards the centre of the gravitational field. **All bodies within the gravitational field of the Earth, near the Earth's surface, will be accelerated towards the centre of the Earth at 9.81 metres per second per second (9.81 metres/sec²),** a value of acceleration referred to by the symbol **g** and regarded as being constant up to an altitude above the surface of the Earth well above the greatest altitude at which aircraft fly. The relationship between **weight, mass** and **g**, the **acceleration due to gravity,** is given by the formula

weight (N) = mass (kg) × g (9.81 metres/sec²)

Weight is given in **Newtons (N)** if the mass is in **kilograms** and acceleration is in **metres/sec²**. The **weight** of a **body** always acts towards the centre of the gravitational field in which the body is located. On Earth, the **weight** of a **body** always acts **vertically downwards** towards the centre of the Earth.

MOMENTUM: Momentum is the name given to the physical property possessed by a body by virtue of its mass and the velocity at which it is travelling.

Momentum = mass × velocity. The units of momentum are **kilogram-metres per second**, which are simply the units of mass (kilograms) and velocity (metres per second) multiplied together.

Momentum is often defined as a measure of how difficult it is to stop a moving object.

A body which is stationary possesses no **momentum**, no matter how massive it is.

Momentum is one of the most fundamental concepts in science. **Momentum** is related to another fundamental physical concept, **force**, by **Newton's Laws of Motion. Newton's Laws of Motion** teach us that any moving body will continue to move in a straight line with uniform velocity unless acted upon by a **force** (Newton's 1st Law) and that **the momentum** of a body will, thus, remain constant unless the body is acted upon by a **resultant force**. When a **resultant force** acts on a body, over a given period of time, it causes a **change in the momentum** of the body. Newton's 2nd Law teaches us that the **rate of change of that momentum is proportional to the magnitude of the applied resultant force.**

FORCE: A **force** is a push or a pull.   The **force** acting on a body is related to the **momentum** of that body by **Newton's Laws of Motion**, as described above. The standard **unit of force** is called the **Newton**, in honour of the English physicist **Sir Isaac Newton. Force** has both **direction** and **magnitude; force** is, therefore, a **vector quantity (see page 15).**

FRICTION: Friction is a special kind of **force** which acts to stop two materials from **sliding over each other**. Between sandpaper and wood, **friction** is high, which is why the surface of both materials is worn away by **friction**. Conversely, there is so little **friction** between skates and ice that the skater can glide effortlessly across the ice. Between the various moving metal parts of a reciprocating internal combustion engine, the **friction** generated is so high that the engine would quickly seize and the moving parts fuse together, if a **lubricant** such as oil were not introduced between the moving parts to keep **friction** to a minimum.

The magnitude of the force of **friction acting between two surfaces** is dependent on the **nature of the two surfaces** in contact with each other and **the force which pushes the two surfaces together**.

VISCOSITY: Viscosity is a measure of the resistance of a fluid to deformation when a force is applied to it. **Viscosity** may also be thought of as the **resistance of a fluid to flow**. **Viscosity** is sometimes considered as being the **thickness of a fluid**, which again is an indication of its **resistance to pouring**.

Viscosity may also be seen as a **measure of fluid friction**.

It follows, then, that **water and petrol have low viscosity**, while **treacle and heavy-duty oil have a relatively high viscosity**.

MOMENTS: The word **moment** is used to describe a **turning force** which acts on a body, causing the object to rotate about a **pivot**. In order for a **moment** to be present, a **force must act at a distance from the pivot, and act perpendicularly to a straight line passing through the pivot**.

The **magnitude of a moment** is calculated by **multiplying the magnitude of the force which tends to cause a body to turn by the perpendicular distance between the force and the pivot point about which the body tends to turn**.

While the scientific unit of a **moment** is the **Newton-metre**, in aircraft mass and balance calculations, you will mostly meet **pound-inches** and **kilogram-metres**.

For a body to be in **equilibrium, the sum of the moments acting on a body must be zero**. That is that **the sum of the moments acting in a clockwise direction must equal the sum of the moments acting on a body in an anti-clockwise direction**. The diagram below depicts two **moments** acting in opposite directions on a beam. The two **moments** cancel each other out so the **resultant moment is zero** and the beam is in **equilibrium**.

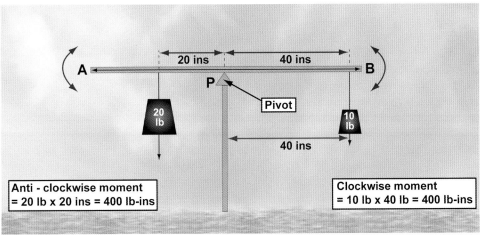

Figure 1.2 Two moments of 400 lb-ins balancing each other out. The beam is in equilibrium.

TORQUE: In the study of engines and propellers, a **moment** or **turning force** is also sometimes called **torque**. **Torque** can be thought of as **rotational force** which causes a change in rotational motion. **Torque,** like a moment, is defined by the linear force causing a rotation about a pivot multiplied by the perpendicular distance from the pivot of the point at which the force is applied. The standard units of **torque** are **Newton-metres**, as for **moments**. You may also meet older units such as **foot-pounds, pound-inches, kilogram-metres etc.**

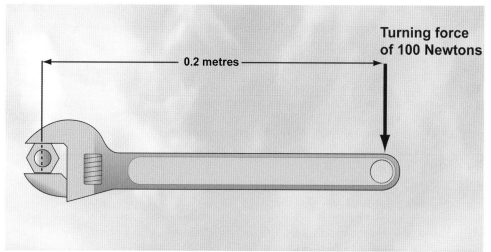

Figure 1.3 A torque of 100 Newtons × 0.2 metres = 20 Newton-metres applied to a nut via a spanner.

The application of **torque** to a mechanism will cause a rotational acceleration until the **applied torque** is balanced by an equal and opposite **resistive torque** from the mechanism, when the mechanism will continue to rotate with constant angular speed.

COUPLES: A **couple** is a **special case of a moment** where **two equal forces** act along parallel lines but in opposite directions and cause a body to tend to rotate about a pivot point. If only one **couple** is acting on a body, the body will rotate, accelerating until an equal and opposite **couple** is generated, when the body will continue to rotate with constant angular speed.

The **magnitude of a couple** is calculated by **multiplying the magnitude of one of the forces which tends to cause a body to turn by the perpendicular distance between the two forces.**

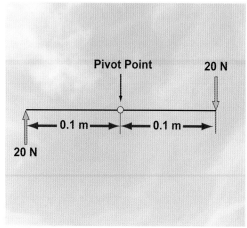

Figure 1.4 A couple of 4 Newton-metres (20N × 0.2m = 4 N-m).

EQUILIBRIUM: Equilibrium is a Latin word meaning **balance**. In science, a body is said to be in **equilibrium** (in **balance**) when all the external forces acting on the body, and all the turning moments acting on the body cancel one another out. Another way of saying this is that **a body is in equilibrium when the vector sum of all the forces and moments acting on the body is zero**. When a body is in **equilibrium,**

it must be either **at rest** or moving in a straight line at constant speed (i.e. travelling at **constant velocity**). If a body is not in **equilibrium,** it will be subject to a resultant force and will be accelerating in some way. You may be able to get an idea of the principle of **equilibrium** from travelling in a car. If you are travelling in a straight line, at constant speed, you will feel exactly the same forces acting on your body as if you were at rest. At constant velocity, there is no resultant force acting on you (except your **weight** due to the force of gravity), and you are in **equilibrium**.

If the car gathers speed rapidly, you experience **acceleration**; if the car brakes suddenly, you experience **deceleration**. (**Deceleration** is simply the name given to a **negative acceleration**.) In both cases, a **resultant force** must be acting; you are, therefore, not in **equilibrium** and you feel the **resultant force** either pressing you back into your seat, if **acceleration** is present, or causing you to move forwards, if the car is **decelerating** when braking sharply.

PRESSURE: Pressure is basically an applied **force** spread over a **contact area**.

If a small **force** is spread over a **large area**, the pressure is said to be **low**, whereas if the same small **force** acts over a **very small area**, then the pressure can be **high**.

Pressure is defined as **force per unit area.** To find the magnitude of **pressure**, we divide the magnitude of the **force**, acting perpendicularly (normally) to a **contact area**, by the **contact area**, itself.

$$\textbf{Pressure} = \frac{\textbf{Force acting normal to the surface}}{\textbf{Contact area of surface}}$$

A typical unit of **pressure**, which you might well expect to come out of the above formula, is the **Newton/metre^2**.

The **SI (Système International)** unit of **pressure** is the **Pascal. One Pascal (Pa)** is equal to **One Newton/metre^2**.

By international agreement, meteorologists use, as the preferred unit of pressure, the **hectopascal (hPa)** which is equal to **100 Pa** or **100 Newtons/ metre^2**.

The **hPa** is also the **standard unit of pressure** used in the European (JAA) aviation world.

Sea-level pressure in the **ICAO Standard Atmosphere (ISA)** is **101 325 Newtons/ metre^2** or **1013.2 hPa**.

Quantitively equivalent to the **hectopascal (hPa)** is the **millibar (mb)**. In Britain, and many other countries outside Europe, the aviation world uses the **millibar** as the standard unit of pressure. So **ISA sea-level pressure** may also be expressed as **1013.2 mb**.

Pressure may also be expressed in other units such as **pounds per square inch (lb/in^2),** or even as the height of a column of Mercury (Hg) which may be supported by an applied **pressure** in the arm of a U-tube or manometer. In the United States of America, the world of aviation uses **inches of Mercury** to express **pressure**. **ISA sea-level pressure** in inches of Mercury is **29.92 ins Hg**.

STATIC PRESSURE: Static pressure is the term used in aviation to refer to the **pressure** sensed by a body by virtue of its being **immersed in the Earth's atmosphere**. Of course, this type of **pressure** would be felt by a body **immersed** in any kind of fluid: liquid or gas.

Static pressure acts on all bodies whether they are moving or stationary (i.e. **static**). The magnitude of the **static pressure** acting on a body depends on the density of the fluid in which the body is immersed and the body's depth below the surface of the fluid. So, the **static pressure** experienced by a body in the Earth's atmosphere is the pressure caused by the weight of air above the body pressing in on the body. The higher a body rises in the atmosphere, away from the Earth's surface, the lower will be the **static pressure**. As we mention above, **atmospheric static pressure, at sea-level, in the ICAO Standard Atmosphere, is 1013.2 hPa, 1013.2 mb, 29.92 in Hg, 101 325 Newtons/metre² or 14.7 lbs/ in².**

Static pressure is exerted in all directions over the entire area of the surface of any object immersed in a gas or liquid.

DYNAMIC PRESSURE: If a body is **moving** through a gas or liquid, **in addition to the static pressure** acting on it, the body also experiences a **pressure resulting from its motion**. This additional pressure is called **dynamic pressure**. So, while a stationary body within a gas or liquid will experience static pressure, **the frontal surfaces of a moving body will experience both static pressure and dynamic pressure**.

Dynamic pressure is exerted on an aircraft moving through air because the air is brought to rest on the cross sectional area of the frontal surfaces of the aircraft. In being brought to rest, the air applies a **force** on the object. If we divide that **force** by the **frontal cross sectional area**, we can measure the **dynamic pressure** being exerted.

The **total pressure** experienced by the **frontal surfaces** of an aircraft in flight, therefore, is equal to **dynamic pressure plus static pressure**. Those parts of the aircraft which are not exposed to the airflow, and against which the air is not brought to rest, will experience only **static pressure**.

WORK: When a force moves through a distance, **work** is done. The amount of **work done** is calculated by multiplying the **force** by the **distance** through which it moves. The standard unit of **force** is the **Newton** and the standard unit of **distance** is the **metre**; so if a **200 Newton force** moves through **10 metres, 2 000 Newton-metres of work** is done. **One Newton-metre** is called a **Joule**, in honour of the English Physicist **James Prescott Joule**, so **2 000 Newton-metres of work done** may also be expressed as **2 000 Joules**.

If you wish to lift a child weighing **30 kg** (scientifically speaking, of mass 30 kg) onto the seat of a chair ½ **metre** from the ground, on Earth, you first need to find the **force** pulling the child to the ground (his **weight**) and which you have to counter in order to lift him. On Earth, the relationship between **mass in kilograms** and **force in Newtons** is the **acceleration due to gravity** which is approximately **10 metres/sec²**. A **30 kg** child, therefore, **weighs**, in scientific units, **300 Newtons**. So to lift the child onto the chair, you would have to do **150 Newton-metres or 150 Joules of work (300 N × ½ m)**. To lift the child twice as high, you would have to do twice the amount of **work**.

POWER: **Power** is defined as being the **rate of doing work**. Looking again at the simple case of a **30 kg** child being lifted through ½ **metre**, if one person lifts the child slowly while another performs the same task quickly, both people are doing **150 Joules of work**, but the person who performs that work quicker develops the greater **power**. **High-power** engines perform work at a higher rate than **low-power** engines.

Thus, an aircraft, with engines of **low power** may transport a given load across the Atlantic in a given time. An aircraft with **very powerful** engines may transport the same load over the same distance in a shorter time. Both aircraft do the same amount of **work**, but the aircraft which performs that **work at the higher rate** is the more **powerful** aircraft of the two.

ENERGY: **Energy** is not the most simple concept when analysed scientifically, but for our purposes we can describe it with a high degree of accuracy as being the **ability to do work**.

Substances and phenomena such as **gasoline (petrol)**, **heat**, **movement**, **position**, **stretched or compressed springs**, **batteries** etc have the ability to do **work** when they are part of a system designed to perform **work**.

Although it is difficult to measure **energy** absolutely, it is not difficult to measure the physical effects of **energy**, such as **heat** and **movement**. Phenomena such as **heat** and **movement** can be used, therefore, to calculate an actual value for other forms of **energy**.

Energy has the units **Joules**, the same units as can be used for **work**. A body or system which possesses **150 Joules** of **energy** is able to do **150 Joules of work**.

(Note that whereas either **Newton-metres** or **Joules** can be used as the units of **work**, only **Joules** are used to measure **energy**.)

One form of **energy** that we are especially concerned with in flying is **kinetic energy**. **Kinetic energy** is the **energy** possessed by a body by virtue of its **movement**. When a **moving body** is brought to a halt, **work is done** on the object stopping the moving body, by virtue of the moving body's **kinetic energy**. In the case of a car colliding with a wall or other solid object, the deformation to the car's structure is evidence of the **work done** in stopping the car. Obviously, an aircraft in flight possesses **kinetic energy**. The air moving over the aircraft's structure, by virtue of its relative motion with the aircraft, also possesses **kinetic energy**. When moving air is brought to a stop in the pitot tube of an airspeed indicator system, the **work done** by the air can be used to set in motion a mechanism which indicates to the pilot how fast the aircraft is moving through the air.

THE CONSERVATION OF ENERGY: The fact that the **total energy** in a closed system always remains constant gives us **the law of the conservation of energy**. The **law of the conservation of energy** teaches us that **energy cannot be created or destroyed**; it can only be converted from one form to another. The **law of the conservation of energy** is a natural law of immense importance, because it applies to almost every aspect of **Physics**. You may not be surprised to learn that many people are still unsure of the exact meaning of this law. For instance, you will often hear people talking about "**burning energy**", or "**using up energy**". Words of this kind are misleading because they imply that energy is being destroyed.

But if **energy** cannot be created or destroyed, how does **energy** do work? The answer lies in the explanation that while the **total energy** of a body or system **cannot be used up**, one or more **types of energy** within a body or system can be **converted to another type of energy.** For example, the **chemical energy** contained in an aircraft's fuel is converted to **heat energy** in the aircraft's engine or engines. That **heat energy** is then converted to **mechanical energy** which turns a propeller. The propeller accelerates air rearwards generating **kinetic energy**; the temperature of the accelerated air will be raised by a measurable amount, adding to the air's **heat energy.** This **heat energy** will be dissipated throughout the atmosphere, but in whatever closed system (e.g. the engine or the atmosphere) is being observed, the **total energy remains the same.**

James Joule found that when **work** was done on an object the amount of **heat** absorbed by the object could be calculated, and that, for a given amount of **mechanical work done**, the **heat** absorbed by the object was always the same, **thereby equating work done with energy transfer or conversion.**

MOTION – NEWTON'S LAWS: Every body which is in motion at speeds well below the speed of light (speed of light = 299 792 458 metres per second, or about 186 000 miles per second) is subject to **Newton's Laws of Motion. Newton's Laws** illustrate the relationship between the **motion of a body** and the f**orces acting on the body.**

Newton's Laws are a good basis for the explanation of the **motion** of everyday objects such as cricket balls, motor vehicles and aircraft, under the conditions normally experienced on Earth.

Newton's 1ˢᵗ Law of Motion: *A body at rest remains at rest, and a body in motion continues to move in a straight line with a constant speed unless a resultant external force acts upon the body.*

In other words, an object which is at rest will not move until an **external resultant force** acts upon it, and an object which is in motion will move at constant velocity (i.e. without changing speed or direction) as long as no **external resultant force** acts upon it.

Newton's 2ⁿᵈ Law of Motion: *The rate of change of momentum of a body is directly proportional to the applied external resultant force and takes place in the direction in which the force acts.*

Newton's 3ʳᵈ Law of Motion: *To every action (applied external resultant force) there is an equal and opposite reaction (equal force in the opposite direction). Action and reaction take place on different bodies.*

In other words, if object A exerts a force on object B, then object B exerts a force of the same magnitude on object A, in the opposite direction.

INERTIA: Inertia is that quality of a body which resists any change in velocity. Thus, a body's **inertia** means that if the body is in a state of rest, it will tend to remain at rest, and if the body is travelling with uniform motion in a straight line, it will tend to continue at that constant velocity. This is, in fact, a state of affairs described by **Newton's 1ˢᵗ Law,** (see above), which is sometimes known as the **law of inertia.** The amount of **inertia** possessed by a body is a function of the body's **mass.** Thus, a body possessing great mass will have a greater **inertia** than a body of small mass.

SCALAR QUANTITIES: A **scalar quantity** is a quantity, usually expressed in terms of a number with units, which possesses **magnitude (i.e. size) only**. **Scalar quantities** may be compared with **vector quantities** which have both **magnitude and direction**; (see below). **Mass** is a **scalar quantity**. When expressing the mass of a body, in kilograms or pounds, for instance, we are describing magnitude only; mass is the amount of matter possessed by a body and cannot be defined in terms of direction.

Speed is another **scalar quantity** (measured in units such as metres per second, miles per hour, knots etc). When we talk about the **speed** of an aircraft, we describe only how fast or slowly it is moving. Although the aircraft will necessarily be moving in a certain direction, that direction is not defined by the **scalar quantity**: **speed**.

VECTOR QUANTITIES: In comparison to a **scalar quantity** which gives us information on **magnitude** only, a **vector quantity** contains information on both **magnitude and direction**. In science, **force** and **velocity** are **vector quantities**. **Vector quantities** are often represented graphically by arrows. If, for instance, we wish to represent a **force** acting in a particular direction, an arrow is drawn to a scale such that **the length of the arrow indicates the magnitude of the force** (a **40 Newton** force would be represented by an arrow twice as long as an arrow representing a **20 Newton** force) and **the orientation of the arrow indicates the direction in which the force is acting**.

In a similar manner, when representing the **velocity** of a body by an arrow (for instance, the **velocity** of an aircraft in a navigation problem), the **length** of the arrow indicates the **magnitude** of the **velocity** (i.e. the aircraft's speed, either through the air or over the ground) and the **orientation** of the arrow (e.g. North, North-West, South-East etc) indicates the **direction of flight** of the aircraft. The arrows, themselves, because they indicate **magnitude** and **direction,** are often referred to as **vectors**.

SPEED: See **Scalar Quantities**, above. When **speed** is mentioned, in science, it refers only to how fast or how slowly a body is moving; no information is given about direction.

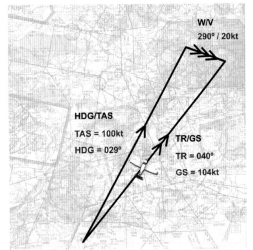

Figure 1.5 Three vectors in a triangle of velocities, indicating magnitude and direction: Wind Velocity (W/V) , an aircraft's Heading and True Airspeed (HDG/TAS) and the aircrafts Track over the ground and Groundspeed (TR/GS).

In aviation studies, and particularly in navigation, a difference is made between aircraft **speeds** such as **True Airspeed** (the actual **speed** of the aircraft relative to the air), its **Indicated Airspeed** (the **speed** read from the aircraft's Airspeed Indicator), and **Ground Speed** (the speed with which the aircraft moves over the Earth's surface). These **speeds** are explained in the relevant chapters of this book.

VELOCITY: See **Vector Quantities**, above. In science and navigation, when considering the **velocity** of a body, **velocity** is expressed in terms of both **magnitude** and **direction**. For instance, when planning a cross-country flight, a pilot will define the expected progress of his aircraft in terms of **speed** and **direction**. He will, for instance, plan to follow a track defined by its bearing measured relative to True or Magnetic North, say 045 degrees (North-East), and plan to fly at a given indicated airspeed, say 110 knots. In defining the progress of his aircraft in this way, the pilot has defined the **velocity** of his aircraft.

Be aware that, in everyday language, you will often hear the word **velocity** used to express magnitude only (i.e. speed). Everyday words often differ in detail and accuracy from words used technically and scientifically. The important thing for you, as a pilot, is that you appreciate and understand these differences.

ACCELERATION: Acceleration is a **vector quantity** which defines **rate of change** in **velocity**. In everyday language, the word **acceleration** is used to mean a rate of increase in velocity, but, in science, it can mean either rate of increase in velocity or a rate of <u>decrease</u> in velocity. A rate of decrease in velocity is a **negative acceleration** and is commonly referred to as a **deceleration**.

CIRCULAR MOTION: **Circular motion** is motion following a circular path. The important thing to grasp about **circular motion** is that although a body, such as an aircraft in turning flight, may be moving around the circumference of a circle at a **constant linear speed** (for an aircraft, say, at 70 knots in a turn) the **velocity of the body is continually changing** because the **direction of motion is continually changing**. As **velocity is continually changing**, a body moving in a circle is also, by definition, **continually accelerating**. The direction of this **acceleration** (called **centripetal acceleration**) is towards the centre of the circle. If the **centripetal acceleration** were not present, the body would fly off in a straight line in accordance with **Newton's 1st Law**.

Circular motion can have as its units either linear units such as **metres per second** or **miles per hour,** which describe how fast or slow a body is moving around the circumferential path, or may be described using units such as **degrees per second** or **radians per second** which define change of **angular displacement**. When dealing with engines and propellers, common units are **revolutions per minute (rpm)**.

CONVENTIONS USED IN EQUATIONS: Although this book on **Principles of Flight** does not contain much mathematics, a few mathematical and scientific equations necessarily appear in a subject of this nature.

When equations are included, certain symbols are used such as ρ for air density, C_L for coefficient of lift, S for wing area, **v** for velocity, and so on.

Be aware that when symbols are written together such as: **Lift $= C_L \frac{1}{2}\rho v^2 S$**, the symbols $C_L \frac{1}{2}\rho v^2 S$ are considered as being multiplied together. So, $C_L \frac{1}{2}\rho v^2 S$ means exactly the same as $C_L \times \frac{1}{2} \times \rho \times v^2 \times S$

So, if letters in an equation are placed next to one another in this way: **Lift $= C_L \frac{1}{2}\rho v^2 S$**, their meaning is exactly the same as if multiplication signs were placed between them.

CHAPTER 2
THE ATMOSPHERE

THE ATMOSPHERE.

Aircraft.
All aircraft, by the very definition of the word, can fly only when immersed in the air.

Lighter-than-air craft such as hot-air balloons are called **aerostats**, while heavier-than-air craft which require relative movement between the air and their lifting surfaces are called **aerodynes**.

Of the aerodynes, fixed-wing craft are called generically **aeroplanes**. In the word **aeroplane**, the word-element **plane** refers to the **mainplanes**, more commonly known as **wings**, and the **tail-plane**, which the Americans often refer to as the **horizontal stabiliser**. The **fin** of an aeroplane is a plane, too; the Americans call it a **vertical stabiliser**. So, you see, **plane** has a particular technical meaning when referring to aircraft, but the word **plane** certainly does not refer to the complete aircraft. The complete aircraft may, though, be called an **aeroplane**. In everyday speech you will often hear people talking about "passenger planes" and "military planes". But because you are a pilot, you might choose to use the more correct words; it is a personal choice.

Rotary-wing craft are known collectively as **helicopters**, from the Greek *pteron* meaning wing and the Greek *helios* meaning "sun", the picture imagined, one might suppose, being that of a rotating wing suggesting the rays of the sun.

In this book on **Principles of Flight** we shall be considering the flight of aeroplanes only. Throughout the book, the words **aeroplane** and **aircraft** will be used synonymously.

The Composition of the Atmosphere.

The Principal Gases.
As it is the relative movement of aeroplanes and air which generates the aerodynamic forces which enable an aircraft to fly, we may logically begin our study of the **Principles of Flight** by examining the nature of the Earth's atmosphere.

The gaseous atmosphere which surrounds our Earth is similar to a giant ocean of air. The light aircraft flown by most private-pilot licence-holders operate in the lower 10 000 feet of the atmosphere, whereas jet airliners regularly fly at altitudes up to about 40 000 feet. The total depth of the atmosphere has been calculated to be about 500 miles (800 km), but about 90% of the mass of air lies in the lower 50 000 feet (9 miles or 15 km) of the atmosphere.

The air in our atmosphere is made up primarily of **Nitrogen** (78%) and **Oxygen** (21%). *(See Figure 2.1)* The remaining 1% consists mainly of **Argon** and **Carbon Dioxide**, with traces of Carbon Monoxide, Helium, Methane, Hydrogen and Ozone. It is this mixture of gases which not only enables an aeroplane to fly but which also makes up the air which sustains human life and enables the combustion of fuel to take place to drive piston engines and gas turbine engines.

> *The air in the atmosphere is made up primarily of Nitrogen (78%) and Oxygen (21%). The remaining 1% is mainly Carbon Dioxide and Argon.*

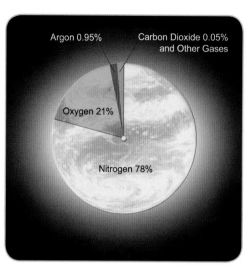

Figure 2.1 The four main gasses which make up the Atmosphere.

Water Vapour and Humidity.

Atmospheric air also contains a small amount of **water vapour** of varying quantity. The measure of the amount of water vapour contained in an air mass is termed **humidity**. Meteorologists measure humidity in several ways: for example, mass of water vapour per unit volume of air (say, 5 gm/m³), or mass of water vapour per unit mass of air (say, 3 gm/kg). As we have said, atmospheric air contains very little water vapour (it is never more than 4% by volume), but the influence of this water vapour is significant, especially on our weather.

Despite the presence of water vapour in the air, the air is normally invisible because water vapour can exist in the air as an invisible gas. The higher the temperature of the air, the more water the air can hold in its gaseous form. As temperature decreases, the natural movement of water molecules slows down and water condenses out onto microscopic impurities in the air, or onto surfaces in contact with the air. This is why you can see your breath on a cold day, why breathing onto a cold glass surface will cause the glass to mist up, and, of course, it is the reason why clouds form.

> *When air cools to its saturation point, or dew point, the invisible gas water vapour condenses out to its liquid state, and cloud is formed.*

When air can no longer hold any more water vapour as gas, the air is said to have reached its saturation point. The temperature of air at its **saturation point**, that is, the air temperature at which water vapour condenses out to water, is called the **dew point**. The more water vapour there is in the air, the higher the dew point will be.

Figure 2.2 Air is normally invisible but condensed water vapour in the air is visible as cloud.

20

And, of course, on the Earth's surface, at an airfield for instance, for any given content of water vapour, the nearer the dew point is to the actual temperature of the air, the greater the danger that the saturation point will be reached, causing condensation to occur and mist or fog to ensue.

Even unsaturated air, as it rises in the atmosphere, under whatever influence, will cool, and its temperature decreases sufficiently for the rising air eventually to reach its saturation point. At the saturation point, cloud is formed. Mist and fog, of course, are just cases of low level cloud. There is mist if the visibility is 1 000 m or more. There is fog if the visibility is less than 1 000 m.

You will often hear the term **relative humidity** used in aviation circles. **Relative humidity** is an expression of the ratio of the amount of water vapour actually present in the air to the amount of water vapour the air can "hold" at any given temperature. When the temperature of the air falls to the **dew point**, relative humidity will become 100%. The air will then be saturated and the water vapour will condense out, changing from the gaseous to the liquid state.

Water vapour is lighter than the same volume of dry air at equal pressure. Therefore, for a given temperature and pressure, a mixture of air and water vapour will be less dense if the water vapour content is high than if the water vapour content is low *(see Figure 2.3)*.

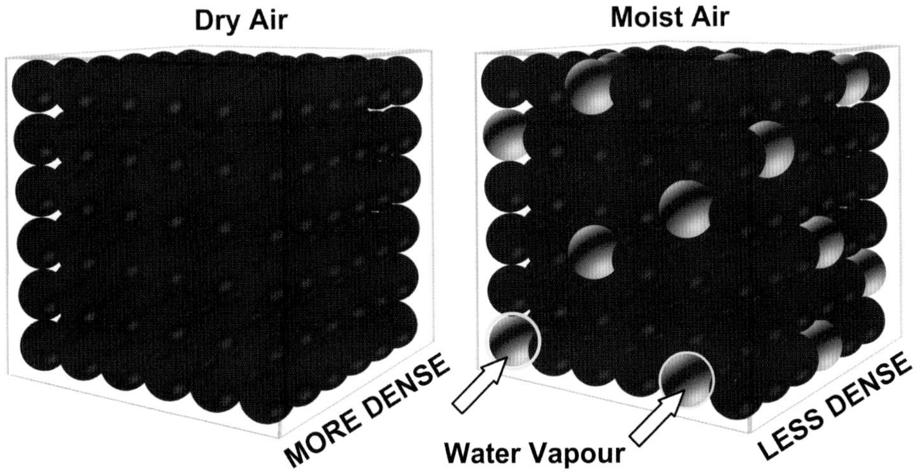

Relative humidity is the ratio of the amount of water vapour present in the air to the amount of water vapour the air can hold at the same temperature.

When temperature falls to the dewpoint, relative humidity is 100%, and water vapour condenses out into its liquid state.

If the water vapour content of air increases, air density will decrease at constant temperature and pressure.

Dry Air   **Moist Air**

MORE DENSE   **Water Vapour**   LESS DENSE

Figure 2.3 Moist air is less dense than dry air.

Air Pressure and Air Density.
The atmosphere was first formed when its gases were released from the Earth during the Earth's formation, over 4 billion years ago. The gases which now make up the air of our atmosphere were prevented from escaping into space by the Earth's force of gravity, so, over an unknown period of time, molecules of air spread out to cover the entire surface of our planet. The gravitational force acting between objects is greater, the greater the mass of those objects, but gets weaker as the distance between the objects increases; so many more tiny air molecules are held in contact with the Earth's surface than are present in the higher reaches of the atmosphere. This fact and the fact that the air near the surface is compressed by the weight of the mass of air above it mean that **air pressure** and **air density** are greatest near the surface of the Earth, and decrease with increasing altitude.

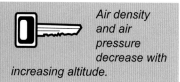

Air density and air pressure decrease with increasing altitude.

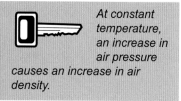

At constant temperature, an increase in air pressure causes an increase in air density.

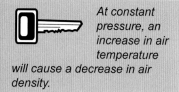

At constant pressure, an increase in air temperature will cause a decrease in air density.

A useful analogy of the variation of pressure and density with altitude is to consider foam rubber blocks piled on top of one another. If we consider any one of the blocks, we can see, in our mind's eye, that it is compressed by an amount which is proportional to the number and weight of blocks above it, and that the maximum compression is experienced by the block at the very bottom of the pile. Similarly, air pressure and air density are highest at the Earth's surface. *(See Figure 2.4).*

Air density refers to the number of air molecules contained within a given volume of air and is measured in terms of **mass per unit volume**. The standard units of air density are kilograms per

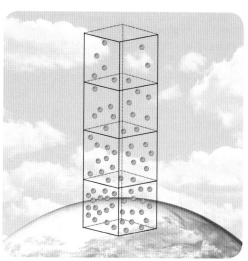

Figure 2.4 Air Density and Pressure decrease with increasing altitude.

cubic metre. The greater the pressure acting on a given volume of air, the greater the number of air molecules that are contained within that volume. Consequently, air density is directly proportional to pressure. When a given mass of air is heated at constant pressure it expands and its volume increases. Because of this increase in volume, the molecules of air are contained within a larger space and, thus, the mass per unit volume of the air – that is the density of the air – decreases. Air density, then, is inversely proportional to temperature; that is, it decreases with increasing temperature.

In general, both engine and flight performance decrease with decreasing air density which is why pilots need to be especially careful in their performance calculations when operating from airfields which are "hot and high": on the continent of Africa, for example.

Both pressure and temperature decrease with increasing altitude. But although a decrease in pressure will cause density to decrease while a decrease in temperature causes density to increase, the effect of the decreasing pressure on air density is the greater.

Air density is of considerable importance for the measurement of aircraft performance. **Lift**, **service ceiling**, and **indicated airspeed** all depend on air density. If air density is low, not only will the lift generated by the wings be less for any given true airspeed, but the power output of the engine will be lower too. Consequently, in low density conditions at an airfield (e.g. high temperature, and high airfield elevation), longer take-off runs will be required for an aircraft of any given take-off mass.

Pressure is a description of the way in which a force is spread over a contact area. **Pressure** is defined as **"force per unit area"**. In **Principles of Flight**, the pressure exerted by the atmosphere on objects immersed in it, when neither the air nor the object is in motion, is known as **atmospheric pressure** or **static pressure**. The standard unit of pressure is the **Newton per square metre**, but, in **Principles of Flight** you will rarely, if ever, hear pressure expressed in those units. In Britain and, especially, the United States, you might still hear pressure expressed, generally, in

pounds per square inch. In engineering, the **bar** or **millibar** is often used, as is the **Pascal** or **hectopascal**. The **millibar** and the **hectopascal** are also used in Meteorology and Altimetry. In the United States, **inches of Mercury** are the units of pressure in Altimetry. Like air density, atmospheric pressure (static pressure) decreases with increasing altitude.

Though the pressure exerted by the atmosphere at the Earth's surface, varies from day to day for reasons you will learn about in Meteorology, at sea level, atmospheric pressure is in the order of 100 000 Newtons per square metre, 1 bar, 1 000 millibars, 1 000 hectopascal, 14.7 pounds per square inch or 30 inches of Mercury.

The pressure of the atmosphere acts in all directions, acting on every square inch of every object immersed in it. *(See Figure 2.5)* For instance, a 6 foot (1.83 metres) human being on the surface of the Earth carries a total load of over ten tons. This is, of course, the equivalent of a force of 14.7 lbs (6.7 kg force) acting on every square inch of his body surface. But despite the fact that atmospheric pressure on the surface of the Earth is very high, we do not notice the pressure, because the pressure inside our own bodies balances this atmospheric pressure. But when the pressure inside any hollow object is less than atmospheric pressure, the difference in pressure can be withstood only by the strength of the object's structure. You have probably all witnessed during school Physics lessons that an empty tin can will collapse if the air inside it is removed.

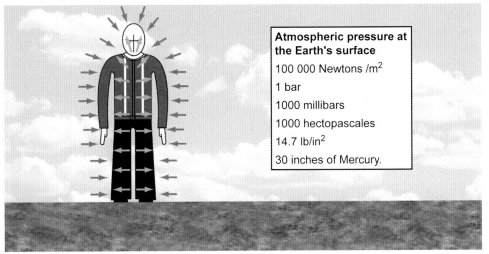

Atmospheric pressure, also known as static pressure, acts in all directions on a body immersed in the atmosphere.

Atmospheric pressure at the Earth's surface

100 000 Newtons /m^2

1 bar

1000 millibars

1000 hectopascales

14.7 lb/in^2

30 inches of Mercury.

Figure 2.5 Atmospheric pressure acts in all directions.

We see then that air possess mass, and that the force of gravity acting on that mass gives air weight which is the ultimate reason why our atmosphere exerts a pressure on objects immersed in it, and why the pressure and the density of the air decrease with altitude. As you will learn in subsequent chapters, these are the properties of air which enable aeroplanes to fly.

Variations in atmospheric pressure and density, along with variations in humidity, have a significant influence on aircraft performance and on the functioning of flight instruments, as you will learn in the **Aeroplanes (General)** volume of this series.

The Temperature of the Atmosphere.

The temperature of atmospheric air, like air density and atmospheric pressure, also decreases with increasing altitude. The air is not heated directly by the sun. The sun's short wave radiation passes through the atmosphere without heat being absorbed by the air. The Earth's surface, however, is heated up by solar radiation, and it is the Earth which heats up the air in contact with, and near, its surface by conduction, convection and long-wave radiation. Not surprisingly, then, it is the lowest layer of atmospheric air which is heated through its proximity to the Earth's surface and it is in that lowest layer where a clear and steady decrease in temperature with increasing altitude occurs. *(See Figure 2.7.)* The lowest layer of the atmosphere is known as the **Troposphere**, from the Greek word **tropos** meaning **mixing** or **turning**, which undoubtedly refers to the fact that it is in the Troposphere that temperature and pressure changes cause the meeting and mixing of air which gives rise to our weather. Almost all of the Earth's weather occurs in the Troposphere, so if you find yourself flying in an airliner on a European route, at 38 000 feet, you are indeed, in all probability, flying above the weather.

The Troposphere rises from the Earth's surface to about 50 000 feet over the Equator, 25 000 feet over the Poles, and about 36 000 feet at mid-latitudes. The Troposphere contains approximately 75% of the total mass of the atmosphere, and all of the water vapour.

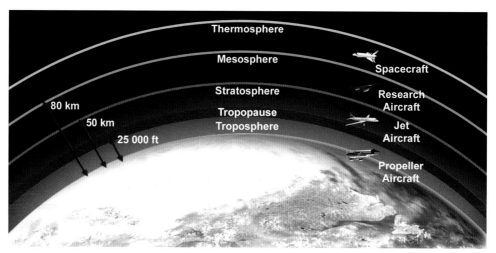

Figure 2.6 The various layers of the atmosphere with approximate heights in kilometres, one kilometre being 3 281 feet.

The boundary between the Troposphere and the layer immediately above it, the Stratosphere, is called the Tropopause. At the Tropopause, the temperature is around - 56.5° Celsius (- 69° Fahrenheit), and this temperature remains constant to an altitude of about 18 miles, or 35 kilometres. At altitudes greater than that, the temperature begins to rise again. But 18 miles high is 95 000 feet, so we will end our account of temperature variation with altitude there, and leave these higher regions to astronauts.

The Atmosphere and Flight.

The important facts to retain about the physical properties of the atmosphere in terms of your study of the **Principles of Flight**, is that air has **mass**, and that the **pressure**, **density**, **temperature** and **relative humidity** of the air change in certain circumstances. Another property of the air which is important in **Principles of Flight** is its **viscosity**. The viscosity of air is a measure of its resistance to flow because of a kind of internal friction acting between the air molecules as they move relative to one another. The viscosity of a fluid is often being described when we talk of a fluid being thick or thin. Air and water have a low viscosity and might be described as thin, whereas treacle and tar have a high viscosity and are seen as thick fluids. The viscosity of air, then, is low, but air <u>does</u> possess a measurable degree of viscosity and this viscosity has consequences for an aircraft in flight.

The ICAO Standard Atmosphere (ISA).

Changes of **air pressure**, **air density**, **air temperature** and humidity within the atmosphere greatly affect the performance of an aircraft in flight as well as the readings of certain flight instruments. In the real atmosphere, of course, these properties are changing continuously with altitude, with passing time and from place to place. In order, therefore, that aerodynamicists, aircraft manufacturers and engineers might have a set of standard values for pressure, density temperature etc, against which to measure aircraft performance and to calibrate instruments, a so-called **standard atmosphere** was defined by the **International Civil Aviation Organisation (ICAO)** in 1964. **The ICAO Standard Atmosphere**, generally known by its initials **ISA,** shows a standard variation of pressure, temperature, density, and viscosity, with altitude. ISA, then, serves as an international standard reference so that, when dealing with the measurement of aircraft performance and the calibration of instruments, everyone can be sure that they are working to the same set of atmospheric conditions.

Changes of pressure, density, and humidity of the air, all affect aircraft performance.

The ICAO Standard Atmosphere, with its significant values for the variation of temperature, pressure and density with altitude, is illustrated at *Figure 2.7*. Mean Sea Level air pressure in the ICAO Standard Atmosphere (which we will, henceforth in this volume, refer to as **ISA**) is 1013.2 millibars (1013.2 hectopascals) or 29.92 inches of Mercury. The ISA temperature at Mean Sea Level is 15° Celsius. In the ISA, temperature decreases with altitude at approximately 2° Celsius for every 1 000 ft.

Density, and pressure decrease with altitude, and temperature decreases with altitude up to the tropopause.

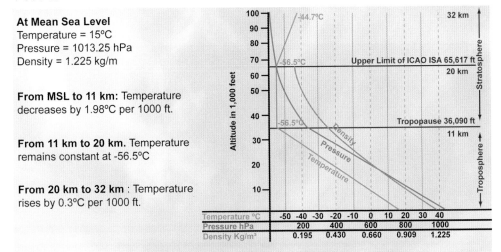

Figure 2.7 The ICAO Standard Atmosphere.

Any values for atmospheric pressure, density and temperature given in this volume will be ISA values. It is important that you remember, though, that the actual values for atmospheric pressure, density and temperature which prevail on any given day are inevitably different from the ISA values. (It would be in the order of a million to one chance that actual values were the same as ISA values.) Consequently, as the calibrations of flight instruments, such as the altimeter and the air speed indicator, as well as manufacturers' figures for aircraft performance, assume that an aircraft is flying in ISA conditions, it is very important, when reading instruments and measuring aircraft performance, on an actual flight, that pilots and engineers understand the effect that the atmosphere's deviation from ISA conditions has on the information they are reading. The topic of **ISA Deviations** is dealt with in detail in the **Meteorology** and **Aircraft (General)** volumes in this series.

The ISA sea level pressure of 1013.2 millibars is also the altimeter subscale setting, which a pilot selects when reading his altitude in terms of **Flight Level**. Flight Levels are also known as **Pressure Altitudes**.

The Measurement of Temperature.
Before we leave our brief look at the atmosphere, there is one more observation that needs to be made on the measurement of temperature.

The standard unit of measurement of temperature in the aviation world, outside the United States, is degrees Celsius (formerly Centigrade). However, the Fahrenheit scale was the primary scale of temperature measurement for non-scientific purposes in most English-speaking countries until the 1960s. Consequently, you will meet degrees Fahrenheit frequently in the United States, and still occasionally in Britain. So, although aviation meteorological reports and forecasts mention temperature in degress Celsius, it is still useful to be able to convert between the two scales.

In degrees Fahrenheit, water freezes at 32°F and boils at 212°F; in degrees Celsius, 0°C degrees is the freezing point of water, and 100°C its boiling point. So in the Fahrenheit scale there are 180° between the boiling points of water, whereas, in the Celsius scale, there are, of course, 100°. Therefore, one Fahrenheit degree is only 5/9 the value of a Celsius degree, (100/180 = 5/9).

The formulae for converting from one scale to the other are:

Conversion from	To	Formula
Fahrenheit	Celsius	°C = (°F - 32) × 5/9
Celsius	Fahrenheit	°F = (°C × 9/5) + 32

Representative PPL - type questions to test your theoretical knowledge of The Atmosphere.

1. Density:

    a. reduces as altitude increases
    b. is unaffected by temperature change
    c. increases with altitude increase
    d. reduces with temperature reduction

2. The presence of water vapour:

    a. in air will increase its density
    b. in the atmosphere will increase the power output of a piston engine
    c. in the atmosphere will increase the amount of lift generated by an aircraft for a given true airspeed
    d. in air will reduce its density

3. Atmospheric pressure:

    a. acts only vertically downwards
    b. is measured in Pascals per square inch
    c. acts in all directions
    d. increases with altitude

4. The air pressure that acts on anything immersed in it:

    a. is also known as Dynamic Pressure
    b. is also known as Static Pressure
    c. is greater at altitude than at sea level
    d. is also known as Total Pressure

5. What properties of the Earth's atmosphere most influence the performance of aircraft?

    a. Its carbon dioxide content, temperature, pressure and humidity
    b. Its oxygen content, pressure, and water vapour content
    c. Its water vapour content, temperature, pressure and density
    d. Its nitrogen content, oxygen content, temperature and pressure

6. A piston engine aircraft flies in that layer of the atmosphere called:

    a. the Stratosphere
    b. the Troposphere
    c. the Mesosphere
    d. the Tropopause

7.　　The respective percentages of the four most abundant gases that make up the atmosphere are?

　　　a. Nitrogen 78%　Oxygen 21%　Argon 0.95%　Carbon Dioxide 0.05%
　　　b. Oxygen 78%　Nitrogen 21%　Argon 0.95%　Carbon Dioxide 0.05%
　　　c. Nitrogen 78%　Oxygen 21%　Argon 0.95%　Carbon Monoxide 0.05%
　　　d. Oxygen 78%　Nitrogen 21%　Argon 0.95%　Carbon Monoxide 0.05%

8.　　When considering the changes in density of the air with altitude, which of the following four options is correct?

　　　a.　　The temperature increase with increasing altitude causes density to increase
　　　b.　　The reduction in pressure with increasing altitude causes density to reduce
　　　c.　　The temperature reduction with increasing altitude causes density to increase
　　　d.　　The increase in pressure with increasing altitude causes density to reduce

9.　　Assuming that the pressure at sea level is ISA, but the temperature is 10°C higher than ISA, the density will be:

　　　a.　　as per ISA
　　　b.　　greater than ISA
　　　c.　　less than ISA
　　　d.　　unaffected

10.　　Which of the following options contains the main constituent gases of the Earth's atmosphere?

　　　a.　　Hydrogen, Carbon Dioxide and Helium
　　　b.　　Nitrogen, Oxygen and Water Vapour
　　　c.　　Nitrogen, Argon and Carbon Dioxide
　　　d.　　Helium, Nitrogen and Carbon Monoxide

11.　　Complete the following sentence to give the most correct statement.

　　　At constant air temperature and volume, if the pressure of the air increases:

　　　a.　　its density will decrease
　　　b.　　its density will be unaffected because the volume remains constant
　　　c.　　its density will be unaffected because the temperature remains constant
　　　d.　　its density will increase

12. What is the definition of Relative Humidity?

    a. The amount of water vapour present in a mass of air, at any temperature, expressed as a percentage of the maximum amount of water vapour that the air could support at the ISA sea-level temperature
    b. The amount of water vapour present in a mass of air relative to the density of air
    c. The amount of water vapour present in a mass of air expressed as a percentage of the maximum amount of water vapour that the air can support at the same temperature
    d. The amount of water vapour present in a given volume of air expressed as a percentage of the total mass of the air

13. What will be the effect on air density of a reduction in air pressure while humidity and temperature remain constant?

    a. The air density will decrease
    b. The air density will increase
    c. The air density will remain unchanged
    d. The density of the air is independent of pressure at constant volume

14. What is the equivalent temperature in Celsius of 77° Fahrenheit?

    a. 45° Celsius
    b. 25° Celsius
    c. 60° Celsius
    d. 172° Celsius

15. If, on a given day, the actual outside air temperature at 3 000 feet is 12°C, what is the approximate difference between the actual and ISA temperature?

    a. 1° C
    b. 11° C
    c. 7° C
    d. 3° C

Question	1	2	3	4	5	6	7	8	9	10	11	12
Answer												

Question	13	14	15
Answer			

The answers to these questions can be found at the end of this book.

CHAPTER 3
LIFT

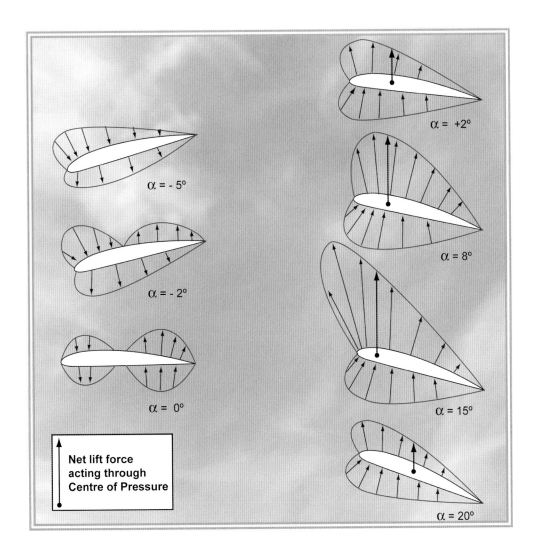

α = - 5°

α = - 2°

α = 0°

α = +2°

α = 8°

α = 15°

α = 20°

Net lift force
acting through
Centre of Pressure

INTRODUCTION.

The first half of this book deals in some depth with the principal forces which act on an aircraft in flight. In this Chapter, we briefly introduce all four main forces and then go on to examine the nature of the force of **lift**, which is the force which sustains an aircraft in the air.

An aircraft, like any physical body, possesses **mass**. The Earth's **force of gravity** acting on the aircraft's **mass** gives the aircraft **weight** which acts vertically downwards towards the centre of the Earth. When an aircraft has no forward speed, its weight keeps it firmly on the ground. (Unless the aircraft is a Harrier, of course; but that is another story.)

In order that an aircraft may fly, its **weight** has to be counter-balanced by a force of equal magnitude to its weight and which acts in the opposite direction. This force is called **lift**. As we will learn, **lift** is generated as a result of the flow of air over the aircraft's surfaces, principally its mainplanes or wings. In order to create this flow of air, the aircraft is propelled forwards through the air by a force to which we give the name **thrust**. But as soon as the aircraft begins to move under the influence of **thrust**, a force arises which opposes the **thrust** force, and acts against the direction of the aircraft's motion. This force is called **drag**. The four forces we have just mentioned, **weight, lift, thrust and drag**, which act on any powered aircraft in flight, are illustrated in *Figure 3.1*. The diagram also depicts a force which is identified as the **tailplane force**. The tailplane force is not one of the principal flight forces; it is a balancing force. Do not concern yourself with it for the moment; you will meet tailplane force at the appropriate time.

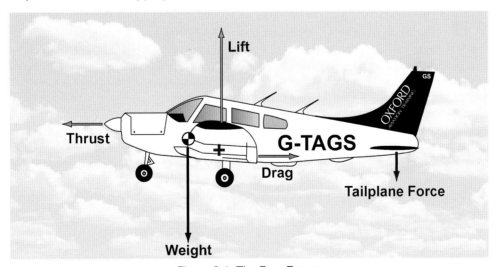

Figure 3.1 The Four Forces.

The four principal forces acting on an aircraft in flight are inextricably interconnected. A pilot must have an adequate knowledge of the way in which these forces interact with one another in order to understand what governs his aircraft's performance in any given phase of flight or in any particular manoeuvre.

The greater the **weight** of an aircraft, the more **lift** will be required to get the aircraft into the air and to maintain steady, straight flight, whether level, climbing or descending.

As the aircraft manoeuvres, it accelerates. Positive accelerations increase the aircraft's effective weight and require more lift to be generated by the wings. An increase in lift inevitably causes drag to increase. As drag increases, more thrust must be applied to balance the greater drag; and so on.

You will find that you have to consider this interrelationship between the four principal flight forces quite often in your study of the **Principles of Flight**. But, for now, let us take a closer look at the first of the four forces: **lift**.

LIFT.

The Primary Cause of Lift.
Lift is the force which sustains an aircraft in the air and enables it to manoeuvre. But how does an aeroplane generate **lift**?

Well, one of the most important properties of air, you will recall, is that it possesses **mass**. For instance, the air which fills a typical living room in an average family home has a **mass** of around 60 kilograms (132 pounds). So when a solid body moves through air, the resulting displacement of the air **mass** causes an opposing force to be exerted on the body which is doing the displacing. (*See Figure 3.2*) The way in which this reaction force acts on the body (i.e. the magnitude and direction of the force) depends on the manner in which the body is moving and the shape and orientation of the body.

First of all, let us consider the general case of how air might be displaced in order to produce **lift** when disturbed by a body which moves through it.

At this early stage in our consideration of lift, we do not want to look too closely at the fine detail of how lift is generated; that will come later. We just need to see the big picture for the moment. Let us, therefore, first of all consider how a body of **undefined characteristics** might affect the air through which it is moving.

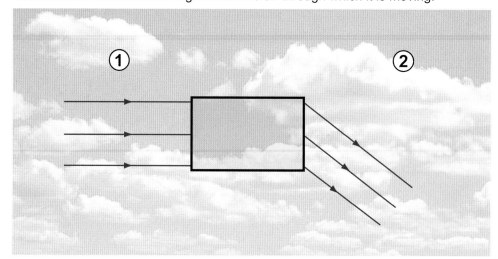

Figure 3.2 The undefined body behind the screen has exerted a force on the air to deflect the air downwards.

The diagram in *Figure 3.2*, which we are viewing from "side-on" represents a screen behind which is concealed the **"body of undefined characteristics"** that we have mentioned. The body and the screen are moving together through the air, thereby causing air to flow over the body. The arrows represent the direction of the relative motion of the free-stream airflow which, in the diagram, is seen passing behind the box. (Remember, in aerodynamics, it does not matter whether we are considering a body moving through the air, or moving air passing over a stationary body. The physical effects are the same.) At Point 1, we see that the flow of air is horizontal; but at Point 2 we observe that the airflow is inclined downwards. Consequently, because we know from **Newton's First Law of Motion** (See Page 14) that any moving mass will continue to move at constant speed in a straight line (in other words, at **constant velocity**) unless acted on by a **force**, we can see that some kind of **force**, acting in a downwards direction, has been applied to the air mass as it passed behind the box. Well, the only object which is behind the box is our **"body of undefined characteristics"**; so it must have exerted a **force** on the air **mass**. We can see, then, from **Newton's Third Law of Motion** (See Page 14) that the **undefined body** behind the screen which is exerting the **downwards force** on the air **mass** must, itself, be experiencing an equal reaction force acting in the opposite direction; that is, **in an upwards direction**.

Now, if we assume that the **undefined body** which is turning the air downwards is the wing of an aircraft, the **upwards reaction force** being experienced by the wing contributes to the force that aerodynamicists call **lift**. We will now go on to look at this **upwards reaction force** in more detail *(see Figure 3.3)*.

A wing turns the airflow downwards. The reaction force acting on the wing, in an upwards direction, contributes to lift.

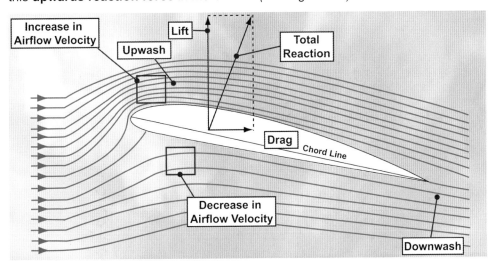

Figure 3.3 Streamlines in an Airflow meeting a wing.

The Nature of Lift - Newton and Bernoulli.

In describing the generation of **lift** by a moving fluid, we have to consider several laws of Physics. In fact, we must simultaneously consider the **principle of the conservation of mass**, the **principle of the conservation of momentum**, and the **principle of the conservation of energy**. (See Page 13) A complete discussion of the scientific theory of how a wing produces **lift** would be very complex, requiring us to be proficient in advanced mathematics, and would be well beyond the scope of this book. Such a formal treatment of **lift** would also be unnecessary for the average pilot, whether amateur or professional. However, in the remainder of this chapter we will be looking at **lift-theory** in enough detail to give what we trust is a convincing and comprehensive explanation of **lift**, which in no way misleads the student and which is of sufficient depth for the practical pilot.

Assumptions.

In the following explanations and discussions of the generation of **lift** by an aircraft's wings, we consider the air as an ideal fluid. Consequently, we make three major **assumptions** about the physical properties of the airflow.

- **The Compressibility of the Airflow.** It is assumed throughout this book, that the airflow over a wing is **incompressible**. Now, you will, of course, realise that air <u>can</u> be compressed very easily. Air in an inflated balloon is at higher than atmospheric pressure, as a child discovers when he releases a blown-up balloon and sees it propelled around a room as if it were an errant rocket. If you have ever inflated a bicycle tyre, you may have felt the heat generated in the end of the pump chamber as you do work on the air to compress it and force it into the tyre. And, of course, skin divers carry air bottles on their backs which contain what is actually called "compressed air".

- However, when air flows over the wing of an aircraft in flight, provided the speed is low and nowhere reaches a value of more than half the local speed of sound (Mach 0.5), the airflow is not compressed and, in any given atmospheric conditions, and at constant altitude, will maintain constant density. This assumption that air is incompressible works well for low-speed flight and simplifies the analysis of lift generation. The assumption is important for light aircraft pilots because if the speed of the airflow exceeds Mach 0.5, the compressibility of air does become an issue. But then we would be in the realms of high-speed flight and beyond the scope of this book. For your reference, the speed of sound, at sea-level, in the ICAO Standard Atmosphere, is about 662 knots (340.3 metres/sec or 1 116.4 feet/sec); so a light aircraft will always be flying at far less than half that speed.

- **The Viscosity of the Airflow.** When considering **lift**, we assume that air is inviscid; that is, that air is of a viscosity approaching zero (See Page 9). In reality, air does possess a measurable amount of viscosity. However, the viscosity of air is very low, and air flowing around a wing does act **as if it were inviscid**, except in the very thin layers immediately next to the surface of the wing, which we call the **boundary layer**. We must note, though, that if air really were inviscid, we could not account for the force of drag. So, to sum up, **our consideration of lift assumes that air has zero viscosity**, but, **in discussing drag, we must take the low viscosity of air into account.**

- **Steady Flow.** In our treatment of lift, we assume that the airflow around the wing is steady. This means that the pattern of the airflow around the wing does not change with time. This does not mean that the velocity at all points in the flow is constant but it does mean that, at any given point in the airflow, velocity is constant.

The Flat-Plate Wing.

One of the simplest ways of changing the direction of a horizontal airflow, so that the air is directed downwards, is to move a flat plate through the air inclined at a small positive angle to the airflow *(See Figure 3.4).* You will probably be familiar with wings which have a "flat plate" cross-section from the simple type of wing used on model aircraft produced for children of all ages. Note that the angle between the plate and the undisturbed airflow, before the flow is modified by the wing, is called the **angle of attack** and is designated by the greek letter, α.

> *Though air is a gas that can be easily compressed, when air flows over a wing at speeds less than half the speed of sound, it is considered to be incompressible.*

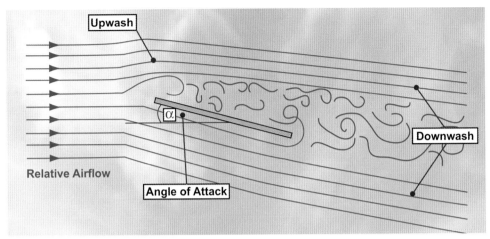

Figure 3.4 The Flat Plate Wing.

> The relative airflow flows parallel to the direction of movement of the aircraft, but in the opposite direction.

We depict the airflow in *Figure 3.4* as being horizontal, but, of course, when an aircraft is in flight its direction of flight is often not horizontal. The **angle of attack**, then, must be understood as being the angle between the wing and what we will henceforth refer to as the **relative airflow**. A light aircraft in steady, cruising flight typically has an angle of attack of around 4°.

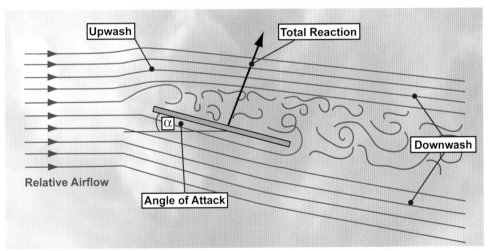

Figure 3.5 The Flat Plate Wing, showing the Total Reaction Force.

Figure 3.6 Total Reaction.

When a flat plate wing moves through the air, as shown in the diagram, it induces a small **upwash** in front of the plate followed by a small downturn or **downwash** in the air flowing over it. This "turning" of the air mass causes a reaction force to act on the flat plate wing directed both backwards and upwards *(See Figure 3.5)*. In **Principles of Flight**, we call this reaction force the **total reaction**. You have doubtless felt this type of total reaction force if you have ever held you hand out of the window of a moving car, at an angle to the airflow, as illustrated in *Figure 3.6.*

> The wing exerts a force on the air, and turns the air downwards. In turn, the wing experiences a reaction force, acting upwards and rearwards, known as the Total Reaction.

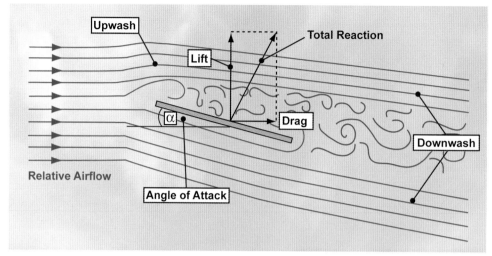

Figure 3.7 The Flat Plate Wing.

Lift is the
name given
to the
component of
the total reaction acting at right
angles to the relative airflow.

The **total reaction** is just what its name suggests it to be. The **total reaction** has the magnitude and direction of the sum of the forces which act on the flat plate wing because of its motion through the air. **Lift** is the name that we give to the **component of the total reaction force acting at right angles to the relative airflow**. The component of the total reaction force acting in the direction of the relative airflow is called **drag**. *(See Figure 3.7)* Drag will be the subject of the next chapter.

The Wing of Aerofoil Cross-section.

Following early experiments with wings of thin, flat, rectangular cross-section, pioneers of aviation soon discovered that **greater lift** could be produced for much **lower drag** by using a wing of curved cross section similar to the wing of a bird. This discovery led to the type of wing, with its distinctive **aerofoil** cross section, that is still used on light aircraft today *(See Figure 3.8)*. As monoplanes replaced biplanes, it was also realised that the curved surfaces and depth of wings with aerofoil cross sections enabled wings to be built with the structural strength required by higher performance **cantilever monoplane** aircraft. *(See Figure 3.8)*.

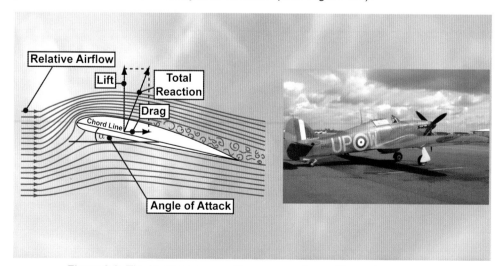

Figure 3.8 The Hurricane: a cantilever monoplane of legendary renown.

Air flows over a wing of aerofoil cross section much more smoothly than over a flat plate wing, at equal angle of attack. Notice that, on the curved aerofoil, the **angle of attack** is measured as the angle between the undisturbed **relative airflow** and a straight line, called the **chord line**, joining the leading edge and the trailing edge of the wing. (See Chapter 4 for the terminology used in the description of aerofoils.) Much less turbulence is caused in the airflow over a wing of aerofoil cross section, and such a wing is much more efficient in producing the **downwards turning of the airflow** which is the key factor in the generation of lift.

The angle between the wing's chord line and the relative airflow is called the angle of attack.

In comparing the airflow over a flat plate wing and a wing of aerofoil cross section, notice, too, that the **total reaction** is less tilted back in the latter case than in the former, and that the ratio of the length of the **lift vector** to that of the **drag vector** is much greater. This factor, together with the smoother airflow and the greater downwash, indicates why an aerofoil is a much more efficient lifting surface than the flat plate.

The importance of the **lift/drag ratio**, and **angle of attack** will be dealt with in later chapters.

Two Ways of Explaining Lift.

We have mentioned that, in describing the exact nature of how lift is generated by air moving, around a wing, we need to have some knowledge of **Physics**. In fact, to understand and explain lift, we have simultaneously to consider the **principle of the conservation of momentum, the principle of the conservation of mass, and the principle of the conservation of energy**. It is the **laws of motion** postulated by the English scientist **Sir Isaac Newton** which concern themselves with the **conservation of momentum**, while the **conservation of energy** within a moving fluid is covered by equations formulated by the Swiss physicist **Daniel Bernoulli**. So the work of both **Newton** and **Bernouilli** contributes to the full explanation of how a wing moving through the air generates lift. In some aeronautical circles, you will find people who favour the Newtonian explanation and those who support the Bernoulli explanation. However, most aerodynamicists treat the two accounts of lift-generation as being two explanations of the same phenomenon, viewed from different perspectives.

First of all, we will look at how **lift** is explained by **Isaac Newton's** explanation of **force** as defined by **rate of change of momentum**; then, we will consider **lift** as explained by the **Principle of the Conservation of Mass and Energy**, which gives us the Bernoulli explanation. (N.B. Bernoulli himself, never attempted to explain the phenomenon of **lift**. It is aerodynamicists who have explained **lift** using Bernoulli's work.)

THE NEWTONIAN EXPLANATION OF LIFT.

So far, we have established that **lift** is generated by a wing because, as it moves through the air at a certain angle of attack, the wing turns the air downwards and, itself, experiences a reaction force acting in an upwards direction. You have already had a glimpse, then, at how **lift** is accounted for by **Newton's Laws of Motion**.

You have also learnt that a wing of aerofoil cross section is more efficient than a flat plate in turning air downwards and, thus, in generating **lift**. We must now look a little more closely at the nature of this turning action on the air and examine how that action can be interpreted in the light of **Newton's Laws** to explain the nature of **lift**.

First of all, you must **not** fall under the misconception that when airflow meets a wing the air is in any way deflected downwards by "bouncing" off the inclined undersurface of the wing. This is not what happens.

Experiments show that if a solid body, such as a wing, moves through a fluid, such as air, and if the body is so shaped or inclined that it deflects or turns the fluid from its relative path, this turning action occurs because the fluid tends to stay in contact with the body and, so, is influenced by the body's shape or angle of inclination. *(See Figure 3.9).*

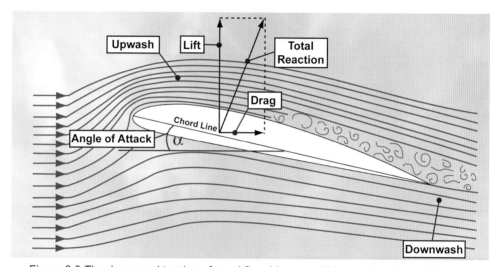

Figure 3.9 The downward turning of an airflow (downwash) by a wing of aerofoil cross-section.

So, when looking for an explanation of **lift**, we should note, primarily, that the wing is changing the direction of flow of an air mass. Now, even if the speed of the airflow were to remain unaltered, the fact that the wing is changing the direction of flow of the air means that the wing is causing a **change in the velocity** of the airflow, because velocity has both magnitude (speed) and direction. If either speed or direction changes, the velocity changes. Now a change in velocity over a given time is, by definition, **a rate of change of velocity**, in other words, **an acceleration** (See Page 16). So, in turning the air downwards, the wing is causing the air to change its velocity and, thus, to accelerate. The **force** which the wing applies to the air, in order to accelerate it, is given by the following formula derived from **Newton's 2nd Law of Motion**:

Force = mass × acceleration

But not only does the wing exert **a force on the air** causing it to change its velocity downwards (that is, causing it to **accelerate** downwards) but this change in velocity of the air also generates **a reaction force on the wing** acting in an upwards direction.

This principle - every action has an equal and opposite reaction - is the principle expressed by Newton's 3rd Law of Motion (See Page 14) and which, helps explain the nature of lift.

The reaction force experienced by the wing is the **total reaction** that we have already considered. The component of the **total reaction acting at right angles to the relative airflow is the lift force**. The higher the aircraft's speed, the greater is the **rate of change of velocity (acceleration)** imparted to the air by the wing, the greater is the **total reaction** force experienced by the wing, and, so, the greater is the **lift force**. *(See Figure 3.8.)*

As we mentioned earlier on, **Newton's Laws** concern themselves with the **principle of the conservation of momentum**, which is one of the fundamental principles of **Physics**. So let us take a very slightly different perspective on lift generation than the one we have just taken and consider the **momentum** implications in the production of **lift**. The air, because of its **mass** and its **velocity** relative to the moving wing, possesses **momentum**. **Momentum is a concept which expresses the quantity of motion possessed by a body or substance.** (See Page 8) **Momentum** is related to **mass** and **velocity** as follows:

Momentum = mass × velocity

Therefore, in imparting a downwash to the air and, thus, causing a change in the velocity of the airflow, the wing is also bringing about a **change in momentum** of the air. Now, **Newton's 1st Law** teaches us that any physical substance which is in motion will continue moving at the same velocity (that is, at the same speed and in the same straight line direction) unless acted upon by a resultant force. So, in order to turn the air downwards, thereby changing the velocity and, thus, **momentum** of the air flowing over it, the wing must exert a force on the air. If we measure this **change of momentum** of the air, over a given lapse of time, we observe a particular **rate of change of momentum**. **Newton's 2nd Law** states that the *magnitude of the resultant force acting on a body is proportional to the rate of change of momentum of the body brought about by that force*. At the same time, in order to satisfy the **principle of conservation of momentum**, **Newton's 3rd Law** tells us that any resultant force which acts on a body gives rise to an equal and opposite reaction force, which acts on the object which was the cause of the first action. In the case we are considering, the reaction predicted by **Newton's 3rd Law** is an explanation of the generation of **lift** by a wing.

Lift can be explained, then by considering the momentum implications in the following way:

In accordance with **Newton's 2nd Law**, the downwards acting force, **F**, exerted by a wing on the air flowing over it is equal to the rate of change of momentum of the airflow.

Now, **momentum = mass × velocity**

and, considering a unit mass of air, **m**

with the initial velocity of air, v_1

being changed to a final velocity, v_2 over a period of time, **t**,

the Force, **F**, exerted by the wing on the airflow may be expressed in a simplified manner by the formula:

$$F = m \times \frac{(v_2 - v_1)}{t}$$

Of course, $\frac{(v_2 - v_1)}{t}$ expresses the rate of change of velocity, which is the same as acceleration, **a**.

Therefore, we arrive again at the formula **F = m × a** which is the definition of **Force** given by **Newton's 2nd Law**. It follows, then, by **Newton's 3rd Law**, which states that **action and reaction are equal and opposite, and act on different bodies**, that the wing experiences a reaction force, known as the **total reaction, TR,** which can be expressed by:

TR = m × a

Lift, itself, of course, as you have learned, is the **vertical component of the total reaction** which acts perpendicularly to the relative airflow.

The above explanation of **lift**, then, shows how the **lift force** acting on a wing is accounted for by **Newton's Laws of Motion**. Scientists are able to confirm that the aerodynamic lift force acting on a wing in a wind tunnel, (and which can easily be measured directly by mechanical means), can be predicted accurately by **Newton's Laws** and the **principle of the conservation of momentum**.

THE BERNOULLI EXPLANATION OF LIFT.

But the Newtonian explanation of **lift**, which accounts for the **lift force** as being a reaction force acting on the wing as a result of the wing causing a downward deflection of the relative airflow, is <u>not</u> the whole story.

We have learnt that when air flows over a wing, the airflow is turned downwards by the influence of the wing. Therefore, as we have seen, the velocity of the airflow is changed. In fact, it can be observed and measured in wind-tunnel experiments that the velocity of the air varies in both magnitude (speed) and direction, at different places near the surface of the wing. This observation is a key factor in the Bernoulli explanation of lift.

Let us now look at how Daniel **Bernoulli's** teachings explain how a moving fluid can generate **lift**.

Bernoulli's Principle is concerned with the **conservation of energy**. Bernoulli taught that the **total energy** in a moving mass of fluid consists of **potential energy** (the energy due to height differences above a given datum position), **kinetic energy,** (energy due to the fluid's velocity) and energy due to the fluid's **pressure**. **Bernoulli's Principle states that for the steady flow of an ideal fluid, the sum of the three types of energy is constant**. In other words, the **total energy** in a system of fluid flow is constant. For the <u>horizontal</u> flow of an ideal fluid, then, **Bernoulli's Principle** shows that as the velocity of a fluid flow (its kinetic energy) changes, the pressure of the fluid changes as well: an increase in velocity causing a decrease in pressure, and vice versa.

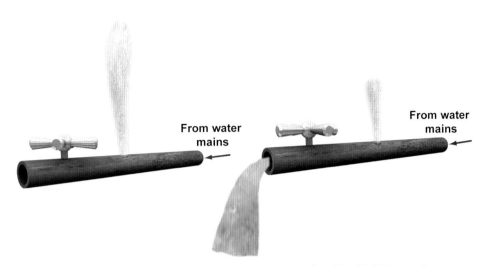

Figure 3.10 Bernoulli's Principle: The total energy of an ideal fluid is constant.

Bernoulli's Principle may be illustrated by an experiment conducted with water under pressure in a pipe. *(See Figure 3.10)* If we were to take a water pipe connected to the mains and closed off by a tap, and drill a small hole in the side of the pipe, we would see a jet of water of a certain length spurt out from the hole. The length of the jet would depend on the pressure in the pipe. If we were to open the tap a little so that the main water stream began to flow, we would notice that the jet of water spurting from the hole grows shorter. The more we opened the tap to increase the velocity of flow of the main jet, the shorter would become the jet of water spurting from the hole.

With the tap closed, there is no water flow along the pipe so the **kinetic energy** of the water is zero and all the energy in the water consists of **pressure energy**. As the tap is progressively opened, water begins to flow from the tap with increasing velocity, and the jet of water spurting from the hole gets shorter. This is because, with the tap open, the water now possesses **kinetic energy** by virtue of its velocity, or more accurately, the rate of flow of its mass. As the velocity of the water flow increases, its **kinetic energy** also increases, and so, **Bernoulli's Principle** teaches us that, the water's **pressure energy** decreases and the jet grows shorter. If the tap is closed again, the water's **kinetic energy** will decrease and its **pressure energy** rise, causing the jet from the hole to increase in length again. The **total energy** of the water **remains constant** throughout the experiment.

Aerodynamicists have discovered that **Bernoulli's Principle** of pressure variation with velocity change can accurately predict the **lift force** developed by a wing, in the same way as Newton's Laws can.

The measurement of steady, horizontal airflow around a wing, which is at a small positive angle of attack to the airflow, irrespective of whether the wing is of flat-plate or aerofoil cross-section *(see Figure 3.11, overleaf)*, shows that, when compared to the velocity of the free airstream, the air flowing over the upper surface of a wing increases in speed while the air flowing under the lower surface of the wing decreases in speed.

When compared to the speed of the freestream airflow, the air flowing over the upper surface of a wing increases in speed while the air flowing under the lower surface of the wing decreases in speed.

In accordance with **Bernoulli's Principle**, where the **kinetic energy** of the air is highest the **pressure energy** of the air is lowest and where the **kinetic energy** is

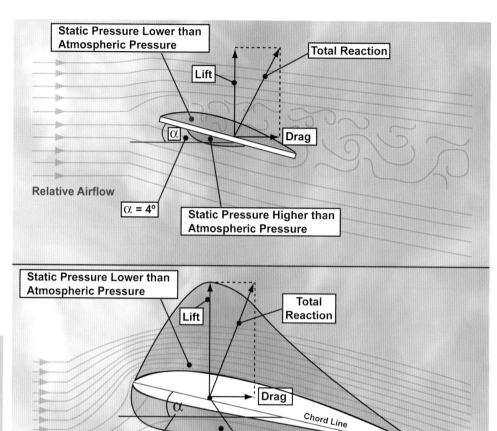

Figure 3.11 Lift force explained by the pressure differential across the upper and lower surface of a flat-plate wing and a wing of aerofoil cross-section.

The air flowing around a wing has a higher velocity over the upper surface than at the under surface. Pressure on the upper surface is, thus, lower than on the under surface. A pressure difference, therefore, exists across the wing, giving rise to an upwards acting force which is called lift.

lowest, the **pressure energy** is highest. In other words, as air flowing around a wing has a higher velocity on the upper surface than at the lower surface, the pressure at the upper surface is less than at the lower surface in such a way that a **pressure differential exists across the wing**, giving rise to a force acting in an upwards direction.

The relationship between pressure and force is expressed by the following simple equations

Pressure = $\dfrac{\text{Force}}{\text{Area}}$ Therefore, **Force = Pressure × Area**

And so, in the case of a wing, **the lift force will be proportional to the pressure differential across the wing multiplied by the surface area of the wing.**

As we have already seen, at equal angle of attack, a wing of aerofoil cross section is much more efficient than the flat plate in producing the **downwards turning of the airflow** which is the primary cause of the differences in the velocity of the airflow. It flows around the wing. Consequently, the pressure differential across a wing of aerofoil cross section is greater than that across a flat-plate wing, and the **lift-force** will be greater and the **drag** lower for the same wing surface area.

The Centre of Pressure.

Note that the **total reaction**, and the two components of the **total reaction: lift** and **drag**, are all shown originating at a point called the **Centre of Pressure.** *(See Figure 3.11 and 3.12).* **The Centre of Pressure** is defined as the point on a body through which the **total reaction** of all the aerodynamic forces affecting that body acts. When an aircraft is in cruising flight, the angle of attack is small, about 4°, and the **Centre of Pressure** lies approximately 1/3 of the way back from the wing's leading edge.

The Centre of Pressure on a wing is the point through which the total reaction and its components, the lift and drag force, are considered to act on the wing.

Do not confuse the **Centre of Pressure** with the aircraft's **Centre of Gravity** which is the point through which the **total weight** of the aircraft acts.

Low-Speed Airflow over a Wing.

So we see that variations in velocity and pressure within a mass of air flowing around an aerofoil can account for the lift generated by a wing, in accordance with the application of **Bernoulli's Principle** to the flow of an ideal fluid.

Remember, we can consider air as an ideal fluid as long as the velocity of the airflow over a wing is less than half the local speed of sound. So far, though, we have simply stated **Bernoulli's Principle**. And although by observing the downwards turning (change in direction) of air flowing around a wing, we can be certain that the velocity of the air is changing, we have not yet learned how that velocity change can be seen.

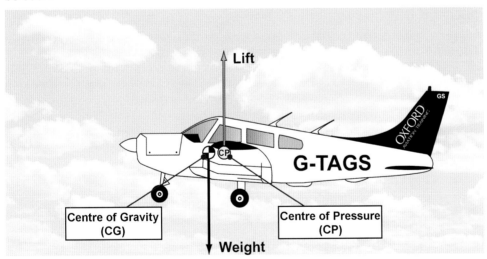

Figure 3.12 The Centre of Gravity and Centre of Pressure.

We will now, therefore, examine the airflow over a wing a little more closely and consider how the equation which illustrates **Bernoulli' s Principle** is derived. In order to do this, we must define two important terms used when describing fluid flow: **streamlines**, and **mass flow**.

Streamlines.

A **streamline** is an imaginary line within a **steady flow** of an **ideal fluid**. At every point on a **streamline** the velocity of a fluid particle is always at a tangent to the line. *(See Figure 3.13, overleaf).*

In the steady flow of an ideal fluid, only one **streamline** can pass through any given point within the airflow. Obviously, then, **streamlines** cannot cross because, if they

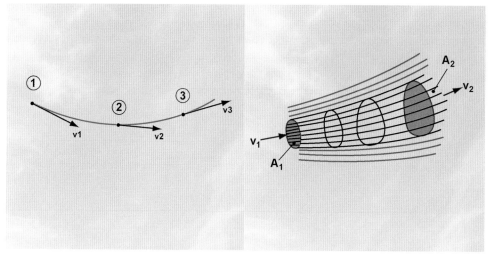

Figure 3.13 A streamline and a stream tube within a steady flow of fluid.

did, a fluid particle would be moving in two directions at once, which is impossible. In the streamline depicted in *Figure 3.13*, for instance, every fluid particle arriving at **Point 1** will have the velocity indicated by arrow v_1. The same is true for fluid particles passing through **Points 2** and **3**; they will have velocities v_2 and v_3, respectively

If we consider a region within a fluid flow containing a number of streamlines, we can define that region as being a stream tube.

The Continuity Equation (Conservation of Mass).

Let us consider the steady flow of an ideal fluid through the stream tube shown in *Figure 3.13*. The areas of cross sections of the stream tube at **Point 1** and **Point 2** are **A1** and **A2**, respectively. The velocity of the fluid at **Point 1** is v_1 and the velocity of the airflow at **Point 2** is v_2. As the fluid is non compressible (i.e. of constant density ρ), and as there can be no flow across the streamlines, it follows that the **mass** of fluid flowing across the two cross sections, over any given period of time, must be the same. This principle, which is an expression of the concept of Conservation of Mass, is known as the **Principle of Continuity**. The **Principle of Continuity** is developed in the blue box below. If you are not interested in the mathematics, just skip the box.

The **Principle of Continuity** states that, for a stream tube, such as the one depicted in *(Figure 3.13)*, the **rate of mass flow** at Point 1 must be the same as the **rate of mass flow** at Point 2.

Now, **mass flow** can be considered as **mass per unit time**; i.e. $\dfrac{\text{mass}}{\text{time}}$

But density $(\rho) = \dfrac{\text{mass}}{\text{Volume}} = \dfrac{\text{mass}}{\text{Area (A)} \times \text{distance}}$

distance $=$ velocity $(v) \times$ time

So, $\rho = \dfrac{\text{mass}}{\text{A} \times \text{v} \times \text{time}}$ and, from this, $\dfrac{\text{mass}}{\text{time}} = \rho \times A \times v$

Therefore, rate of mass flow $= \rho Av$

And, from the **Principle of Continuity**, as rate of mass flow entering the stream tube equals the rate of mass flow leaving the stream tube:

$\rho_1 A_1 v1 = \rho_2 A_2 v_2$

And, since ρ is a constant for an incompressible fluid,

$A_1 v_1 = A_2 v_2$

And so, the **Principle of Continuity** teaches us that the product **Av** must have the same value at any point in the **stream tube**. We can, therefore, deduce that:

Av = constant for any region of flow of an ideal fluid

This equation is known as the **Continuity Equation**.

The **Continuity Equation** derived from the **Principle of Continuity** tells us that, in any region of fluid flow, the cross-sectional area, **A**, of the stream tube multiplied by the velocity, **v**, of the fluid always gives us the same constant value, and when **A** increases, **v** must decrease, and vice versa.

The **Continuity Equation** also enables us to interpret the streamline picture. If the cross-sectional area of a stream tube decreases, the distance between individual streamlines which make up the stream tube decreases, too, so the streamlines are closer together. But as velocity, **v**, multiplied by cross-sectional area, **A**, is a constant, as **A** decreases **v** must increase. Therefore, we see that widely spaced streamlines within any region of fluid flow indicate a lower flow velocity than the velocity of the fluid in a region of flow where the streamlines are close together.

So, in summary, for the steady flow of an ideal fluid:

increase in cross-sectional area = **decrease in velocity of**
of stream tube **fluid flow**

decrease in cross-sectional area = **increase in velocity of**
of stream tube **fluid flow**

tightly packed streamlines = higher velocity

widely spaced streamlines = lower velocity

Looking back at *Figure 3.13*, we can see that because **A2** is larger than **A$_1$**, the velocity **v$_2$** must be less than **v$_1$**; and, so, the fluid particles in the stream tube must have been decelerated in moving from **A$_1$** to **A$_2$**. Newton's 2nd Law tells us that for this to happen, a resultant force must have been applied in the direction from **A$_2$** towards **A$_1$**. Now, if the flow is horizontal, gravitational force is constant over the whole length of flow. But, the deceleration __can__ have been caused by a greater internal pressure **(Force/Area)** acting at **A$_2$** than at **A$_1$**. We can conclude, therefore, that **in the steady, horizontal flow of an ideal (incompressible) fluid, the internal pressure of the fluid is greatest where the speed of the airflow is lowest, and *vice versa*.** (This, of course, is the same statement as that made by **Bernoulli's Principle** and provides a clue as to the close relationship between the Bernoulli and the Newtonian theories of lift.)

The Principle of Continuity teaches that the rate of mass flow of an incompressible fluid through a stream tube is constant.

The Principle of Continuity teaches that in a streamtube of decreasing cross-sectional area, the speed of an incompressible airflow will increase.

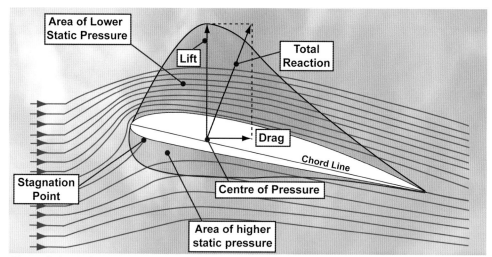

Figure 3.14 Airflow around an aerofoil at a small angle of attack – streamlines and variations in static pressure within the airflow.

Let us now consider the case of steady low-speed airflow around an aerofoil, knowing that, in these conditions, air can be assumed to be an ideal fluid. The study of airflow around aerofoils is often conducted in a wind tunnel. And if smoke is introduced into the airflow, it distributes itself within the airflow to form **streamlines** which make it actually possible to see the airflow around the aerofoil.

If we observe such a situation where an aerofoil is angled to the relative airflow at a small positive angle of attack, we can observe that the streamlines made visible by the smoke are closer together in the air flowing over the aerofoil than those in the airflow passing underneath the aerofoil. This situation is depicted in *Figure 3.14, above*.

Just under the leading edge of the aerofoil, the airflow is brought to rest; this is called the **stagnation point**. There is a second, less important, **stagnation point** at the trailing edge.

We can, thus, now see for ourselves, from the streamlines, the correctness of the prediction that the turning effect of the wing on the air flowing around an aerofoil causes a change in the local speed of the airflow such that the speed over the upper surface of a wing is higher than the speed of the air flowing underneath the wing. As we have just learnt, where the speed (or velocity) of flow is lowest, the pressure of the airflow is highest and where airflow speed is highest the pressure is lowest. Therefore, there exists a pressure differential across the wing, which generates a net force (pressure differential × wing area) acting in an upwards direction.

The explanation just given is a simple expression of how **Bernoulli's Principle** of **pressure variation** with **velocity change** accounts for **lift force**.

Let us now look at how **Bernoulli's Principle** is expressed through **Bernoulli's Equation**.

BERNOULLI'S PRINCIPLE.

Bernoulli's Principle concerning the relationship between pressure variations and the velocity changes in a fluid flow expresses a fundamental relationship of fluid mechanics, and is derived from **Newton's Laws**. This close connection between **Bernoulli's Principle** and **Newton's Laws** reveals, perhaps, that the two interpretations of lift that we have been considering – pressure differential across the wing, on the one hand, and rate of change of momentum of the air flow, on the other – boil down, ultimately, to one and the same thing: **a unitary theory of lift**. That depth of analysis goes beyond the scope of this book, but it is fitting that, as pilots, you be aware of the current scientific discussions on the important subject of lift.

As we have mentioned, the generation of lift by an aircraft wing involves three fundamental principles of Physics: the **Conservation of Momentum,** the **Conservation of Mass,** and the **Conservation of Energy**. You have learnt that the explanation of lift using **Bernoulli's Principle** concentrates on the issue of the **Conservation of Energy**, but, inevitably, the other two principles are involved, too.

We have already seen from the **Continuity Equation** – expressing **Conservation of Mass** - that the rate of mass flow of an ideal fluid is constant at all points along a stream tube. The **Continuity Equation** has also taught us that, within any region of flow, where the streamlines are widely spaced, a lower velocity of flow is indicated, and where the streamlines are close together a higher flow-velocity is indicated. We have also deduced from the **Continuity Equation** that the pressure of the fluid is greatest where the speed of flow is lowest, and *vice versa*.

The total energy within an ideal fluid flow is constant. For a horizontal flow, total energy consists of kinetic energy and pressure energy.

Bernoulli's Principle states that the <u>total energy</u> **within an ideal fluid flow is** <u>constant</u>. You have also learnt that for a <u>horizontal</u> flow of ideal fluid, such as the flow of low speed air around a wing, the **total energy** in the airflow consists of the **kinetic energy** of airflow, that is the energy it possesses by virtue of its mass and its velocity, plus the airflow's **pressure energy**, that is, the energy due to the pressure of the air acting in all directions within the flow.

The pressure that moving air exerts on an object, by virtue of the air's velocity, is called dynamic pressure.

Dynamic and Static Pressure in an Airflow.
If moving air is brought to rest, its **kinetic energy** does work on the object which brings it to rest. In being brought to rest, the air applies a force on the object - which of course will have a certain frontal area - and, therefore, the air will exert a pressure on that object due, solely, to the initial velocity of the air. The name that aerodynamicists give to this kind of pressure is **dynamic pressure**. *Figure 3.15 overleaf*, illustrates how the **dynamic pressure** of an airflow may be approximately registered by a flat plate attached to a wall by a spring. We will assume that atmospheric static pressure acts on every square inch of the plate, on both the front and back surfaces. So, the value of pressure sensed by the spring will be the value of the **dynamic pressure**, and the compression of the spring is due to the **dynamic pressure** alone. (As we have mentioned, this method registers **dynamic pressure** only approximately. To measure **dynamic pressure** <u>exactly</u>, it is equivalent to the **static pressure**, exerted within the moving airflow which would have to be acting on the rear of the plate, not atmospheric pressure. However, the present reasoning is accurate enough to give you an initial idea of the nature of dynamic pressure.)

You can feel dynamic pressure for yourself, if you hold your hand out of the window of a moving car, with your palm perpendicular to the air flow *(see Figure 3.16, overleaf)*.

To contrast **dynamic pressure** with what Bernoulli's Principle calls, simply, the **pressure energy** in an airflow - that is, the pressure in the airflow which acts in all

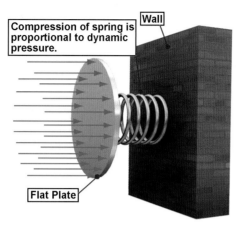

Figure 3.15 Dynamic pressure: Airflow
striking a plate.

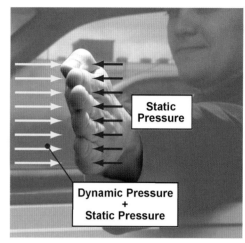

Figure 3.16 You can feel **dynamic pressure**
for yourself.

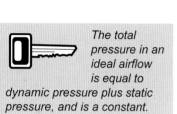

The total pressure in an ideal airflow is equal to dynamic pressure plus static pressure, and is a constant.

directions - **pressure energy** is referred to in most text books for pilots as **static pressure**. So, if we think of all the energy in a moving mass of air as being pressure, we can re-state **Bernoulli's Principle** for airflow as follows:

Total Pressure = Dynamic Pressure + Static Pressure = Constant

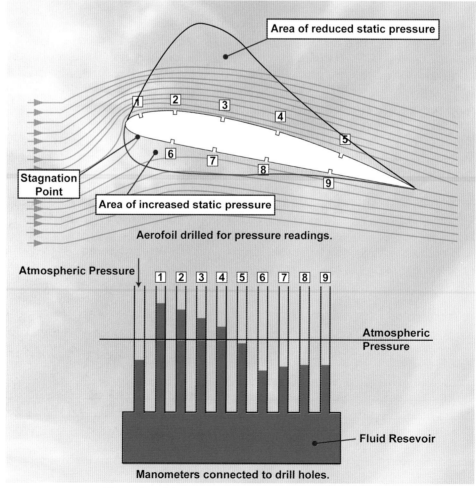

In a horizontal ideal airflow around a wing, when dynamic pressure increases, static pressure decreases, and vice versa.

Figure 3.17 Measuring static pressure around a wing.

N.B. When we are considering **Bernoulli's Principle** applied to airflow around the wings and/or fuselage of an aircraft in flight, do not confuse **static pressure** with the ambient atmospheric pressure. **In Bernoulli's Principle, static pressure refers to the pressure exerted in all directions within the air flow, itself, not the ambient atmospheric pressure measured by a stationary observer.**

Static pressure is exerted in all directions.

The variation in static pressure in the airflow around a wing has traditionally been measured in wind tunnels by using an aerofoil with small holes drilled into the upper and lower surfaces and connecting these holes to manometer tubes containing a suitable liquid. The different heights of the liquid within the tubes shows the distribution of static pressure around the aerofoil. *(See Figure 3.17, previous page.)*

So we may now, in the light of what we have learned so far, reword **Bernoulli's Principle** applied to the airflow which meets an aerofoil at a small positive angle of attack, at speeds below half the local speed of sound, as follows:

Total pressure in the airflow around an aerofoil is constant. Over the upper surface of the wing, where there is an increase in velocity, the dynamic pressure increases and the static pressure falls. Below the wing where there is a decrease in the velocity of the airflow, the static pressure increases and the dynamic pressure falls.

Over the upper surface of a wing, the velocity of the airflow increases and static pressure falls. Under the wing, velocity decreases and static pressure rises.

The static pressure is highest of all at the **stagnation point**, just under the leading edge of the aerofoil.

From **Bernoulli's Principle**, then, we can conclude that the **pressure differential which exists across the aerofoil can account for the lift force which acts upwards from the area of higher pressure to the area of lower pressure.**

Bernoulli's Equation.
Let us now look at the equation which expresses **Bernoulli's Principle** mathematically. The derivation of **Bernoulli's Equation** is beyond the scope of a book of this nature, but for those of you who are curious to know how it is derived, the derivation is placed at the end of this chapter, before the questions section.

The pressure differential acting across the aerofoil acts in an upwards direction and can account for the lift force developed by a wing.

Here we will just state **Bernoulli's Equation** for air of density ρ, flowing horizontally over an aircraft flying at a velocity, **v**, well below 300 knots, so that we can make all the assumptions we have mentioned in the chapter about the air being treated as an ideal fluid. Expressed as an equation, then, for this particular case, **Bernoulli's Principle** may be written:

p + ½ρv² = constant

This is **Bernoulli's Equation**, where ½ρv² represents the **dynamic pressure** of the air flow, sometimes referred to by the symbol **Q**, and **p** represents the **static pressure** in the airflow.

Any increase in the speed of an incompressible airflow will result in an increase in dynamic pressure and a reduction in static pressure.

The total pressure of the airflow, **p + ½ρv²** is a **constant**, so that any increase in velocity will result in an increase in **dynamic pressure** and a reduction in **static pressure**.

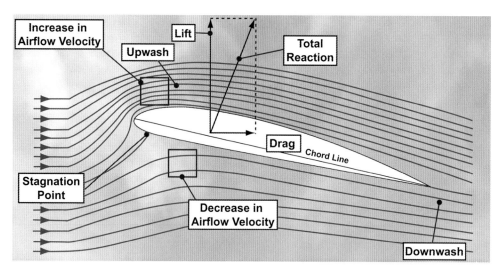

Figure 3.18 Streamlines in an airflow meeting a wing.

How Bernoulli's Equation Predicts the Lift Force Generated by a Wing.

Let us now review all of what we have learnt about how Bernoulli's Principle explains the lift force on a wing.

Figure 3.18, represents a wing of aerofoil cross section in a wind tunnel where smoke has been introduced into make the streamlines visible to us. There is a small positive angle of attack between the wing and the relative airflow. The exact value of this angle of attack need not concern us for the moment, but, it will lie between +2° and +8°. The angle in the diagram is not drawn to scale.

The streamlines show an **upwash** in the airflow just upstream of the wing and a **downwash** downstream of the wing. This **turning effect** of the wing on the airflow causes a **rate of change of momentum** in the air mass which, in turn, is the cause of the variations in the velocity of the airflow around the wing. The streamlines are relatively close together close to one another, just above the upper surface of the wing and relatively far apart below the wing's under surface.

As we have learnt from our study of the **Continuity Equation**, widely spaced streamlines within any region of airflow indicate a lower air velocity than the air velocity in a region of flow where the streamlines are close together, and vice versa. We can see, therefore, from our observation of the streamlines that the speed of the airflow over the upper surface of the wing is higher than the free stream airflow in front of the wing and that the speed of the airflow beneath the wing is lower than the free stream airflow.

Bernoulli's Equation, $p + \frac{1}{2}\rho v^2$ = constant, teaches us that while the total pressure energy within an airflow is constant, where there are variations in the <u>velocity</u> of the airflow, there will be corresponding variations in **static** and **dynamic pressure**. Where the speed of the airflow is highest, dynamic pressure will be highest and **static pressure** will be lowest. Conversely, where the speed of the airflow is lowest, **dynamic pressure** will be lowest and **static pressure** will be highest.

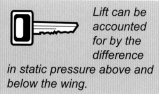
Lift can be accounted for by the difference in static pressure above and below the wing.

As it is **static pressure** which acts in all directions (whereas **dynamic pressure** acts only in the direction of flow), it is the difference in **static pressure** above and below the wing which causes the **pressure differential** across the wing and the corresponding **lift force**. The pattern of pressure distribution over the wing that we are considering is depicted in *Figure 3.19*. The aerodynamic force acts from the **higher relative static pressure** beneath the wing upwards in the direction of the **lower static pressure** above the wing. This force can be measured in a wind tunnel and is predicted by **Bernoulli's Equation**.

The streamlines show us that the speed of the airflow is highest <u>over</u> the forward section of the wing and lowest <u>under</u> the forward section of the wing. Consequently, we see that the pressure differential across the wing is not evenly distributed. **Both the decrease in pressure acting on the upper surface of the wing and the increase in pressure acting on the lower surface of the wing are most pronounced over the wing's forward section.**

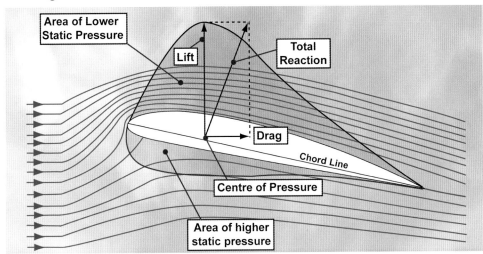

Figure 3.19 Pressure distribution over a wing.

We observe, then, and Bernoulli predicts, that, where the local speed of the airflow is greatest, the static pressure is lowest, the upwards-directed pressure differential is greatest and, therefore, the lift force is also the greatest. You should note, too, that, at a constant angle of attack, if the speed of the free-stream airflow increases, the result of this general increase in speed will be to increase the value of the pressure differential across the wing and to further increase the lift force.

Remember that the point on the wing through which the **total reaction** of all the aerodynamic forces acts is called the **Centre of Pressure**.

VARIATION OF LIFT AND PRESSURE DISTRIBUTION WITH ANGLE OF ATTACK.

The pattern of the lift and pressure distribution around a wing of typical aerofoil cross section changes with **angle of attack. This change** is shown in *Figure 3.20, overleaf,* where we assume that the velocity of the free-stream airflow is constant for all angles of attack.

We have already discussed the reason why aircraft have wings of aerofoil cross section. Typically, the wing of a light training aircraft will have an upper surface of pronounced positive camber and an under surface which is straighter. (Aerofoil terminology is covered in the next chapter.) The angle of attack is the angle between the aerofoil's chord line and the relative (free stream) airflow. Angle of attack is usually represented by the symbol α (the Greek letter "alpha"). The relative airflow is not shown in *Figure 3.20*, but the angle of attack is indicated.

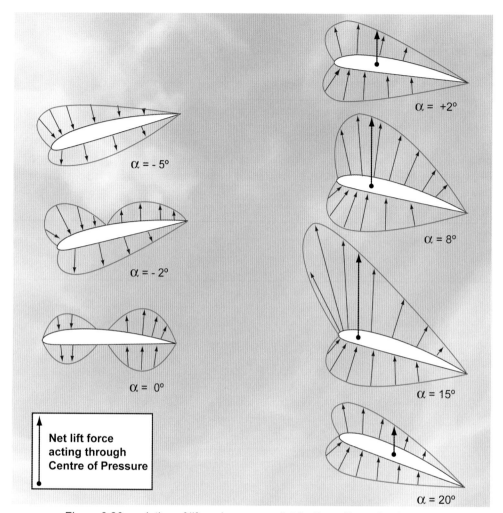

Figure 3.20 variation of lift and pressure distribution with angle of attack.

In *Figure 3.20,* the relative pressures are represented by arrows. A higher relative pressure is depicted by arrows pointing into the surface of the aerofoil, while arrows pointing outwards from the surface represent a lower relative pressure. With an angle of attack of about -5° the **stagnation point** in the airflow is on the upper surface of the wing, and the lift is negative.

-2° is a typical angle of attack for zero-lift - that is, when the upwards - acting force is equal to the downward acting force. The **stagnation point** remains on the upper surface of the wing. Note that even though the upward and downward acting forces are equal, the distribution of the lines of action of the forces gives the wing a nose-down **pitching moment.**

At 0° angle of attack, there is a net upwards-acting lift force but the distribution of the forces still causes a nose-down **pitching moment** on the aerofoil (though not necessarily on the aircraft a whole).

Lift can be considered as acting through the Centre of Pressure.

At 2° angle of attack, the **stagnation point** is on the lower surface of the wing. Lift is positive and we show the lift component of the total reaction force acting through the **Centre of Pressure** which is at a typical position on the aerofoil, forward of the aerofoil's geometric centre.

During flight, the angle of attack is usually between 2° and 8°. During your flying training, though, you will experience angles of attack of 16° and greater when learning to recognize and recover from a stall. Therefore, we have shown representative angles of attack up to 20°. The diagrams of the aerofoils between 2° and 20° angle of attack include a depiction of the lift force.

As the angle of attack increases from 2° to 15° the **Centre of Pressure** gradually moves forwards and the resultant lift force increases in magnitude, until reaching about 16° (this is a typical stalling angle of attack for many light training aircraft). Beyond this lift force decreases abruptly and the **Centre of Pressure** moves rearwards again. This abrupt decrease in lift and rearwards movement of the **Centre of Pressure** is due to the separation of the airflow from the wing's upper surface. You will learn about separation in the Chapter on Stalling.

Lift increases with increasing angle of attack until reaching the stalling angle of attack of around 16°, at which point lift decreases abruptly.

Notice that the gradual forwards movement of the **Centre of Pressure** with increasing angle of attack (up to the stalling angle of attack) tends to cause the angle of attack to increase even more, which, in turn, will cause the **Centre of Pressure** to move further forwards, and so on to the stall. This phenomenon is called instability and is one of the problems that aircraft designers have to deal with. Instability of this nature is, of course, why conventional aircraft have tailplanes (horizontal stabilisers)

One final point that you should note from the pressure distribution patterns in *Figure 3.20* is that where the lift force is relatively large (angles of attack from 2° to 15°), the greater contribution to the lift is made by the upper surface of the wing. Notice that the value of the higher pressure on the under surface of the wing changes relatively little between 2° and 20° angle of attack. You will not be surprised, therefore, to learn from your flying instructor that keeping the upper surface of an aircraft wing free from contamination (for example, through accumulations of ice and/or water) is critical.

Angle of Attack.

As we defined earlier, the **angle of attack** is the angle between the aerofoil's chord line and the relative (free stream) airflow. See *Figure 3.21*. Do not confuse the **angle of attack** with the **pitch attitude** of the aircraft. Your flying instructor will have a lot to say to you about **pitch attitude** and will define **attitude** for you precisely. As an approximate definition, we may say that **pitch attitude** is the angle of the aircraft's nose relative to the horizon.

Angle of attack is the angle between an aerofoil's chord line and the relative airflow.

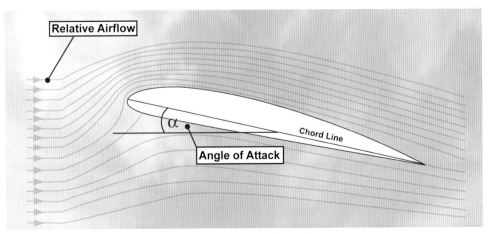

Figure 3.21 Angle of Attack.

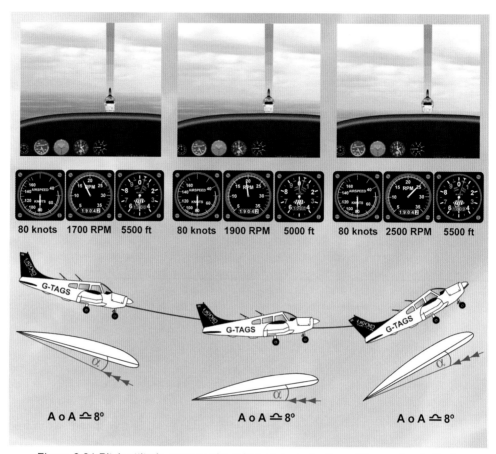

Figure 3.21 Pitch attitude must not be taken as an indication of the angle of attack.

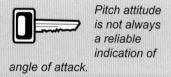

Pitch attitude is not always a reliable indication of angle of attack.

An aircraft is rarely following the line of flight in which its nose is pointing and, therefore, **pitch attitude** is mostly <u>not</u> a good indication of **angle of attack**. Certainly, in maintaining level flight at different airspeeds and power settings, the angle of attack is increased (to fly slower) or decreased (to fly faster) by raising or lowering the nose of the aircraft, but this relationship between **angle of attack** and **pitch attitude** can not be assumed in all cases.

At a given aircraft weight, a given angle of attack corresponds to a particular airspeed. The pilot of an aircraft may elect to descend at, say, 80 knots, fly straight and level at 80 knots, or climb at 80 knots *(see Figure 3.21)*. **Because the airspeed remains the same, the angle of attack will be the same in all cases. Pitch attitude** (and power) will, however, <u>not</u> be the same in all cases because the aircraft is, respectively, descending, flying level or climbing.

Remember, then, you must <u>not</u> treat the **pitch attitude** of the aircraft as an indication of the **angle of attack** between the wing and the relative airflow.

SUMMARY OF THE NATURE OF LIFT.

As we said earlier in this chapter, both the Bernoulli and the Newtonian explanations of **lift** accurately predict the magnitude and direction of the resultant aerodynamic force acting on a wing. Both the **rate of change of momentum of the downwards deflected airflow** over the wing and **the pressure differential across the wing** account for the **aerodynamic lift** that the wing generates. Furthermore, **Bernoulli's Principle** concerning the relationship between pressure variations and velocity changes in a fluid flow is ultimately derived from **Newton's Laws**.

Though the advanced mathematical treatment of **lift**, which is required to fully explain this most important of forces in terms of the **Principles of Flight**, is beyond the scope of this book, it is important for all pilots who wish to understand the nature of **lift** to know that the Bernoulli and Newtonian predictions of the **lift force** measurable in a wind tunnel are <u>both</u> accurate.

A very concise explanation of the way the aerodynamic force generated by a wing is accounted for by both **Bernoulli's Principle** and **Newton's Laws** is given on the website of the National Aeronautics and Space Administration (NASA) of the United States of America. NASA writes that:

"Lift and drag are mechanical forces generated on the surface of an object as it interacts with a fluid. The net fluid force is generated by the pressure acting over the entire surface of a closed body [Bernoulli]. The pressure varies around a body in a moving fluid because it is related to the fluid momentum (mass × velocity). The velocity varies around the body because of the flow deflection [Newton]..." (Our brackets.)

THE GENERAL LIFT EQUATION AND THE COEFFICIENT OF LIFT.

In our consideration of **lift** up to now, we have assumed that the speed of the free stream airflow is constant. Furthermore, one of our initial assumptions was that air flowing at low speeds typical of light aircraft flight is **incompressible** so, because we have not considered airflow at different altitudes and in different atmospheric conditions, we have taken **density** to be constant, too.

We have also discussed briefly that if the angle of attack remains constant, and the speed of the airflow increases, **lift** will increase.

The above are general observations, but if we wish to calculate the lift produced by any aerofoil in any conditions we have to take into account not only variations in angle of attack, airspeed and air density, we also have to consider the shape of the aerofoil, particularly the amount of camber on its upper surface. All these factors are taken into consideration by the **Lift Formula:**

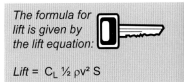

The formula for lift is given by the lift equation:

Lift = C_L ½ ρv^2 S

Lift = C_L ½ ρv^2 S

The **Lift Formula** is one of the few formulae that you will be required to remember for the PPL theoretical knowledge examination. **Lift, remember, is a force acting perpendicularly to the free-stream relative airflow.** In the **Lift Formula:**

C_L is the **coefficient of lift** which takes account of the **shape** of the aerofoil and the aerofoil's **angle of attack** with the relative airflow. C_L has no units

½   is a constant which is arrived at by experiment.

ρ   is a Greek letter (pronounced "roe") which represents the density of the air. ρ has the units **kg/m³**

v   is the **velocity** of the free-stream relative airflow which is the same as the **true airspeed** of the aircraft. Notice that lift varies according to the **square** of the velocity; **v** has the units **m/sec**

S   is the surface area of the wing. **S** has the units **m²**.

The **Lift Equation** reveals that the **lift force** produced by a wing is proportional to dynamic pressure, ½ ρv², to the area of the wing **S** and to the coefficient of lift **C_L**, which represents the **shape** of the wing and **angle of attack** of the wing with the relative airflow.

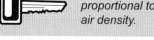

Lift is directly proportional to air density.

So what does the **Lift Equation, Lift = C_L ½ ρv² S**, tell us which is of practical use to the pilot?

Well, it tells him several things of varying degrees of usefulness:

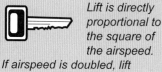

Lift is directly proportional to the square of the airspeed. If airspeed is doubled, lift increases by a factor of 4.

- **Lift is directly proportional to air density**. This information is not very useful because a pilot can do nothing about **air density**, although he might deduce that the higher he flies, the lower will be the **air density**, and he might suspect that this fact might somehow affect the aircraft's performance.

- **Lift is directly proportional to wing area.** That can be useful knowledge if an aircraft is fitted with Fowler Flaps which extend from the wing, and so increase area. The pilot might deduce, for instance, that with Fowler Flaps extended, he can generate the same lift at lower airspeeds.

- **Lift is directly proportional to the square of the airspeed;** so, if the aircraft flies twice as fast, the lift generated by the wings will increase fourfold. This is very useful information, because the pilot will see immediately that his ability to control the aircraft's speed gives him direct control over the lift produced by the wings.

- **Lift is directly proportional to the Coefficient of Lift, C_L.** This is also very useful information. We have learnt that **C_L** includes both the **shape** of the wing and the **angle of attack** of the wing with the free-stream relative airflow. By increasing the **angle of attack**, the pilot can increase **C_L** and so increase the lift produced by the wing, **but not beyond the angle of attack for maximum lift.** By selecting flap, the pilot can also modify the **shape** of his aircraft's wing and, therefore also modify the value of **C_L**. He will understand, therefore, that the selection or deselection of flap will affect the lift generated by the wing.

The **Lift Equation** also reveals a relationship between the speed of an aircraft and angle of attack. For any phase of straight, steady flight the aircraft's weight must be exactly balanced by lift. Thus, assuming that air density, wing surface area, and wing shape are constant, we see that any change in airspeed, **v**, must require a corresponding change in **C_L** if Lift is to remain constant and steady flight maintained. Now, the only part of **C_L** that the pilot can control is the **angle of attack**. So if airspeed, **v**, is increased, the **angle of attack** must be decreased and *vice versa*.

From this fact, we may deduce that in conditions of steady flight, **for each airspeed a specific angle of attack, C_L is required**. This relationship reveals one of the fundamental principles of flying a light aircraft: that is, in steady, straight flight, **airspeed is determined primarily by angle of attack**. And, in steady, straight flight, the angle of attack is controlled by the pilot by selecting an appropriate pitch attitude with the control column or control wheel. At the same time, he uses the throttle to adjust engine power to maintain level flight, or a constant rate of descent or climb. Whether the pilot changes angle of attack first, or engine power, when selecting a new airspeed, is something you will be taught by your flying instructor.

You will appreciate, then, that by referring to the **Lift Equation**, the pilot may at all times recall the fundamental relationships which affect the performance of his aircraft.

Variation of Coefficient of Lift with Angle of Attack

To bring this chapter on **lift** to a close, let us examine a graph illustrating how the Coefficient of Lift, C_L, and so (because **lift** is directly proportional to C_L) the **total lift** produced by any given wing, varies with **angle of attack**.

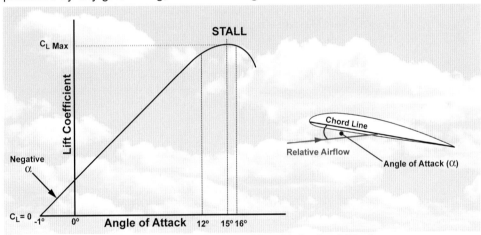

Figure 3.22 The variation of C_L with Angle of Attack.

Figure 3.22 shows the graph of C_L against **angle of attack** for a typical aerofoil. The principal points to note from the graph are:

- As we are considering an aerofoil cross section, the wing will produce a net lift force even at 0° **angle of attack**, and even at a very small negative angles of attack. This is a property of most non-symmetrical aerofoils with a cambered upper surface. A flat plate and a symmetrical aerofoil would generate no lift at 0° **angle of attack**.

- The graph is a straight line between 0° and 12°, indicating a uniform increase in lift with increasing **angle of attack**.

- Beyond 12° angle of attack, the graph begins to curve over towards a maximum value of lift. In this region, there is only a small increase in lift with increasing angle of attack.

- Lift reaches a maximum at about 15° to 16° **angle of attack**. Above this angle, the graph begins to curve downwards indicating that the lift is decreasing.

The Coefficient of Lift, C_L, reaches a maximum just before the wing stalls.

We see, therefore, that, for small angles of attack, any increase in the angle at which the wing meets the relative air flow leads to an increase in lift. But, after a given angle is reached (i.e. the angle of attack for maximum lift), any further increase in angle of attack will cause a relatively rapid decrease in lift, as shown by the sharp downturn in the graph. The angle at which lift begins to decrease is called the **stalling angle of attack**. You will learn more about stalling in a later chapter, but you should note here the important fact that **a wing stalls at a given angle of attack, not at a given speed,** although you will often come across the term stalling speed when considering stalling from straight and level flight.

SUMMARY.

In this chapter, we have attempted to explain the nature of the **lift force** generated by an aircraft wing and to investigate the factors which affect that **lift force**. When considering the motion of a wing through the air (remember, it is the relative motion of the air and the wing which is important), we have looked at the three very important scientific principles of the **Conservation of Mass**, the **Conservation of Momentum** and the **Conservation of Energy**. We have seen how **Newton's Laws of Motion** (conservation of momentum) and **Bernoulli's Principle** (conservation of energy) <u>both</u> account for the generation of **lift** by a wing. **Lift** can be accounted for as a reaction to the downward turning of the airflow (Newton), <u>and</u> by the upwards acting pressure differential across the wing (Bernoulli). In some aeronautical circles you will find people who favour the Newtonian explanation and those who support the Bernoulli explanation. Most aerodynamicists, however, treat the two accounts of lift generation as being two explanations of the same phenomenon, viewed from different perspectives.

For the pilot, the deep science is not of prime importance as long as he understands the **basic nature of lift**.

It is generally recognised that the **Lift Equation, Lift = $C_L \frac{1}{2} \rho v^2 S$,** permits the pilot to keep the various factors affecting **lift** and **airspeed** clearly in mind. By committing the **lift equation** to memory and referring to it as required, the pilot may readily appreciate how **lift** is influenced by **angle of attack**, the **shape** of the wing cross-section, the **density** of the air, **airspeed** and the **area** of the wings. The pilot should, therefore, have a good basic understanding of how the lift force is acting on his aircraft in flight, whatever manoeuvre he is performing.

Representative PPL - type questions to test your theoretical knowledge of Lift.

1.   Dynamic pressure equals:

    a.   total pressure plus static pressure
    b.   static pressure minus total pressure
    c.   total pressure divided by static pressure
    d.   total pressure minus static pressure

2.   Relative airflow is _____ and _____ the movement of the aircraft.

    a.   perpendicular to   opposite to
    b.   parallel to   opposite to
    c.   perpendicular to   in the same direction as
    d.   parallel to   in the same direction as

3.   In straight and level flight, the free stream airflow pressure compared to the pressure of the air flowing under the forward section of a wing is:

    a.   equal
    b.   higher
    c.   lower
    d.   of equal pressure but travelling faster

4.   The velocity of air flowing over the upper surface of the wing of a typical training light-aircraft increases when compared to the velocity of the free airflow. Which of the options below best describes the pressure considerations of the air flowing over the wing:

    a.   its dynamic pressure will decrease and its static pressure increase
    b.   its dynamic pressure will remain constant and its static pressure will decrease
    c.   its dynamic pressure will increase and its static pressure decrease
    d.   its dynamic pressure will decrease and its static pressure remain constant

5.   The air flow over the wing's upper surface in straight and level flight, when compared with the airflow that is unaffected by the wing, will have:

    a.   a higher velocity
    b.   a higher density
    c.   a reduced velocity
    d.   the same velocity

6.   Which of the four answer options most correctly completes the sentence?

      Increasing speed also increases lift because

      a.   lift is directly proportional to velocity
      b.   lift is directly proportional to the square of the airspeed
      c.   the increased velocity of the relative wind overcomes the increased drag
      d.   increasing speed decreases drag

7.   1 - Air has mass
      2 - Air is not compressible
      3 - Air is able to flow or change its shape when subject to even small pressures
      4 - The viscosity of air is very high
      5 - Moving air has kinetic energy

      The correct combination of true statements, from the above options, is:

      a.   1, 2, 3 and 5
      b.   2, 3 and 4
      c.   1 and 4
      d.   1, 3, and 5

8.   A moving mass of air possesses kinetic energy. An object placed in the path of such a moving mass of air will be subject to:

      a.   static pressure and dynamic pressure
      b.   static pressure
      c.   dynamic pressure
      d.   dynamic pressure minus static pressure

9.   The Principle of Continuity states that, in a Streamtube of decreasing cross-sectional area, the speed of a subsonic and incompressible airflow will:

      a.   remain the same
      b.   decrease
      c.   increase
      d.   always become sonic

10.   The angle of attack of an aerofoil is defined as:

      a.   the angle between the chord line of the aerofoil and the horizon
      b.   the angle between the chord line of the aerofoil and the relative airflow
      c.   the angle between the chord line of the aerofoil and the aircraft's longitudinal axis
      d.   the angle between the mean camber line of the aerofoil and the relative airflow

11.   An aerofoil section is designed to produce lift resulting from a difference in the:

        a.   negative air pressure below and a vacuum above the surface
        b.   higher air pressure below the surface and lower air pressure above the surface
        c.   vacuum below the surface and greater air pressure above the surface
        d.   higher air pressure at the leading edge than at the trailing edge

12.   Which of the sentences below makes the most correct statement about Lift?

        a.   Lift acts perpendicularly to the wing chord line
        b.   Lift acts parallel to the wing chord line
        c.   Lift acts perpendicularly to the wing mean camber line
        d.   Lift acts perpendicularly to the relative airflow

13.   On an aerofoil section, the force of lift acts perpendicular to and the force of drag acts parallel to the:

        a.   relative airflow
        b.   longitudinal axis
        c.   chord line
        d.   aerofoil section upper surface

14.   A positively cambered aerofoil starts to produce lift at an angle of attack of approximately:

        a.   4 to 6 degrees
        b.   0 degrees
        c.   minus 4 degrees
        d.   16 degrees

15.   If the Angle of Attack and other factors remain constant, and the airspeed is doubled, lift will be:

        a.   doubled
        b.   one quarter of what it was
        c.   the same
        d.   quadrupled

16.   Which of the answer options most correctly completes the sentence?

        The amount of lift a wing produces is directly proportional to:

        a.   the dynamic pressure minus the static pressure
        b.   the square root of the velocity of the air flowing over it
        c.   the air density
        d.   the air temperature

17.   The centre of pressure is:

      a.   the force opposing gravity
      b.   the point through which the aircraft weight acts
      c.   the point through which total lift acts
      d.   the central point of the engine oil system

18.   The total lift force is considered to act through which location in an aircraft's wing?

      a.   The wing's upper surface
      b.   Always forward of the Centre of Gravity (C of G)
      c.   The wing's C of G
      d.   The Centre of Pressure

19.   Static pressure acts:

      a.   parallel to airflow
      b.   parallel to dynamic pressure
      c.   in all directions
      d.   downwards

20.   Which of the following statements is correct?

      a.   Lift acts perpendicular to the horizontal and drag parallel in a rearwards direction
      b.   Drag acts parallel to the chord and opposite to the direction of motion of the aircraft and lift acts perpendicular to the chord
      c.   Lift acts at right angles to the top surface of the wing and drag acts at right angles to lift
      d.   Drag acts parallel to the relative airflow, opposing the motion of the aircraft, and Lift acts perpendicularly to the relative airflow

21.   In which of the conditions described below will the Coefficient of Lift of a wing be at its maximum?

      a.   At the aircraft's maximum rate of climb speed
      b.   At or just before the stall
      c.   In level flight at an angle of attack of between 4° and 6°
      d.   At the aircraft's maximum angle of climb speed

22.   The formula for lift is:

      a. $L = W$
      b. $L = \frac{1}{2}\,\rho V\,(C_L)^2\,S$
      c. $L = C_L\,\frac{1}{2}\,\rho V^2\,S$
      d. $L = C_L\,\frac{1}{2}\,\rho^2 V\,S$

23.　　Which of the following statements best accounts for how a lift force can be generated by a wing of aerofoil cross section whose upper surface is positively cambered and whose undersurface is uncambered?

　　　　a.　　The air flowing over the upper surface has a longer distance to travel than the air flowing under the wing

　　　　b.　　An upwards-acting reaction force is generated by the wing as it turns the airflow around it a in downwards direction

　　　　c.　　There is an upwards acting reaction to the airflow which bounces off the under surface of the wing as the airflow strikes the undersurface at a positive angle of attack

　　　　d.　　A wing of the aerofoil section described will naturally produce positive lift at any angle of attack

24.　　Which of the following statements best accounts for how the airflow around a wing of standard aerofoil cross section contributes to the lift force produced by the wing?

　　　　a.　　A wing of standard aerofoil cross acts like an inverted venture tube

　　　　b.　　Because the total energy in the air passing above the wing is greater than the total energy in the air flowing beneath the wing

　　　　c.　　Lift is produced by the wing "skipping" over the airflow in the same way as a flat stone might skip over water

　　　　d.　　The downwards turning of the airflow by the wing produces a rate of change of momentum in the airflow, the reaction to which is a force acting on the wing in an upwards direction

Question	1	2	3	4	5	6	7	8	9	10	11	12
Answer												

Question	13	14	15	16	17	18	19	20	21	22	23	24
Answer												

The answers to these questions can be found at the end of this book.

CHAPTER 4
MORE ABOUT AIRFLOW
AND AEROFOILS.

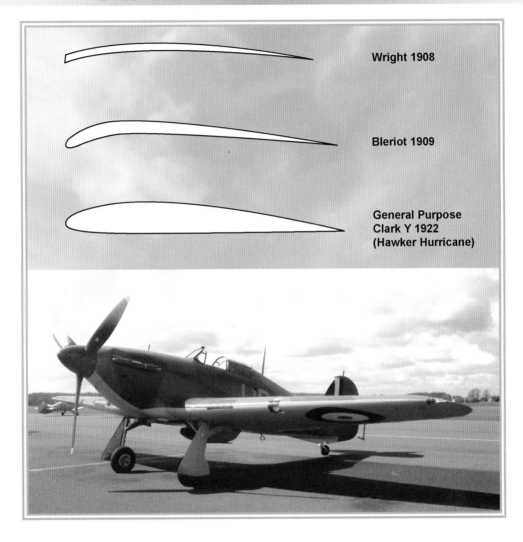

Wright 1908

Bleriot 1909

General Purpose
Clark Y 1922
(Hawker Hurricane)

AIRFLOW.

The Viscosity of Air.

Now that we have investigated the nature of **lift**, and before going on to examine another of the principal forces which acts on an aircraft in flight, the force of **drag**, we must take a second look at **airflow** around an aerofoil.

In our examination of **lift**, one of the major assumptions we made was that air is **inviscid**; in other words, we assumed that air has no **viscosity**. That assumption enabled us to treat air as an **ideal fluid** and to use **Bernoulli's Principle**, concerning **ideal fluids**, as one of the scientific principles which explain how **lift** is generated by a wing.

Air possesses viscosity, even though its viscosity is very low.

Assuming air to be without **viscosity** is a valid assumption when investigating **lift** at low airspeeds because although, in reality, air <u>does</u> possess **viscosity**, the **viscosity of air is so low that it can be discounted**.

However, in order to explain **drag,** we must put aside the assumption that air is **inviscid** and acknowledge that air <u>is</u>, in reality, **viscous**, even though its **viscosity** is very low. The reason why we must now take into account the **viscosity** of air is that scientists have shown that if air were not **viscous**, no **drag force** would act on an aircraft moving through the air, whatever its shape. However, as aerodynamicists and aircraft designers know only too well, and as you will already have discovered from your flying lessons, there <u>is</u> such a thing as **drag**.

Drag is, of course, in most circumstances, a great disadvantage to a pilot. This is the case if a pilot wishes to fly as far as possible and as fast as possible or to obtain the best possible glide performance from his aircraft. On the other hand, **drag** enables a pilot to exert control over his aircraft: for instance, when he wishes to modify the aircraft's **lift/drag ratio** in order to maintain a desired glide-slope at an appropriate approach speed when landing. You will learn more about the **lift/drag ratio** later in this book, and in the section dealing with **Aircraft Performance**.

For the moment, however, let us just accept that although in our examination of **lift** we assumed the air to be **inviscid**, air **must**, in reality, possess some degree of **viscosity** if we are to account for the force of **drag** which acts on an aircraft.

If the air possessed no viscosity, there would be no drag.

The **viscosity** of air also accounts for the true nature of **airflow** around a wing of aerofoil cross section.

Airflow and Friction.

We must now, then, put aside the purely streamlined, non-turbulent view of the flow of air around an aerofoil that we spoke of and depicted in Chapter 3 where we were assuming that air possessed no **viscosity**.

Because air **does** possess **viscosity**, we must now take into account that when one layer of air flows over the layers of air lying next to it, both above and below, the layers rub together causing a **frictional force** to be generated between them which acts parallel to the direction of flow in such a way as to slow down the faster-moving layers of air and to speed up the slower-moving layers. *(See Figure 4.1, overleaf.)* The same type of **frictional force** will be generated between the **airflow** and the surfaces over which the air is flowing, such as the upper and lower surface of a wing.

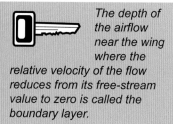

The depth of the airflow near the wing where the relative velocity of the flow reduces from its free-stream value to zero is called the boundary layer.

The **free-stream airflow** at a given distance above, below and in front of the aerofoil, which is unaffected by the presence of the aerofoil, will flow past the aerofoil at a relative velocity equal and opposite to the aerofoil's own velocity through the air. But, wind tunnel experiments show, from the streamlines made visible by smoke, that the **relative velocity of the airflow** nearer to the aerofoil begins to reduce, because of the **frictional forces** which exist between the layers of air, until the particles of air which are actually in contact with the surface of the aerofoil are actually at rest on the aerofoil's surface. *(See Figure 4.1.)* You may have noticed that fine impurities on the surface of an aircraft's wing are not "blown away" during flight.

The **depth of airflow** within which the **frictional forces** generated by the viscosity of air cause the airflow's relative velocity to reduce from its free-stream value to zero on the aerofoil's upper surface constitutes what aerodynamicists call the **boundary layer**. The most common way of representing the changing velocity of the airflow within a boundary layer is to use the velocity profile shown in *Figure 4.1*. The depth of the **boundary layer** depicted in *Figure 4.1* is greatly exaggerated.

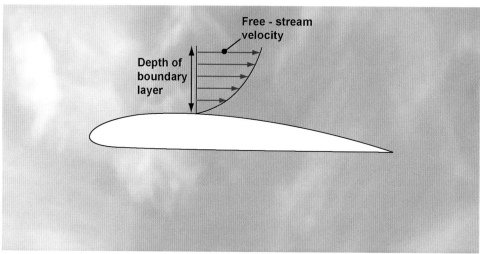

Figure 4.1 The friction forces in real airflow, due to the air's viscosity, cause the relative velocity of the airflow to reduce as it approaches the surface of the wing.

The Boundary Layer.

Depending on several factors which will be mentioned later in this book, the airflow in the **boundary layer** may be either **laminar** or **turbulent**. In normal flight conditions, at an angle of attack well below the stall angle, the **boundary layer** on a wing is typically only a millimetre or so thick.

The boundary layer contains airflow which is both laminar and turbulent.

The **frictional forces** that we have described, and the consequent presence of the **boundary layer**, account for what is known as **skin-friction drag**, about which you will read more, later. You will not be surprised to learn that the smoother the surface of an aerofoil, the lower will be the **skin-friction drag**. However, because of **air viscosity**, **skin-friction drag** can never be eliminated altogether. The best that can be done - and much research has gone into this - is to try to arrange that the airflow within the **boundary layer** remains **laminar** over as much as the aerofoil as possible, so that the layers of air are kept sliding smoothly over each other. Once the **boundary layer** becomes turbulent, the energy losses within the turbulent flow cause **skin-friction drag** to increase significantly.

For our revised view of airflow around a wing we will consider airflow meeting an aerofoil and a very small positive angle of attack of, say, 4°, as shown in *Figure 4.2*. The angle of attack is not indicated on the diagram, and the diagram, for the sake of clarity, is not to scale. In order to keep things simple, we will consider airflow over the upper surface of the aerofoil only. (Remember that the pressure distribution curve above the wing indicates the lowest static pressure at its highest point, and the highest static pressure at its lowest points.)

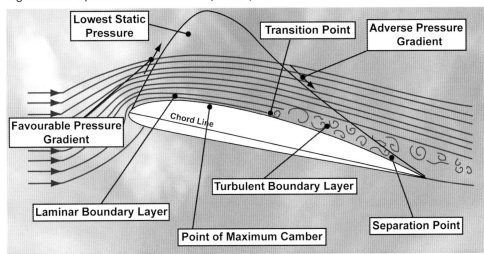

The transition point is the point where the airflow within the boundary layer changes from laminar to turbulent.

Figure 4.2 Airflow in the Boundary Layer and Separation (NB: the depth of boundary layer is greatly exaggerated) .

The point at which the pressure gradient becomes so adverse that the boundary layer separates from the wing's surface is called the separation point.

As depicted in *Figure 4.2*, the **boundary layer** over the leading edge of an aerofoil is **laminar** and produces only little drag. The **boundary layer** tends to remain laminar as long as the airflow continues to accelerate towards a region of lower pressure. Because, as you have learnt, the **camber** of an aerofoil increases the turning effect that a wing has on the airflow, thus generating greater velocity change, the airflow will generally accelerate, and static pressure continue to fall, up to the **point of maximum camber**. Up to the point of maximum camber, then, the **boundary layer** has a good chance of remaining laminar because the **pressure gradient** is favourable – in other words, the air is flowing from a region of higher static pressure to a region of lower static pressure.

The Transition Point.
At a certain point on the aerofoil, however, normally aft of the point of maximum camber, the **pressure gradient** becomes **adverse** causing the airflow in the **boundary layer** to slow down and the **laminar** flow to become **turbulent**, though still attached to the surface. The point at which **boundary layer** flow changes from **laminar** to **turbulent** is called the **transition point**.

Though the **boundary layer** remains very thin for the whole extent of its flow over a wing, it does increase in thickness as it moves towards the trailing edge, especially after the **transition point.**

The Separation Point.
Towards the trailing edge, as the aerofoil cross-section reduces significantly in area, the **pressure gradient** may become so **adverse** that the **boundary layer** actually **separates** from the aerofoil's surface. This is called the **point of separation**. Aft of the **separation point**, the **boundary layer** is replaced by a completely unpredictable

and haphazard region of airflow, sometimes referred to as the "dead air" region. The dead air region is a region whose thickness and extent is of a vastly different scale than that of the **boundary layer**.

Following **separation**, we may consider that the streamlined flow of air over the wing, represented by the thin **boundary layer**, with its **laminar** and **turbulent** regions, has completely broken down.

The principal effects of the separation of the **boundary layer** from the surface of the wing are as follows:

- an area of reduced pressure is established to the rear of the wing which greatly increases **form drag**, a type of drag which will be explained in more detail, later in this book.

- there is an abrupt **decease in the lift force**.

- the air flow becomes **erratic** and **violent**.

As **angle of attack** increases, the **point of separation** moves forward. A wing will eventually stall when the **angle of attack** has reached a value where the **point of separation** moves so far forward that the **lift force** decreases abruptly over the whole wing. Because of the violent and erratic flow in the dead air region, the aircraft is often subject to pronounced buffeting just before the **stall** occurs.

Control of the Boundary Layer.

The **turbulent** section of the **boundary layer** is much thicker than the **laminar** boundary layer. Because of the energy expended in the change of the airflow from **laminar** to **turbulent**, aerodynamicists estimate that a **turbulent boundary layer** causes in the region of five times as much **skin friction drag** as a **laminar boundary layer**. It is the **turbulent boundary layer** which hastens the complete **separation** of the airflow from the surface of a wing.

Because of the adverse effects of **separation** and because of the relationship between the **turbulent boundary layer** and **separation**, aerodynamicists put a lot of thought into how the **boundary layer** can be influenced in such a way as to maintain **laminar flow** within the **boundary layer**, and to avoid or delay **separation**, in order to improve aircraft performance. You will learn that certain types of devices may be fitted to the wing of an aircraft in order to influence the **boundary layer** in the Chapter in this book entitled '**Lift Augmentation**'.

DIFFERENT TYPES OF AEROFOIL.

One definition that aerodynamicists have for **aerofoil** is: "any body which, when set at a suitable angle to a given airflow, produces much more lift than drag."

Having examined airflow around the **aerofoil** of a typical light aircraft wing, let us now look at some different types of **aerofoil** to discover how their characteristics influence the airflow around them and how they are each designed to meet certain performance criteria and to suit different aircraft roles.

You have learnt that the pioneers of aviation discovered, very early on, that wings produced greater **lift** for lower **drag** when the wing was of curved cross section, with a positively cambered upper surface, rather than being just flat. This "curved" type of wing cross section was given the name **aerofoil,** in Britain. (In the United States, the word **airfoil** is used.)

Aerofoils have developed, over the years, from thin cross-sections resembling the wings of a bird (used by Wright and Bleriot) to the deeper type of **aerofoil** which is still used on light aircraft today. The modern light-aircraft type of **aerofoil** has been in use since the 1930s. They are not only efficient lift-generators but also can be constructed to incorporate load-bearing spars so that they possess the necessary structural strength required by the unbraced wings of cantilever monoplanes.

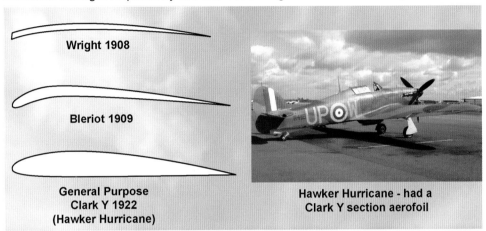

Figure 4.3 The development of the aerofoil cross-section. The wing of the Hawker Hurricane was a Clark Y Section aerofoil

Figure 4.3 depicts three representative aerofoils which show how the aerofoil has developed over the years. The lower aerofoil cross section, is a depiction of the **Clark Y Section** used for the wing of the WW2 fighter aircraft, the **Hawker Hurricane**, and is typical of the type of **aerofoil** still used on light aircraft.

A wing of **aerofoil** cross section is more efficient than a flat wing primarily because it is much more effective in producing the **downwards turning of the airflow** at equal angle of attack, which, as you have learnt, is the key factor in the generation of **lift**. Air also flows over a wing of **aerofoil cross section** much more smoothly (with less turbulence) than over a flat plate wing. This greater extent of **laminar flow** also contributes to efficient **lift** generation and to keeping **drag** as low as possible. *(See Figure 4.4.)*

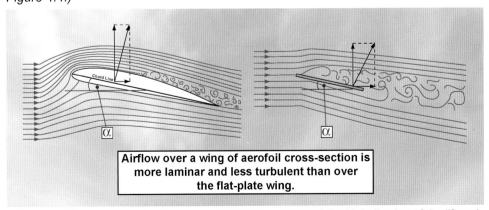

Figure 4.4 Comparison of airflow around flat plate and aerofoil with indication of the lift and drag forces.

73

You see from *Figure 4.4* that, for the aerofoil, the ratio of the length of the **lift vector** to that of the **drag vector** is much greater than for the flat plate. This more favourable **lift drag ratio**, together with the more **laminar** airflow and the greater **downwash**, indicates why a wing of **aerofoil cross section** is a much more efficient lifting surface than a flat-plate type of wing.

AEROFOIL TERMINOLOGY.

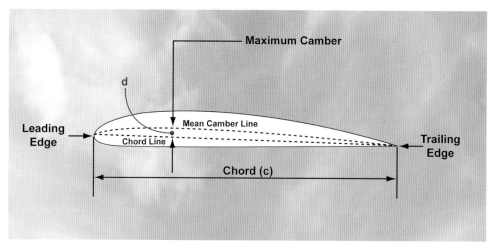

Figure 4.5 Aerofoil terminology.

Certain technical terms are used to refer to the various characteristics of the aerofoil. These terms are defined by the pictures and words below.

- The straight line drawn from the centre of curvature of the **leading edge** to the **trailing edge** is called the **chord line**.

- The **chord** (c) is the distance between the **leading edge** and **trailing edge** measured along the **chord line**.

- The line joining the **leading** and **trailing edges** of the **aerofoil** which is, at all points, equidistant from the upper and lower surfaces is known as the **mean Camber Line**.

- The **maximum camber** of an **aerofoil** is the point at which the distance (d) between the **mean camber line** and the **chord line** is maximum. The **maximum camber** is expressed as a percentage of the **chord**: $\frac{d}{c} \times 100$.

Typical **maximum camber** for a subsonic aerofoil is 3%.

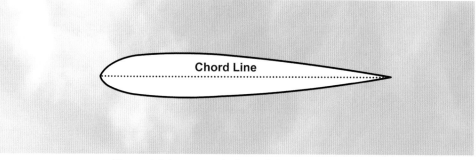

Figure 4.6 A symmetrical aerofoil has no camber

74

•   Symmetrical **aerofoils** are **aerofoils** with a symmetrical cross section. They have no camber since the **chord line** and the **mean camber line** are co-incidental. See *Figure 4.6*. The fin and tailplane of an aircraft are often **symmetrical aerofoils**.

•   The **thickness** (sometimes called **maximum thickness**) is the greatest distance between the upper and lower surfaces of the **aerofoil**. Be aware that the position of **maximum thickness** is not necessarily the same as that of **maximum camber**.

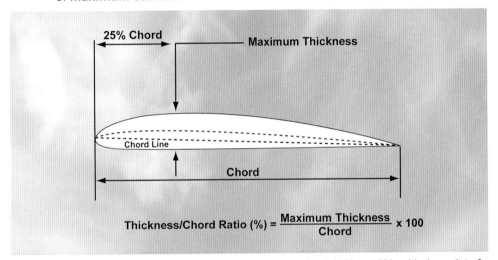

Figure 4.7 Most light aircraft have a thickness-chord ratio of 12% to 15%, with the point of maximum thickness at about 25% chord.

•   The **thickness** of a wing is usually expressed as a fraction of the **chord**. This fraction is called the **thickness/chord ratio**. For subsonic aircraft, the **thickness/chord ratio** is between 12% and 15%.

•   The position of the points of **maximum thickness** and **maximum camber** are expressed as being a fraction of the chord, aft of the leading edge. In the diagram, **maximum thickness** is shown at about 25% chord.

The Significance of the Aerofoil in Wing Design.

Aerodynamicists, when designing an aircraft, choose an aerofoil section which has the optimum characteristics for the aircraft's role.

The main differences to be observed between the various types of aerofoil used for the wings of modern aircraft are in the extent and position of a wing's **maximum camber** and **maximum thickness**, and in the **thickness/chord ratio** of a wing.

As you have learned, any factor which affects the overall shape of a wing and, especially, its ability to **turn** or **deflect** the airflow will also affect the wing's **Coefficient of Lift** at any given **angle of attack**. For instance, at zero degrees angle of attack, the symmetrical aerofoil cross section shown in *Figure 4.6* will not turn the airflow at all and will, consequently, not generate any **lift**.

A symmetrical aerofoil will not cause downwash at 0° angle of attack and, thus, generates no aerodynamic force at 0° AoA.

On the other hand, an aerofoil with a pronounced upper surface **camber** will cause a marked **turning** of the airflow, even at zero degrees angle of attack, and, therefore, generate a measurable amount of **lift**. This point is illustrated in *Figure 4.8* which is

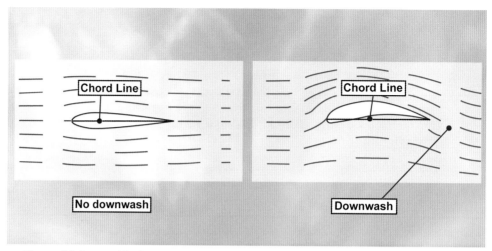

Figure 4.8 Symmetrical and cambered aerofoils at 0° Angle of Attack showing how they affect airflow.

a highly simplified representation of the airflow around symmetrical and cambered aerofoils at 0° angle of attack.

You have seen in *Figure 4.3* how **camber**, **thickness** and **thickness/chord ratio** of the wings of early aircraft evolved rapidly. *Figure 4.9* below, shows the four basic aerofoil sections which are met in relatively modern types of wing design.

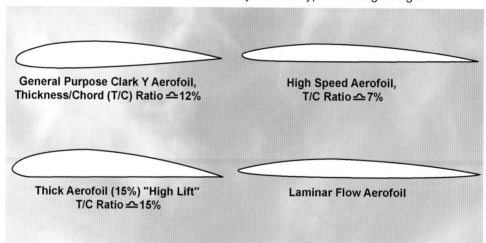

Figure 4.9 Typical aerofoil sections used in modern wing design.

A typical light training aircraft might have a wing with a **thickness/chord ratio** of 10%, with its **maximum camber** at about 40% **chord**.

The **Clark-Y aerofoil**, for instance, which is the top left aerofoil of *Figure 4.9* and is typical of a modern, light-aircraft, general-purpose wing, has a **thickness/chord ratio** of just under 12%, a **camber** of 3.55% with a **maximum camber** at about 35 to 40% **chord**. This type of wing has reasonably high **lift** for low **drag**, at typical light-aircraft speeds, and possesses smooth stall characteristics.

Relatively thick aerofoils (**thickness/chord ratio** about 15%) are high-lift aerofoils, best for low speed operations and, in larger aircraft, for carrying heavy payloads at low speeds.

Laminar flow wings generate good lift for low drag, but they may have poor characteristics in the stall.

Thin aerofoils (**thickness/chord ratio** about 7%) are best for high speeds. The Concorde had a thickness/chord ratio of only about 3%.

The wing section on the **Piper PA28 Warrior**, a popular training aircraft, is a **laminar flow** aerofoil *(see Figure 4.9)* . This type of aerofoil, typically, has a **thickness/chord ratio** of about 12% and is so designed that the point of minimum static pressure (point of **maximum camber**) on the wing is at 50% chord so that the airflow is speeded up gradually to the half way point of the wing chord, giving the aircraft good performance in the cruise at small angles of attack, but poor characteristics at the stall. **Laminar flow** wing sections generate good lift for low drag, and are often used on high performance sailplanes. The principal disadvantage of **laminar flow** wings is that they are sensitive to slight changes in wing contour. Therefore, **laminar flow** wings, especially the leading-edge area of the wing, must be kept free of contamination from insects, raindrops, and the like, at all times,. Contamination on the surface of **laminar flow** wings can easily break up the **laminar airflow** and cause aircraft handling problems for the pilot.

Laminar flow wings are sensitive to slight changes in contour, and must be kept free of contamination, especially the leading edge.

The different types of aerofoil mentioned above, with their different values for **thickness/chord ratio**, **maximum thickness**, **maximum camber**, and the position of these latter two along the chord, **turn** or **deflect** the airflow to different extents. That, in turn, will affect the **air velocity** and **pressure distribution** around the wing. Consequently, each different type of aerofoil will have a different **Coefficient of Lift** and **Coefficient of Drag** for any given **angle of attack**. This situation is illustrated for **Coefficient of Lift** in *Figure 4.10*.

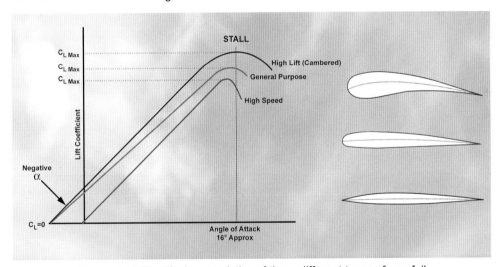

Figure 4.10 The lift characteristics of three different types of aerofoil.

AIRFLOW THROUGH A VENTURI TUBE.

In a venturi tube, where the velocity of air is highest, its static pressure will be lowest.

In our examination of airflow, we must take a look at what is known as the **venturi effect**. In the chapter on **Lift**, you learnt about the **Bernoulli Principle** and the **Bernoulli Equation**. One of the most common examples of the practical application of the **Bernoulli Principle** is the **venturi tube**. The most common type of **venturi tube,** used in practice, is a tube which narrows to what is called the **throat**, and then gradually widens out again, as shown in *Figure 4.11, overleaf*. As you have already learnt, if we assume – as we do throughout this book – that air is **incompressible** at speeds well below the speed of sound, the **rate of mass flow** through the venturi

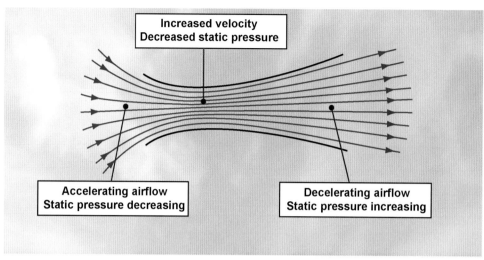

Figure 4.11 Airflow through a Venturi Tube.

tube must be **constant**. Therefore, as the cross-section of the tube decreases, the velocity of the airflow will increase, reaching its maximum velocity at the throat. **Bernoulli's Equation** tells us that **where velocity is greatest, static pressure will be lowest**. So, as the airflow approaches the throat, static pressure will fall, and increase again as the tube cross section increases in diameter and the airflow velocity decreases.

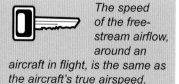
The venturi tube creates low static pressure at its throat.

Figure 4.12 Venturi Tube fitted to Auster J6.

A **venturi tube**, then, is used to create a decrease in pressure, lower than that of the atmosphere. Carburettors employ the **venturi effect** for their basic function. On older aircraft, **venturi tubes** are also used in the operating systems of some flight instruments (such as the **direction indicator** or **artificial horizon**) which operate on the so-called "partial vacuum" system. You can read about both these uses of **venturi tubes** in the **Aeroplanes (General)** volume, in this series of manuals.

The **venturi tube principle** may also be used to create areas of high airflow velocity; for example, in a wind tunnel.

MEASURING AIRSPEED.

The speed of the free-stream airflow, around an aircraft in flight, is the same as the aircraft's true airspeed.

It is convenient for you to note at this point that when an aircraft is in motion, either on the ground, during the take-off and landing roll, or in the air, the relative airflow is used to measure the speed of the aircraft through the air.

Now, the speed of the free-stream airflow around an aircraft in flight is, naturally, equal to the forward speed of the aircraft relative to the air, referred to by pilots as the aircraft's **true airspeed**.

Free stream airflow

Speed of free-stream airflow = True airspeed of aircraft.

Figure 4.13 The speed of the free-stream airflow is the same as the aircraft's true airspeed.

You learnt in the chapter on **Lift** that the **dynamic pressure** exerted by a moving, ideal fluid on a body is the pressure exerted by virtue of the velocity and density of the fluid. Therefore, we may reasonably deduce that an aircraft's **airspeed** is a function of the **dynamic pressure** exerted by the airflow it encounters in flight. You may remember the following equation for dynamic pressure, which can be extracted from Bernoulli's Equation:

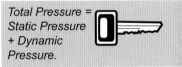

An aircraft's true airspeed is a function of the dynamic pressure acting on the aircraft in flight.

Dynamic pressure (Q) = ½ ρ v²

You may also recall that the **total pressure** in a fluid in motion, horizontally, is given by the relationship:

Total Pressure = Static Pressure + Dynamic Pressure.

Total Pressure = Static Pressure (p) + Dynamic pressure (Q)   or

Total Pressure = p + ½ ρ v²

So, if we measure the **total pressure** and the **static pressure** of an airflow, and if we know the **density** of the air (ρ), we can obtain quite an accurate value for the **dynamic pressure** of the air, and, therefore, deduce the aircraft's **true airspeed**. Knowing the **true airspeed (TAS)** and the **wind velocity** (W/V), a pilot can then calculate his speed over the ground (which, in Navigation, is called **groundspeed** (GS)), as well as the **heading** (HDG) he should fly to achieve a desired **track** (TR) over the ground *(See Figure 4.14)*. You will learn how to do all these calculations in the **'Navigation & Radio Aids'** volume of this series.

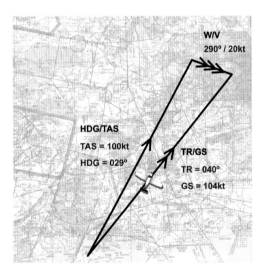

Figure 4.14 A pilot needs to know his True Airspeed in order to navigate his aircraft.

The instrument which displays to the pilot an aircraft's **indicated airspeed** is known, simply, as the **airspeed indicator**.

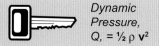

Dynamic Pressure, Q, = ½ ρ v²

The detailed function of the airspeed indicator is covered in our **'Aeroplanes (General)'** book. Here we will examine only those theoretical aspects of measuring airspeed which are relevant to the **Principles of Flight**.

Basically, the **airspeed indicator (ASI)** is an instrument whose operating system "subtracts" **static pressure** from **total pressure**, in the air flowing around the aircraft, in order to give the pilot an indication of the **dynamic pressure, Q,** of the airflow.

Q = ½ ρ v² = Total Pressure - p

Figure 4.15 An Airspeed Indicator (ASI) indicating 95 knots.

The ASI is calibrated in such a way that the pilot reads from the instrument the **indicated airspeed** of his aircraft. When the pilot corrects **indicated airspeed** by taking into consideration the actual **density** of the air (ρ), he will obtain the aircraft's **true airspeed**. The **indicated airspeed** in *Figure 4.15* is 95 knots.

The total pressure of the airflow is measured by an open tube, called a **pitot tube**, whose open end faces the oncoming free-stream airflow. A hole or holes (known as static vents) facing "side-on" to the airflow, so that no air flows into the static vents, sense the static pressure within the airflow. The static vents may be fitted in the fuselage of an aircraft, as shown in *Figure 4.16*, or they may be incorporated into the circumference of a pitot tube to form a **pitot-static tube**, as depicted in *Figure 4.17*.

The **total pressure** sensed by the **pitot tube** is fed to one side of a pressure-measuring device, (usually a sensitive diaphragm) within the **airspeed indicator (ASI)** system while the **static pressure** sensed by the static vents is fed to the other end of the **ASI's** pressure-measuring device. This arrangement is illustrated in *Figure 4.18*.

Figure 4.16 A Static Vent.

The **pressure difference** sensed by the ASI is the **difference between the total pressure in the relative airflow and the static pressure within the relative airflow**. This difference is, of course, a measure of the **dynamic pressure, Q,** of the airflow, ½ ρ v². The dial of the **ASI** can, therefore, be calibrated to read, the speed of the airflow, **v**, directly, for a given value of ρ.

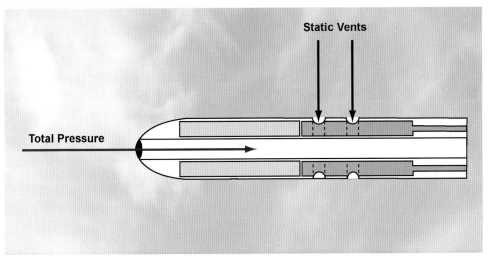

Figure 4.17 A pitot-static tube which senses both total and static pressure in the relative airflow.

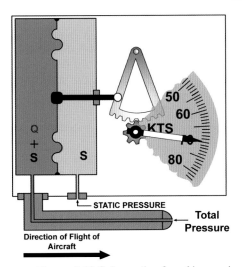

Figure 4.18 Schematic of an Airspeed Indicator (ASI) System.

As we have seen, an aircraft's **airspeed** – in other words, its speed relative to the air through which it is flying - is necessarily equal to the speed of the airflow over the aircraft. So, the ASI, in measuring the **v** of ½ ρ **v**² is measuring the airspeed of the aircraft. The airspeed measured by the **ASI** is called the **indicated airspeed**. The **ASI** will measure the aircraft's **true airspeed** only if the local density of the air in which the aircraft is flying is equal to the value of ρ assumed by the manufacture of the ASI when the ASI was calibrated. At all other values, the pilot must apply corrections to the reading on the **ASI** in order to obtain his aircraft's **true airspeed**. As you have already learnt, it is the **true airspeed** that a pilot needs for navigation calculations.

The ASI "subtracts" static pressure from total pressure to allow dynamic pressure to be indicated on the ASI instrument face.

So, what is the relationship between **true airspeed** and the airspeed that a pilot reads from the ASI?

In the calibration of **ASIs**, the assumed atmospheric conditions, including, most importantly, the **air density**, ρ, are the conditions which prevail **at sea-level in the ICAO Standard Atmosphere (ISA).** The **ASI**, then, will be calibrated assuming an **air density** of **1.225 kg per cubic metre**, and a **temperature** of **15° C**. It follows, therefore, that the **indicated airspeed** that a pilot reads from his **ASI** will be different from his aircraft's **true airspeed** at all times, **unless the air in which the aircraft is flying corresponds exactly to ISA sea-level conditions**.

As you might imagine, in reality, even at sea level, ISA conditions hardly ever prevail. Therefore, a pilot invariably has to apply corrections to the **indicated airspeed (IAS)** to obtain his aircraft's **true airspeed (TAS)**. In correcting **IAS** to obtain **TAS** there are several errors to take into account. The most significant errors are **density error, temperature error, instrument error** and **position error**. **Instrument error** and **position error** are dealt with briefly below, but, except for the **density error** and **temperature error**, the other errors are either compensated for within the **ASI**, itself, or may be disregarded by the light-aircraft pilot flying at altitudes below 10 000 ft above sea-level.

Indicated airspeed corrected for **instrument error** and **position error** is known as **calibrated airspeed** or **rectified airspeed**. We will use the expression **calibrated airspeed**. In practice, **ASIs** are tested extensively, on the bench and in flight, by the manufacturer. In light aircraft, **position error** and **instrument error**, including temperature errors, are largely compensated for within the **ASI** <u>before</u> it is released for service.

Consequently, a light aircraft pilot flying at typical light aircraft cruising levels can assume that **the airspeed he reads from his ASI, the indicated airspeed, approximates very closely to the calibrated airspeed.**

However, because **density** and **temperature**, both decrease at a significant rate with increasing altitude, these two factors cannot be ignored, and a pilot <u>must</u> apply **density** and **temperature** corrections to his aircraft's **indicated airspeed** (which we assume to be equal to the **calibrated airspeed**) in order to obtain **true airspeed**. You will learn how to calculate **true airspeed**, using a navigation computer *(see Figure 4.19)*, in the **'Navigation & Radio Aids'** volume of this series.

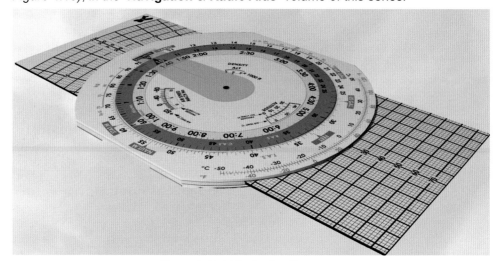

Figure 4.19 A Navigation Computer.

Because, in this chapter, we are considering airspeed as the measurement of **v** in the expression for dynamic pressure, ½ ρ **v²**, which is **true airspeed**, let us examine a little more closely how **indicated airspeed** and **true airspeed** are related by different values of air density, ρ. You may skip the maths in the blue box, if you wish.

In calibrating the ASI, the value for ρ is assumed to be the air density in ISA sea-level conditions. We will indicate this value of air density by the symbol ρ_{SL}.

We have also said that the indicated airspeed, as read directly from the ASI, and corrected for instrument and position error is called calibrated airspeed. We will represent **indicated airspeed** (which we assume to be equal to **calibrated airspeed**) by the symbol v_i.

Now, in the expression for dynamic pressure $\frac{1}{2}\rho v^2$, v is the true airspeed.

But v_i will be the true airspeed only where $\rho = \rho_{SL}$

Therefore, $\frac{1}{2}\rho v^2 = \frac{1}{2}\rho_{SL}v_i^2$

Therefore, $v^2 = \dfrac{\rho_{SL}v_i^2}{\rho}$

$$v^2 = \dfrac{v_i^2}{\dfrac{\rho}{\rho_{SL}}} \qquad\qquad v = \dfrac{v_i}{\sqrt{\dfrac{\rho}{\rho_{SL}}}}$$

Now, $\dfrac{\rho}{\rho_{SL}}$ = relative density σ

Therefore, $v = \dfrac{v_i}{\sqrt{\sigma}}$

And so, when $\rho = \rho_{SL}$, $\sigma = 1$, and true airspeed, v, is the same as indicated airspeed, v_i. But ρ is rarely, if ever, exactly equal to ρ_{SL}. When the aircraft is operating at altitude, it may be assumed that ρ is almost always less than ρ_{SL}. Consequently, σ and $\sqrt{\sigma}$ will be less that 1. Therefore, at altitude, true airspeed, v, is invariably greater than indicated airspeed.

At sea-level, then, where local air density will be very close to **ISA** air density, the **indicated airspeed** read directly from the ASI may be taken to be close to the **true airspeed**. But, because local air density decreases with increasing altitude, largely because of the decrease in pressure, invariably, air density at altitude, especially above 2 000 ft, will be less than the ISA sea-level air density. **Therefore, at altitude, true airspeed will be greater than indicated airspeed.**

Where air density is less than the ISA sea level value, indicated airspeed will be lower than true airspeed.

Consequently, when a pilot calculates his **true airspeed** during his navigation preparations for a cross-country flight, at a planned indicated airspeed of, say, 110 knots and a planned cruising altitude of 3 000 ft, he will know that he can expect the **true airspeed** to be higher than his planned **indicated airspeed**. It is **true airspeed** that he must use for his navigation calculations.

As we have said you will learn how to carry out these calculations in the volume **Navigation & Radio Aids**. However, it is important that you understand the **airflow** and **Principles of Flight** considerations behind your navigation calculations.

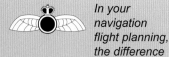
In your navigation flight planning, the difference between indicated airspeed and true airspeed must be taken into account.

Just to give you a feel for the difference you may expect, in a temperate climate like that of much of Europe, between **indicated airspeed** (assumed to be equal to **calibrated airspeed**) and **true airspeed**, an **indicated airspeed** of 110 knots at a pressure altitude (altimeter subscale setting of 1013 millibars) of 2 500 feet, with an outside air temperature (OAT) at that altitude of 5° C, would give a **true airspeed** of just over 112 knots. You would be right to think that this is not a significant difference. But, it will make a discernible difference in your navigation figures and must be taken into account.

If you were to fly at a pressure altitude of 6 000 feet on a hot summers day, with an (Outside Air Temperature (OAT) of 12° C, an **indicated (calibrated) airspeed** of 110 knots would give a **true airspeed** of 122 knots: a significant difference.

More About ASI Errors.

Before we bring this chapter to a close, we will examine the main **errors** in the reading of the **airspeed indicator (ASI)** a little more closely, so that you have an appreciation of the potential that the **ASI** has to deceive the pilot. As we have mentioned, the two principal **ASI** errors are **instrument error** and **position error**. And although these may largely be compensated for during **ASI** manufacture and installation in an aircraft, you must be aware of their existence. As you have learnt, for typical light aircraft navigation flights, especially over short distances, the indicated airspeed shown on the ASI can be assumed to be very close to calibrated airspeed (indicated airspeed corrected for instrument and position error), however, you must consult the aircraft's Flight Manual, or Pilot's Operating Handbook, to confirm this assumption.

Figure 4.20 Correction figures to convert indicated airspeed into calibrated airspeed may be found in the aircraft's Flight Handbook or the Pilot's Operating Handbook

Instrument Error in the ASI.

Instrument Errors in the **ASI** are caused by imperfections in the design and manufacturing processes of the instrument. **Instrument errors** will, therefore, be different in different types and models of **ASI**. In general, **instrument errors** are negligible.

Position Error in the ASI.

Position errors in **ASI** readings can be caused either by inaccurate static pressure sensing, inaccurate total pressure sensing, or by a combination of both. **Position error** in the sensing of static pressure is most common when the static vents are incorporated into a pitot-static head. The accuracy of total pressure sensing may be affected by misalignment of the pitot or pitot-static head; for example, if the pitot tube is inclined at an angle to the free-stream airflow instead of facing directly into the flow. **Position error** will, therefore, also arise in extremes of aircraft attitude, such as flight at high angles of attack near the stall, especially when marked turbulence is present.

ASI errors can be minimised during flight testing by taking a series of ASI readings over a range of airspeeds and attitudes. Instrument calibration corrections can be made based on the results of such tests with a correction being applied to each indicated airspeed.

As we have mentioned, the indicated airspeed, when corrected for instrument and position errors, gives calibrated airspeed. The pilot applies his own temperature and density corrections to calibrated airspeed in order to obtain true airspeed.

At high speeds, in excess of half the local speed of sound (Mach 0.5) compressibility error in the ASI reading must also be taken into account. In this book, we ignore compressibility error as typical light aircraft speeds are far below Mach 0.5.

The Value of Indicated Airspeed Readings.

Although it must be corrected for navigation purposes, **indicated airspeed** is very a useful value in itself.

Indicated airspeed is a measure of the real dynamic pressure, $\frac{1}{2}\rho\mathbf{v}^2$, being exerted on an aircraft as result of its motion through the air, and is, therefore, also an indication of the aerodynamic forces (such as lift and drag) acting on the airframe. As far as the safety of the aircraft is concerned, then, it is often of greater importance to the pilot to have a direct reading of these aerodynamic forces than to be able to read directly his aircraft's true airspeed. For this reason, all aircraft speed limitations are given as indicated airspeed.

Representative PPL - type questions to test your theoretical knowledge of Lift.

1. Total pressure sensed by a Pitot Tube comprises:

    a.   pitot pressure plus dynamic pressure
    b.   pitot pressure minus dynamic pressure
    c.   static pressure plus dynamic pressure
    d.   dynamic pressure minus static pressure

2. Two identical aircraft of the same weight fly at two different altitudes (in straight and level flight and the same angle of attack). Assuming that other factors remain constant, that the air is incompressible, and that ISA conditions prevail, how do the true air speeds of the two aircraft compare?

    a.   They are the same
    b.   The True Air Speed (TAS) of the higher aircraft will be the greater
    c.   The TAS of the lower aircraft will be the greater
    d.   Altitude has no effect on the True Air Speed required to support a given aircraft weight at constant angle of attack

3. In accordance with Bernoulli's Theorem, where PT = Total Pressure, PS = Static pressure and q = Dynamic pressure:

    a.   PT + PS = Q
    b.   PT = PS - Q
    c.   PT - PS = Q
    d.   PS + PT = Q

5. The symbol for dynamic pressure is:

    a.   Q
    b.   P
    c.   R
    d.   D

6. As Indicated Air Speed (IAS) is reduced, in order to maintain altitude, the pilot must:

    a.   increase the angle of attack to maintain the correct lift force
    b.   decrease the angle of attack to reduce the drag
    c.   deploy the speed brakes to increase drag
    d.   reduce the thrust

7. Dynamic Pressure may be expressed by the formula:

    a. $Q = ½ \rho V^2$
    b. $Q = \rho V^2$
    c. $Q = \rho V$
    d. $Q = 2 \rho V$

8.	The smooth flow of air, where each molecule follows the path of the preceding molecule, is a definition of:

	a.	wind
	b.	turbulent flow
	c.	free-stream flow
	d.	laminar flow

9.	If the cross sectional area of an airflow is mechanically reduced:

	a.	the mass flow remains constant and the static pressure increases
	b.	the velocity of the airflow remains constant and the mass flow increases
	c.	the mass flow remains constant and the velocity of the airflow increases
	d.	the velocity of the airflow remains constant and the kinetic energy increases

10.	Dynamic pressure is:

	a.	the pressure change caused by heating when a moving airflow is brought completely to rest
	b.	the pressure due to the mass of air pressing down on the air beneath
	c.	the amount by which the pressure rises at a point where a moving airflow is brought completely to rest
	d.	the total pressure at a point where a moving airflow is brought completely to rest

11.	The dynamic pressure exerted by the air on an aircraft's frontal surface is equal to:

	a.	air density times speed squared
	b.	half the air density times the true airspeed squared
	c.	half the true airspeed times the air density squared
	d.	half the air density times the indicated airspeed squared

12.	The term angle of attack is defined as:

	a.	the angle between the relative airflow and the horizontal axis
	b.	the angle between the wing chord line and the relative airflow
	c.	the angle that determines the magnitude of the lift force
	d.	the angle between the wing and tailplane incidence

13. In sub-sonic airflow, as air passes through a venturi, the mass flow _____, the velocity _____ and the static pressure _____.

   a. decreases then increases   remains constant
   increases then decreases
   b. remains constant   increases then decreases
   decreases then increases
   c. remains constant   increases then decreases
   increases then decreases
   d. decreases then increases   increases then decreases
   increases then decreases

14. An aircraft carries out a given journey, on two separate days. On both days, the pilot flies at an indicated airspeed of 120 knots. On the first day, the air density is greater than on the subsequent day. How will the forces of Lift and Drag acting on the aircraft compare on the two days?

   a. On the first day both Lift and Drag will be less than on the subsequent day
   b. On the first day the Lift will be greater and Drag will be less than on the subsequent day
   c. On the first day the Lift will be less and Drag will be greater than on the subsequent day
   d. The forces of Lift and Drag acting on the aircraft will remain unchanged

Question	1	2	3	4	5	6	7	8	9	10	11	12
Answer												

Question	13	14
Answer		

The answers to these questions can be found at the end of this book.

CHAPTER 5
DRAG

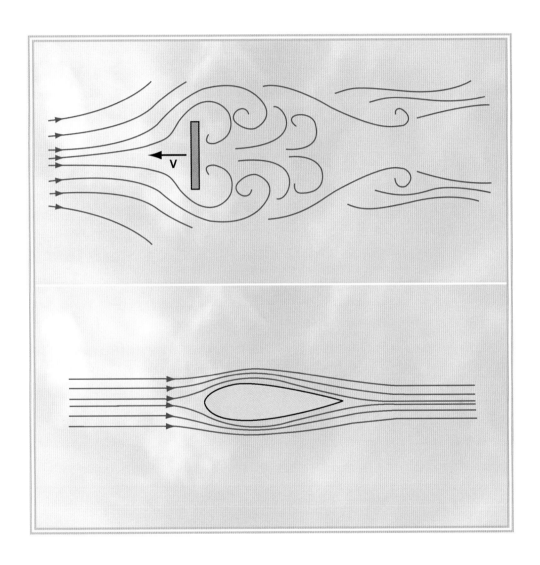

DRAG.

INTRODUCTION.

The concept of **drag** has been touched upon in the chapters dealing with **lift** and **airflow**. Here, we must develop that concept further.

A body moving through a viscous fluid such as air will, because it displaces the air, experience a resistance to its motion which is given the name **drag**.

The chapter on **lift** has already given you an insight into the fact that, as well as lift, a **drag force** is generated by a wing as it moves through the air. In fact, **aerodynamic drag** is an inevitable by-product of **lift** *(See Figure 5.1)*.

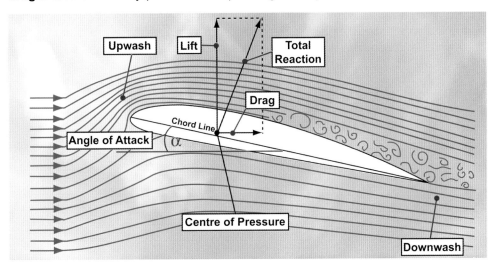

Total drag is made up of parasite drag and induced drag.

Figure 5.1 Drag is an inevitable by-product of lift.

But it is not only the wings which generate **drag**. All other parts of an aircraft's airframe, too, give rise to a **drag force** which acts parallel and opposite to the direction of flight. The combined **drag** produced by the airframe is called **total drag**.

Total drag is divided into two main sub categories: **parasite drag** and **induced drag**.

Parasite drag is the **drag** which is generated as the air flows around the aircraft, by virtue of such things as the aircraft's **shape**, **speed** (dynamic pressure), **frontal area**, and the **texture and condition** of the aircraft's **surface**. You will sometimes hear **parasite drag** referred to as **profile drag** or **zero-lift drag**. **Zero-lift drag** is a good descriptive term for **parasite drag** because it emphasises that this type of **drag** is unconnected to **lift**.

Induced drag is the **drag** which is produced as a <u>by-product</u> of **lift**. **Parasite drag** will be present even if the aircraft is flying at an angle of attack at which the wings are producing no **lift**. When the wings are producing **lift**, some **drag** will be generated which is additional to the **parasite drag**. The <u>additional, lift-dependent</u> drag is called **induced drag**. You may often hear **induced drag** <u>called</u> **lift-dependent drag**.

Drag can almost always be regarded as a disadvantage, though, in some aspects of aircraft control, especially the control by the pilot of his aircraft's approach to land, the presence of **drag** is essential. This is fortunate, because **aerodynamic drag** is an <u>inevitable</u> product of **lift**. Nevertheless, in most phases of flight, when an aircraft is climbing, in the cruise, or gliding for range, **drag** is detrimental to the aircraft's performance.

Consequently, aerodynamicists have put an immense amount of work, over the decades, into finding ways of decreasing the **drag** generated by an aircraft, across the whole range of its operating speeds.

For a powered aircraft, in any phase of steady flight, at whatever speed, each kilogram, Newton or pound of **drag force** acting on the aircraft must be counterbalanced by an equal amount of **thrust** from the engine or engines. So, if **drag** could be reduced, an aircraft could have a superior performance in terms of lifting capacity, speed, range and endurance, when fitted with the same engine. Alternatively, a manufacturer could choose to fit a smaller engine for the same aircraft performance.

We will now examine the various types of **drag** separately.

PARASITE DRAG.

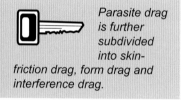
Parasite drag is further subdivided into skin-friction drag, form drag and interference drag.

Parasite drag may be further sub-divided into **skin-friction drag**, **form drag** (sometimes called **profile drag** or **pressure drag**) and **interference drag**. *(See Figure 5.2.)*

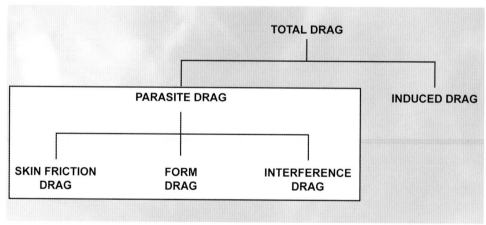

Figure 5.2 The components of Parasite Drag.

Skin-Friction Drag.
We met **skin-friction drag** in the previous chapter during our study of the boundary layer. You learnt, there, that the frictional forces acting between the layers of airflow making up the boundary layer account for **skin-friction drag**.

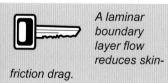
A laminar boundary layer flow reduces skin-friction drag.

If the airflow within the boundary layer remains laminar over as much of the aerofoil as possible, so that the layers of air are kept sliding smoothly over each other, **skin-friction drag** is reduced. The turbulent section of the boundary layer is much thicker than the laminar boundary layer. Because of the energy expended in the change of the airflow from laminar to turbulent, it is estimated that a turbulent boundary layer causes in the region of five times as much **skin-friction drag** as a laminar boundary layer.

Several factors contribute to maintaining a laminar airflow over a wing at cruising angles of attack. Chief amongst these are:

- The profile of the aerofoil which determines the position of the area of minimum static pressure on a wing and, thereby, the nature of the pressure gradient. On a laminar flow wing, the point of maximum camber (minimum static pressure) is at about middle chord, and, consequently, the favourable pressure gradient ensures that laminar flow will be maintained at least until that point.

- The smoothness of the surface of the wing. A smooth surface will also mitigate against laminar flow becoming turbulent. Consequently, the smoother the surface, the lower will be the **skin-friction drag**.

Any roughness on the skin of a leading portion of an aircraft's airframe will induce a turbulent flow and increase skin-friction drag.

A polished aircraft not only looks good, but will fly more efficiently since **skin-friction drag** is reduced. Construction methods can greatly affect skin friction. Flush riveted or bonded metal aircraft will have less skin friction than aircraft with rivet heads that stand proud, or fabric aircraft with pronounced stitching. *(See Figure 5.3.)*

Figure 5.3 The surface area and the surface finish affect skin friction drag.

Many aircraft today are constructed from composite materials, which produce continuous smooth structures with low skin friction values. *(See Figure 5.4.)*

The manufacturer will determine the type of construction of the aircraft, and its inherent skin friction values. In service, the aircraft's surface can become contaminated with dirt, water, ice, frost or snow, which will affect not only the **skin-friction drag** but also the **lift** that can be produced.

Figure 5.4 Composites materials produce continuous smooth structures which have low skin-friction drag.

Keep wing surfaces free of all contamination, especially the leading edges.

Figure 5.5 The surface area and the surface finish affect skin friction drag.

Tests have shown that wing contamination of a thickness and surface roughness similar to medium or coarse sandpaper will reduce **lift** by as much as 30%. *(See Figure 5.5.)*

Any contaminants on the aircraft's surface, especially on the wing, will increase **skin-friction drag**, as well as adversely affecting the aerofoil profile, adding to the weight and, thus, increasing stalling speed. A pilot must always remove such contaminants as ice, snow, or squashed insects from the wings before flight, especially from the leading edge and the area around it.

Because **skin-friction drag** is so closely connected with the nature and characteristics of the boundary layer, boundary layer control is an important issue for designers of jets and other high performance aircraft. Mechanisms used to maintain favourable boundary layer conditions for as large a section of the wing as possible include blowing air into the boundary layer, or sucking air from the boundary layer, through holes in the wing surface.

Boundary layer control methods of this type are not found on a typical light aircraft, but some light aircraft do have a simple form of boundary layer control in the form of leading-edge slots, a device that you will meet in the chapter on **Lift Augmentation**.

Form Drag.
The **form drag** (sometimes called **profile drag** or **pressure drag**) acting on a body moving through a viscous fluid is the name given to the type of drag generated principally by the shape of the body. An aircraft's shape will influence the extent to which the air through which it is moving is disturbed. All aircraft, whatever their shape, cause a very significant disturbance to the air.

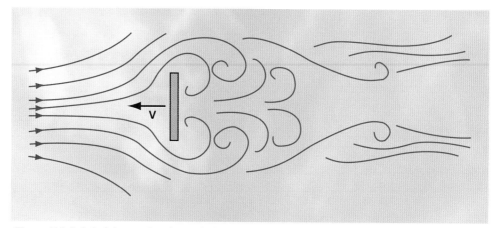

Figure 5.6 A flat plate moving through the air, at a right angle to the airflow, generates a very large amount of form drag.

The greater the disturbance created by the aircraft as it moves through the air, the greater will be the energy required to create the disturbance and the greater will be the **form drag** on the aircraft. If the disturbance can be minimised, **form drag** will be reduced.

An extreme example of the generation of **form drag** is the movement of a flat plate through the air, at a right angle to the airflow, as illustrated in *Figure 5.6*. In the situation shown, the **drag** will be almost entirely due to the vortices generated by the plate, and to the dynamic pressure, $\frac{1}{2}\,\rho v^2$, acting on the plate's frontal surface, against the plate's direction of motion. So, **form drag** is a maximum, while **skin-friction drag** will be negligible.

Reducing Form Drag through Streamlining.

Streamlining reduces form drag.

In the chapter on **lift** you learned that lines which show the direction of flow of a fluid at any particular moment are called **streamlines**. A body so shaped as to produce the least possible turbulence in the air flowing around it is said to be a **streamlined** shape. A **streamlined** shape will, consequently, generate far less **form drag** that a shape of large, flat, frontal cross-sectional area.

Therefore, in the design and manufacture of aircraft, the shapes of aircraft components, as well as the shape of the whole aircraft itself, are designed, where possible, to be of a form and proportion that will cause only a gradual change in the direction of the air which flows over them.

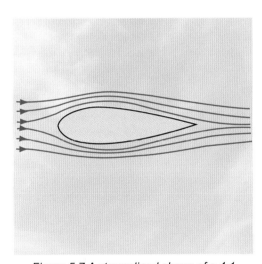

Figure 5.7 A streamlined shape of a 4:1 fineness ratio is optimal for minimising parasite drag.

Aircraft components will, therefore, tend to be of a long, slender shape, with minimal frontal area, as depicted in *Figure 5.7*. Such **streamlined** shapes generate as little as 5% of the **form drag** produced by the flat plate.

However, long, thin shapes can have a significant **surface area** and, therefore, <u>do</u> give rise to **skin-friction drag**. So, obtaining the correct ratio between the length and thickness of a **streamlined shape** is crucial, if minimum **parasite drag** is to be achieved. The ratio of length to thickness is called the **fineness ratio**. For airspeeds up to 300 knots, it has been shown that a **fineness ratio** of about **4:1** is optimal. An optimally-designed, **streamlined** aircraft component, meeting the airflow at a small angle of attack, will generate much less **form drag** than **skin-friction drag**.

Figure 5.8 overleaf, illustrates how the **form drag** caused by an undercarriage wheel is reduced by fitting a **streamlined spat**.

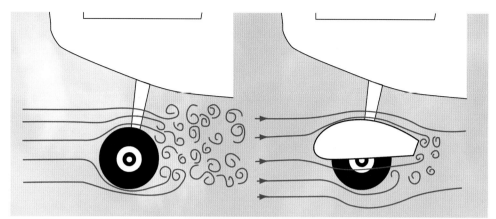

Figure 5.8 The form drag generated by an undercarriage wheel may be reduced by fitting spats.

It is, obviously, of great importance that the **form drag** produced by aircraft components which are directly exposed to the relative airflow should be reduced to a minimum, as an aircraft will perform much more efficiently if its **total drag** is low. Aerodynamicists have proven beyond doubt that enormous performance and efficiency advantages are to be gained by **streamlining** exposed aircraft components such as undercarriage legs and wheel assemblies.

Increase in Form Drag with Increasing Angle of Attack.

We have established, then, that the **form drag** generated by an aircraft increases in proportion as the air is disturbed by the aircraft's passage. You will not be surprised to learn, therefore, that **form drag** increases as a wing's **angle of attack** increases. You may remember that, as **angle of attack** increases, the **separation point**, at which the boundary layer breaks away from the wing, moves forward towards the wing's leading edge, creating an increasing area of erratic and haphazard airflow, aft of the wing. As the **angle of attack** approaches the **stalling angle** (typically 16° for a light training aircraft without sophisticated lift augmentation devices), the erratic, haphazard wake, behind the wing, thickens, causing **form drag** to increase rapidly. *Figure 5.9* illustrates this phenomenon. In order to keep things simple, we depict only the airflow above the wing. The increase in **form drag** with increasing angle of attack explains why **drag** increases markedly at the **point of stall**, to accompany the abrupt decrease in **lift**.

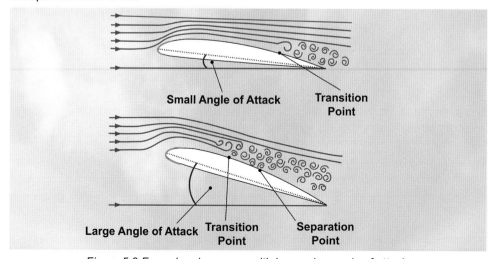

Figure 5.9 Form drag increases with increasing angle of attack.

Interference Drag.

Although the **form drag** of any aircraft component may be minimised by **streamlining**, it is not always the case that two **streamlined** components will generate minimum **form drag**, if those components are joined together. It can be demonstrated by experiment that the **form drag** generated by a complete aircraft is greater than the sum of the separate elements of **form drag** generated by each individual component.

This additional **increment in form drag** is called **interference drag**. **Interference drag** is caused, primarily, by the joining of the wings to the fuselage.

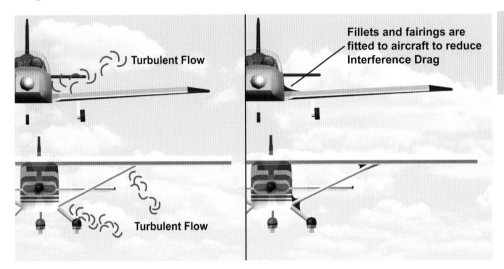

Turbulent Flow

Fillets and fairings are fitted to aircraft to reduce Interference Drag

Turbulent Flow

Interference drag is caused, primarily, by the junctions of wing and fuselage.

Figure 5.10 Interference drag occurs, primarily, at the junction between wing and fuselage, and may be reduced by fitting fairings of fillets.

Interference drag can be reduced at the junctions where components meet by ensuring that no sharp angles are formed by the junctions. This is achieved by fitting **fairings** or **fillets** *(see Figure 5.10)*.

Parasite drag varies directly with the square of the indicated airspeed.

The Variation of Parasite Drag with Aircraft Speed.

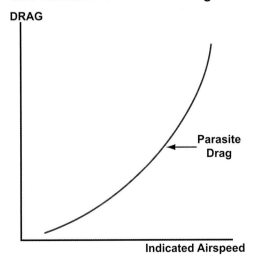

DRAG

Parasite Drag

Indicated Airspeed

Figure 5.11 Parasite drag increases as the square of the indicated airspeed.

Analysis of the **total drag** acting on an aircraft is complex. However, it is fairly accurate to say that **parasite drag increases as the square of the indicated airspeed**.

So if, at 90 knots, the **parasite drag** acting on an aircraft is 200 pounds (lbs) force, (91 kilograms force or 892 Newtons), the **parasite drag** at 180 knots would be four times that value: 800 lbs force, (324 kilograms force or 3 568 Newtons). *Figure 5.11* illustrates graphically how **parasite drag** increases with indicated airspeed. The graph is a curve, because, as we have learnt, the increase in **parasite drag** varies as the **square** of the indicated airspeed.

INDUCED (OR LIFT-DEPENDENT) DRAG.

All parts of an aircraft generate **parasite drag**, but the wings, as the producers of **lift**, generate an additional form of **drag** which is **inextricably bound to their lift-producing function**, and which is called **induced drag**. This type of **drag** bears the name **induced drag** because, in producing **lift**, the regions of differing pressure, above and below the wings, __induce__ vortices, which vary in strength, dimension and **drag effect** with varying **angle of attack**. Because it is inseparable from **lift**, **induced drag** is also known as **lift-dependent drag**. (See *Figure 5.12.*)

> *Induced drag, sometimes called lift-dependent drag, is a by-product of, and inseparable from, lift.*

Figure 5.12 The regions of differing pressure, above and below the wings, induce vortices which vary in drag effect with varying angle of attack.

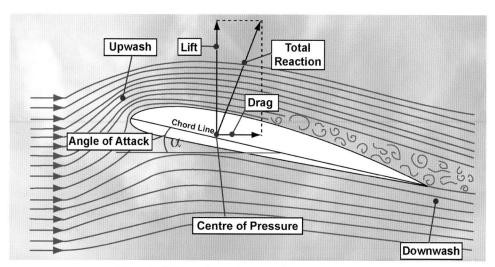

Figure 5.13 Two dimensional air flow around a wing.

In dealing with **parasite drag**, we have considered airflow in two dimensions only: that is, airflow in the sense of the aircraft's longitudinal axis, passing from front to rear, and airflow in the vertical sense, when considering **upwash**, upstream of the wing, and **downwash**, as the air leaves the aft sections of the wing, downstream. *(See Figure 5.13.)*

But, in real life, a wing is not infinitely long. It must have wingtips. In the region of the wingtips, airflow is of a different nature to the **two-dimensional flow** that we have been considering up to this point. The finite length of the wing, and the consequent presence of wingtips, means that, at the wingtips, air flows from the under-surface of the wings (from the region of higher pressure) to the upper-surface of the wings, in a spanwise direction, modifying the airflow across the whole length of the wing, causing the type of **vortices** shown in *Figure 5.12*, and generating **induced drag**. It is this **three-dimensional flow**, then, which lies at the root of **induced drag**.

Three Dimensional Airflow.

In order to modify the two-dimensional picture of airflow depicted in *Figure 5.13*, we must take a look at the **spanwise** pressure distribution around a wing. **Spanwise** pressure distribution is depicted in *Figure 5.14*. Around an actual wing, the precise shape of the pressure distribution envelope will depend on the wing plan form and on the angle of attack between the wing and the relative airflow.

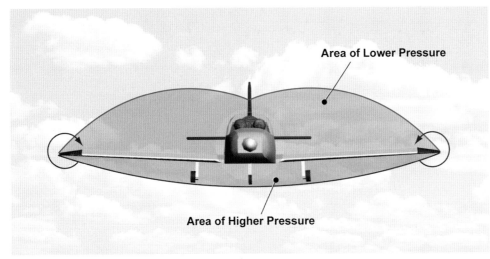

Area of Lower Pressure

Area of Higher Pressure

Wingtip vortices are caused by spillage from the high pressure area under the wing to the low pressure area above the wing.

Figure 5.14 A representative, spanwise, pressure distribution envelope, showing airflow around the wingtips.

As we have already mentioned, the pressure difference between the regions above and below the wings causes air, at the wing tips, to flow from the region of higher pressure below the wing to the region of lower pressure above the wing. This **spillage** of air around the wingtips is also depicted in *Figure 5.14* and influences the whole of the airflow around the wing, along the wing's total span. On the under-surface, because the flow around the wingtips is outwards and upwards, there is a general outward flow across the whole length of the wing's undersurface towards the wingtips. At the wingtips, on the upper surface, spillage causes a downwards-curling, inwards flow which deflects the airflow over the whole length of the wing's upper surface inwards towards the fuselage. *(See Figure 5.15.)*

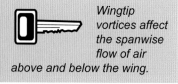

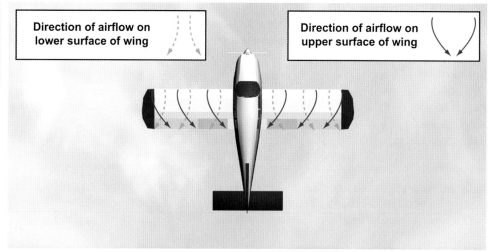

Figure 5.15 Deflection of main airflow spanwise caused by wingtip spillage.

Trailing Edge and Wingtip Vortices.

Where the **spanwise** deflections in the airflow combine with the main longitudinal airflow, at the wing's trailing edge, they meet at an angle to each other to form **vortices** at the trailing edge, as depicted by *Figure 5.16*. When viewed from behind, these **vortices** will be rotating clockwise from the port (left) wing and anti-clockwise from the starboard (right) wing. The **vortex at each wingtip** is particularly large and strong. *(See Figure 5.17.)*

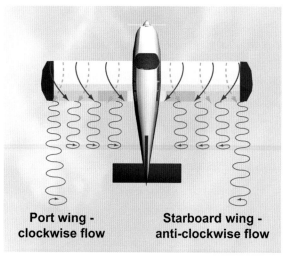

Figure 5.16 When spanwise deflection meets the main airflow, vortices are formed at the trailing edge.

Figure 5.17 The wingtip vortex is particularly large and strong.

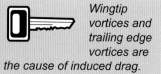

Wingtip vortices and trailing edge vortices are the cause of induced drag.

It is the combination of trailing-edge and wingtip vortices which are the cause of induced drag.

Both wingtip and trailing edge **vortices** will become larger and stronger as the pressure difference between the upper and lower wing surfaces increases. Consequently, if we consider normal operating angles of attack (that is: below the stalling angle of attack), the **vortices will increase in size and strength with increasing angle of attack**.

This fact is the first factor in the explanation of why, unlike **parasite drag**, **induced drag**, in straight flight, increases as airspeed decreases (increasing angles of attack), and decreases as airspeed increases (decreasing angles of attack).

Additional Downwash Caused by the Wingtip Vortices.

Considering the direction of rotation of the large wingtip vortices, we see that they cause an upwards deflection in the airflow on the outside of the wing span and a downwards deflection – or **downwash** - of air within the wingspan, at the trailing edge.

Wingtip vortices increase downwash, cause the lift vector to rotate rearwards, and give rise to induced drag.

This additional downwash of the airflow must not be confused with the downwash caused by the inherent downwards-turning effect on the airflow by the wing which we discussed in the chapter on lift, and which is vital to the production of lift.

It is the <u>additional</u> downwash, caused by the wingtip vortices, which is the primary cause of induced drag.

The **additional downwash**, however, increases the main **downwash** leaving the trailing edge of the wing. For this reason, both the total reaction and the lift force vector acting perpendicularly to the relative airflow are rotated backwards. This situation is depicted in *Figure 5.18*. (Note, that *Figure 5.18* is a highly simplified representation of the rearward tilting of the lift force. No airflow is shown, except for one representative line, and no total reaction is shown.) The rotating rearwards of the lift vector under the influence of the wingtip vortices increases the horizontal component of aerodynamic force (which we originally labelled simply as **drag**) acting against the direction of motion of the aircraft. It is this **increase in the rearwards acting component of the lift force** which is the <u>induced</u> drag.

The higher the angle of attack, the stronger the wingtip vortices and the greater the induced drag.

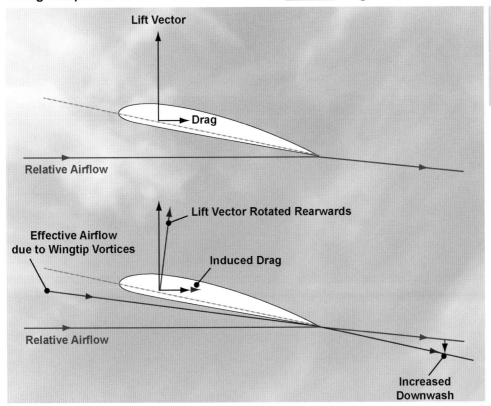

Figure 5.18 The effective airflow is the true airflow.

101

So whenever the wings are producing lift, they are also generating **induced drag**. In particular, in straight flight, the lower the aircraft's speed (greater angle of attack) the greater is the **induced drag**, and the higher the aircraft's speed, the lower is the **induced drag**.

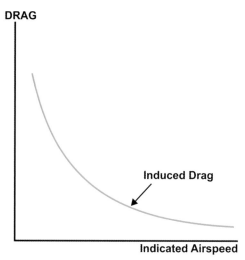

DRAG

Induced Drag

Indicated Airspeed

Figure 5.19 Induced drag is inversely proportional to the square of the airspeed.

In fact, induced drag is inversely proportional to the square of the aircraft's velocity, in straight flight. This relationship is shown in *Figure 5.19.*

This is a totally opposite situation to the case of **parasite drag** which increases as the aircraft's speed increases. (**Parasite drag**, you will remember, is directly proportional to the square of the aircraft's velocity.)

The **wing tip vortices** and, therefore, the **induced drag**, are largest and most powerful at high angles of attack, and disappear altogether at the zero-lift angle of attack; that is, at about -2° for a typical light-aircraft wing.

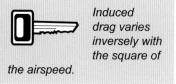

Induced drag varies inversely with the square of the airspeed.

The Effect of Manoeuvres and Weight on Induced Drag.

In level turns flown at any given airspeed, the wings have, of course, to create more **lift** than is required for level flight at the same speed, in order maintain height. To maintain height in a turn, **angle of attack** (and power) must be increased. Consequently, greater **induced drag** will be generated in a turn than in straight flight, at the same speed. In a very steep turn, for instance, at a 60° angle of bank, an aircraft wing has to generate twice the **lift** needed for straight flight. This situation is depicted in *Figure 5.20.*

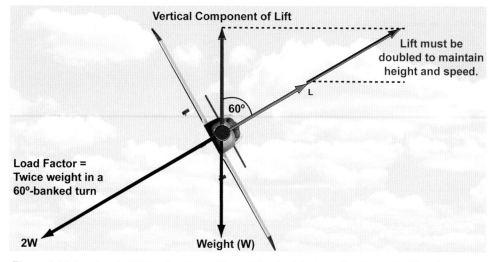

Figure 5.20 In a level, 60°-banked turn, lift must be doubled, leading to a significant increase in induced drag.

If speed is not increased, the extra **lift** needs to be generated by increasing **angle of attack** (and power). And, so, **induced drag**, which is inseparable from lift, will also increase even though there has been no increase in speed. The increase in **induced drag** is, of course, the reason why the pilot has to apply more power in turns, especially in a steep turn, in order to maintain speed and height.

You may have noticed, at air shows, that, when violent manoeuvres are flown by a fighter aircraft, vapour trails can sometimes be seen at the fighter's wingtips. This is because the pressure at the centre of the **wingtip vortices** gets so low that the water vapour in the air condenses into visible trails. The vapour trails, so generated, sometimes illustrate dramatically, by their irregular streaming movement, the agitated nature of the **vortex flow**.

A heavier aircraft must fly with increased angle of attack at any given airspeed and will generate greater induced drag than a lightly-loaded aircraft.

Of course, in turns, when increased **lift** is required to balance the **weight**, the **inertial reaction** to the increased **lift** force applies an extra **load factor** on the wings, acting along the same line of action as the **lift** force but in the opposite direction. The **load factor** in a balanced 60° banked turn is **2**. This **load factor** is an indication of the **apparent increase in weight** of the aircraft and its occupants. In a 60°-banked turn, then, the pilot feels that he **weighs twice as much** as normal and might say, colloquially, that he is **"pulling 2g"**.

Similarly, for any given speed, an aircraft in level flight will need to generate more lift if it is carrying a heavy payload than when it is lightly loaded. This means that, at identical speeds, identical aircraft will have to fly at higher **angles of attack**, the greater their payload. A heavily loaded aircraft, then, will also generate greater **induced drag**, at a given speed, than an identical aircraft which is lightly loaded.

Summary of the Causes of Induced Drag.
Induced drag is inseparable from the **lift-producing** function of the wings. **Wingtip vortices** will be generated as a result of the pressure difference above and below the wings. As the **vortices** increase in size and strength, they induce an increased, **additional downwash** which is superimposed on the main, **lift-producing** downwash. This phenomenon causes the **lift vector** to rotate rearwards. **The rearwards-acting horizontal component arising from the tilting backwards of the lift vector is the induced drag**. At low airspeeds and high angles of attack, the **vortices** are larger and more powerful, the rearwards-tilting of the lift vector is greater, and the **induced drag** is higher. **Induced drag is inversely proportional to the square of the airspeed**, reducing as airspeed increases and **angle of attack** decreases. Compared to straight flight, **angle of attack** must be increased in steep, level turns, flown at the same speed, in order that the wings may generate the increased **lift** required to maintain height. Therefore, in steep turns, greater **induced drag** will act on the aircraft than at the same speed in straight flight.

Methods of Reducing Induced Drag.
A wing of infinite length would, of course, have no wingtips, so there would be no wingtip vortices, no spanwise flow and no **induced drag**. This hypothetical situation is the situation we were considering when we examined parasite drag. An infinitely long, wingtipless wing is obviously an impossibility. In practice, the best methods of minimising **induced drag** involve reducing the vortex-generating effects of wings and wingtips. There are several methods of achieving this aim.

Reducing Induced Drag - Aspect Ratio.

An infinitely long wing, without wingtips, generates no **induced drag**. The best practical approximation to a wing of infinite length is a wing of high **aspect ratio**; that is a wing whose **span** is great relative to its **mean chord**. The notion of **aspect ratio** is illustrated in *Figure 5.21*.

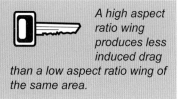

A high aspect ratio wing produces less induced drag than a low aspect ratio wing of the same area.

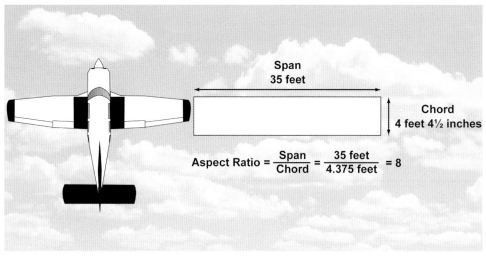

Figure 5.21 A wing of low aspect ratio.

Both the schematics of simple wing plan-forms in *Figures 5.21* and *5.22* have approximately equal wing areas. But the shorter, stubbier wing has a **low aspect ratio** of 8 whereas the longer, more slender wing has a **high aspect ratio** of 25. The aircraft illustrated alongside each plan-form may not have these exact **aspect ratios** in reality, but the illustrations <u>do</u> show how aircraft can have either low or high **aspect ratio** wings.

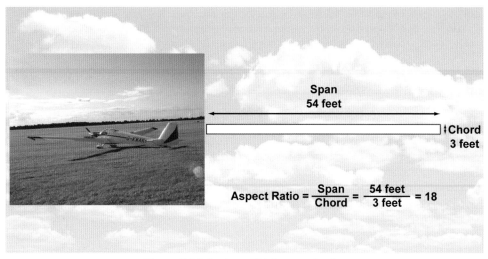

Figure 5.22 A wing of high aspect ratio.

A **light training aircraft**, for instance, might have an **aspect ratio** of 7 or 8, whereas a **touring motor glider** could have an **aspect ratio** of around 14 to 18.

Now, in the design of a wing, area is an important factor in determining what lift the wing can develop **(Lift = C_L ½ ρ v² S)**. But a wing of **high aspect ratio** will generate much **less induced drag** than a wing of **low aspect ratio** of equal area.

This is because the **high aspect ratio** wing is a closer approximation to a wing of infinite length than is a **low aspect ratio** wing. A **high aspect ratio** wing has a smaller wingtip of less vortex-generating significance than a **low aspect ratio** wing of equal area. With the **high aspect ratio** wing, then, there is less spillage of air from the high pressure area below the wing to the low pressure area above it, and, consequently, smaller, less powerful, wingtip vortices are generated, causing less **induced drag**.

Obviously, the production of very **high aspect ratio** wings carries with it structural issues for the designer, but the increasing load bearing and flexing qualities of composite materials is overcoming this problem.

The Shape of the Wing's Plan-form.

We have established that **induced drag** is greatest when the **wingtip vortices** are greatest, so any method of reducing **wingtip vortices** will reduce **induced drag**, too. **High aspect ratio** wings will achieve this reduction in **induced drag**, as we have just seen. Wings of **elliptical plan-form** will achieve the same objective of keeping the wingtip small compared to wing span. The Spitfire is, doubtless, the most famous aircraft to be fitted with wings of **elliptical plan-form**.

Figure 5.23 Spitfires showing elliptical wing plan form.

Elliptical wings are expensive to produce because of the manufacturing processes required to create the wing. It is more common for aircraft designers to consider **tapered wings** which also reduce wingtip size, and, thus, vortex strength. **Tapered wings** are, however, less effective that **elliptical wings** at reducing **induced drag**.

Washout.

You should now be totally at ease with the explanation that **induced drag** is greatest at high **angles of attack**, because of the increased pressure difference between the airflow above and below the wings, and that the **vortices** which cause **induced drag** are strongest at the **wingtips**. Now, the **wingtip angle of attack** can be kept lower than the **mean angle of attack** for the whole wing by constructing the wing with **washout**. On a wing with **washout**, the **angle of incidence** between the wing and the aircraft's longitudinal axis reduces gradually along the length of the wing, as the wingtip is approached. In other words, the wing is slightly twisted along its span, as illustrated in *Figure 5.24, overleaf*.

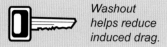

Washout helps reduce induced drag.

This means that, at any given **mean angle of attack** for the whole wing, the **angle of attack** at the **wingtip** will always be less than the mean, reducing **wingtip vortex** size and strength, and so reducing **induced drag**.

Figure 5.24 Washout refers to the reducing angle of incidence from root to tip. Washout also helps to reduce induced drag.

Winglets and Other Wingtip Modifications.

Modifications to wingtips, designed to minimise spillage from the high to low pressure regions, can also reduce **wingtip vortex** strength and, thus, **induced drag**.

Common wingtip modifications, some of which are illustrated in *Figure 5.25*, are: **winglets, shaped wingtips, wing end-plates**, or **wing fences**, and **wingtip tanks**.

Figure 5.25 Wingtip shapes designed to reduce wingtip vortex strength.

TOTAL DRAG.

Total drag as you learnt at the beginning of this chapter is made up of **parasite drag** and **induced drag**. You have also learnt that **parasite drag** <u>increases</u> with the square of the airspeed, whereas **induced drag** <u>decreases</u> with the square of the airspeed. When we consider an aircraft in any phase of flight: take-off, climb, cruise, descent, or landing, the **total drag** acting on the aircraft, at any time, will be made up partly of **parasite drag** and partly of **induced drag**. *Figure 5.26* combines the graphs for the variation of both **parasite** and **induced drag** with speed.

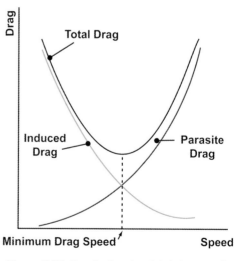

Figure 5.26 Graph showing total drag against speed.

You met the two individual graphs earlier in this chapter. *Figure 5.26*, a combination of the two earlier graphs, shows that **parasite drag** predominates at high speeds, while **induced drag** at high speed is low. At low speeds, the opposite is the case. Based on the values for each of the individual graphs at various speeds, a curve may be drawn illustrating how the **total drag** acting on an aircraft varies with speed.

You should note that the speed at which the **total drag** acting on an aircraft is at a minimum is the speed at which **parasite drag** <u>is equal to</u> **induced drag**, (that is, the point at which the **parasite drag** and **induced drag** curves intersect each other). The speed for **minimum drag** is an important reference value for pilots. **Minimum drag speed** will give a pilot his aircraft's **maximum rate of climb**, **best glide performance**, and **best speed for range** in cruising flight.

Minimum drag occurs when parasite drag equals induced drag, at an angle of attack of approximately 4°.

Minimum drag speed is also the speed for the best **lift/drag ratio**. Each aircraft type will have a **minimum drag speed** which will vary, for that aircraft, depending on such factors as **weight** and **wing loading**. However, **minimum drag speed** will always occur at an **angle of attack** of approximately **4°**.

The Drag Equation.

Having derived a graph showing how **total drag varies with airspeed**, we can see from the graph *(Figure 5.26)* that **total drag** is high at both low and high speeds. In order to relate **total drag** to general aircraft parameters such as **aircraft surface area**, **air density**, **wing shape**, **angle of attack** and, of course, **speed**, aerodynamicists have derived the following **drag equation**:

$$\text{Drag} = C_D \tfrac{1}{2} \rho \, v^2 \, S$$

You will notice that this equation is very similar to the lift equation that you have already met.

$$\text{Lift} = C_L \tfrac{1}{2} \rho \, v^2 \, S$$

Like the **Lift Equation** the **Drag Equation** is one of the few equations that you will be required to remember for the PPL theoretical knowledge examination.

Learn the drag equation:

$\text{Drag} = C_D \tfrac{1}{2} \rho \, v^2 \, S.$

In the **Drag Equation**, the symbols have the following meaning.

C_D	is the **Coefficient of Drag** which is a number which takes into account shape, as well the angle of attack of the relative airflow. C_D has no units
ρ	is the local **air density**; ρ has the standard units **kg/m³**
v	is the aircraft's **true airspeed**. Notice that total drag varies according to the square of the velocity. **v** has the standard units **m/sec**
S	is a reference **surface area**. **S** has the standard units **m²**

The **Drag Equation**, then, reveals that the **total drag** acting on an aircraft in flight is proportional to **dynamic pressure**, $\tfrac{1}{2} \rho \, v^2$, to the **local air density**, ρ, the **reference surface area, S,** and to the **coefficient of drag, C_D**, which takes into account the **shape** of the lifting surface and **angle of attack** of the relative airflow.

The Drag Coefficient C_D.

The **drag coefficient, C_D**, for **total drag**, has to include the effects of both **parasite drag** and **induced drag** and is determined experimentally. The reference surface area, **S**, can be any surface area chosen by the aerodynamicist: **wing area**, **frontal area**, or **aircraft surface area**. For different surface areas, the calculated C_D will be different, but, of course, the measured **total drag** will be the same and the different values for C_D will be related to each other as ratios of the different reference surface areas used.

The coefficient of drag, C_D, takes into account both the shape of the wing and its angle of attack to the relative airflow.

For instance, let us assume that the reference surface area is the frontal cross sectional area of the whole aircraft. Now, in the equation **Drag = C_D ½ ρ v² S**, the expression ½ ρ v² is the **dynamic pressure**, for which we have the symbol, **Q**. So, we can re-write the drag equation as:

Drag = **C_D Q S**   and we can, then, re-arrange this equation to read:

$$C_D = \frac{Drag}{Q \times S}$$

Pressure = $\frac{Force}{Area}$ so Force = Pressure × Area, and

Force produced by Dynamic Pressure = Q × S

We can see, then, that C_D is an expression of the **ratio of the drag force to the force produced by the dynamic pressure (Q × S)**. Being a ratio of quantities (i.e. forces) having the same units, C_D, itself, has no units.

Note that the **drag coefficient, C_D**, for any given aircraft, is **constant** only while the aircraft maintains a **constant angle of attack**. As soon as the pilot selects a different angle of attack with respect to the relative airflow, the frontal area exposed to the airflow will change, the amount of turbulence generated will change, and, of course, the strength of the wing vortices will change. Therefore, C_D will change.

Figure 5.27 shows how the **drag coefficient, C_D**, varies with angle of attack. Knowing the value of C_D, and given the other variables in the **drag equation**, the **total drag** acting on an aircraft can be calculated for any given true airspeed from the drag equation: **Drag = C_D ½ ρ v² S**

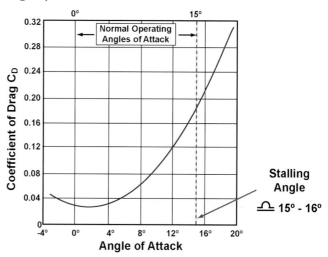

Figure 5.27 Graph of Coefficient of Drag, C_D, against angle of attack.

The graph of C_D against **angle of attack** shows that C_D varies with varying **angle of attack**, being least at a very small positive **angle of attack** and rising at **angles of attack** greater and less than that angle. C_D increases at quite a low rate up to about 8° but, from then on, increases more and more rapidly, especially as the **stalling angle** (typically about 16°) is reached. C_D continues to rise rapidly beyond the **stalling angle** as the airflow becomes very turbulent.

Total drag is high at both very low and very high airspeeds.

C_D is low at small **angles of attack**. Small **angles of attack** are, of course, associated with **high speeds**. So, although C_D in the drag equation is small, **v** will be high, and, as **drag** is directly proportional to v^2, **total drag** will still be very high at high speeds, even though **induced drag** will be low. At high angles of attack, **v** is low, but, now, C_D is very high. In straight and level flight, **high angles of attack** are associated with **low speed**. So, although **parasite drag** is low at low speed, **total drag** is high.

These findings are what we were led to expect by the graph of **total drag** against speed, at *Figure 5.27*.

EFFECTIVE ANGLE OF ATTACK AND GROUND EFFECT.

To conclude this chapter on **drag**, we will look in a little more detail at how the additional downwash caused by **wingtip vortices** are affected by flight in close proximity to the ground. This phenomenon is called **ground effect**. **Ground effect**, in modifying the **wingtip vortices**, also influences **induced drag** and, consequently, the performance and handling characteristics of the aircraft. **Ground effect** is experienced by most pilots during the final phases of the landing.

Effective Angle of Attack or "Downwash Angle".
As you have learnt, **wingtip vortices** *(see Figure 5.28)*, induce a **downwash** in the airflow over the wings which is **additional to the main lift-essential downwash** which we learnt about in the chapter on **lift**.

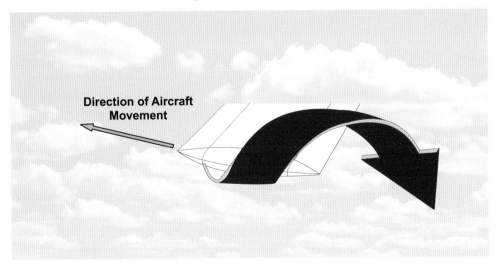

Direction of Aircraft Movement

Figure 5.28 Wingtip vortices are the cause of the additional downwash which is the cause of induced drag.

In fact, the **wingtip vortices**, in increasing the angle of **downwash** aft of the wing, also modify the angle of **upwash** upstream of the wing, as depicted in *Figure 5.29*.

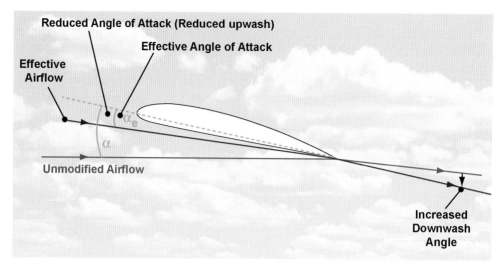

Figure 5.29 Wingtip vortices are the cause of the additional downwash which is the cause of induced drag.

The effect of this modification of the airflow is to change the direction of the **relative airflow** to produce the true or **effective airflow**, as you can see from *Figure 5.29*. The result is a **reduced angle of attack**, measured between the wing chord and the effective airflow, and called the **effective angle of attack**.

Both the **lift** and the **drag** produced by the wing are affected by these changes.

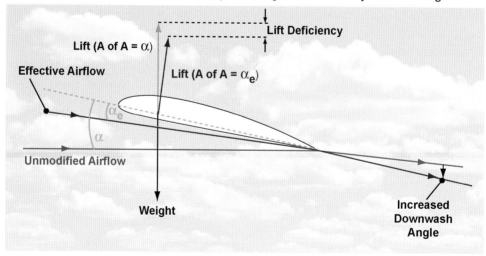

Figure 5.30 Lift deficiency due to increased downwash angle.

The **lift vector** now acts at 90° to the **effective airflow**, as depicted by the red lift arrow in *Figure 5.30*.

The **effective lift vector**, produced by the **effective angle of attack**, α_e, now acts slightly rearwards. You can see, too, that, since the **effective angle of attack** has reduced, the magnitude of the **lift force** has reduced.

Lift must of course equal the **weight** of the aircraft to maintain level flight. So, to restore the **lift** which has been lost due to the **downwash**, as indicated in *Figure 5.30*, the wing must be selected to a higher angle of attack as in *Figure 5.31*.

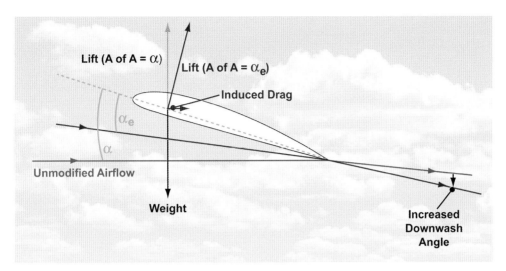

Figure 5.31 A further increase in A of A restores the lift deficiency and generates induced drag.

This, as you now know, increases **drag** by a value that we call **induced drag**. The amount by which the angle of attack is reduced by the effective airflow, $\alpha - \alpha_e$, is called the **downwash angle**.

Ground Effect.

When an aircraft is taking off or landing, the closeness of the wing to the ground prevents full development of the **wingtip vortices**, thus making them much weaker. This **reduction in vortex strength** is called **ground effect**. (*Figure 5.32.*)

An aircraft is in ground effect when within approximately ½ a wing span's distance from the ground.

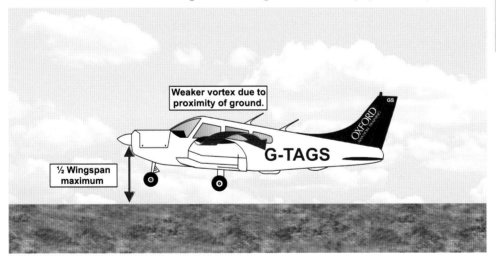

Figure 5.32 Ground effect prevents full development of the wing tip vortices.

An aircraft is subject to **ground effect** when it is within approximately half wingspan distance from the ground.

The **reduction in vortex strength** near the ground causes a **decrease in the additional downwash angle** and, consequently, an increase in the effective angle of attack, and an **increase in lift**.

Ground effect reduces induced drag and increases lift.

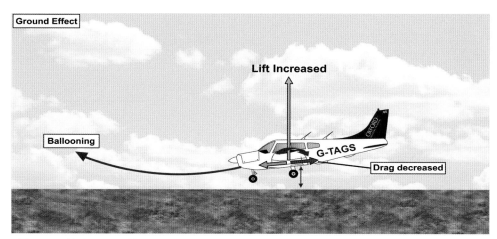

Figure 5.33 Ground effect reduces the wingtip vortices and increases the effective angle of attack, thus increasing lift.

Furthermore, even though the effective angle of attack has increased, the **induced drag** will decrease in **ground effect** due to the **reduced wingtip vortices**. This **reduction in drag** will cause the aircraft to tend to accelerate, and further **increase lift**.

Good speed control on approach helps to achieve a good landing.

The combination of **ground effect** and an approach flown at too high an airspeed, especially with a small flap angle selected, may lead to a balloon landing; a common trait of the student pilot. *(See Figure 5.33.)* For this reason, it is necessary for the pilot to demonstrate good speed control on the approach.

The Effect of Downwash on the Horizontal stabiliser.

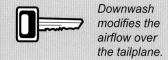

Downwash modifies the airflow over the tailplane.

We must also consider the effect of **additional downwash** on the **horizontal stabiliser** or **tailplane**. You will recall that it is the **tailplane** that provides stability and controllability of the aircraft in pitch.

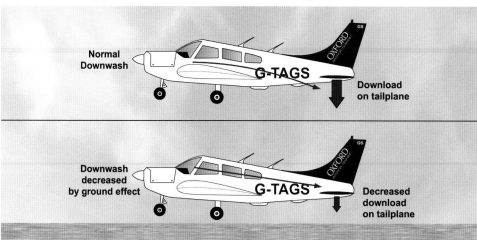

Figure 5.34 Ground effect reduces the wingtip vortices and increases the effective angle of attack, thus increasing lift.

Downwash will affect the aerodynamic characteristics of the tailplane as well as the main wing. The effective angle of attack at the tailplane is modified by the changing **downwash** from the main wing, altering the aircraft's stability and controllability characteristics.

Representative PPL - type questions to test your theoretical knowledge of Drag.

1.   As airspeed increases, induced drag:

   a.   increases
   b.   decreases
   c.   is dependent on the weight of the aircraft
   d.   remains unchanged

2.   As airspeed increases induced drag _____, parasite drag _____ and total drag _____.

   a.   increases   increases   increases
   b.   increases   decreases   increases then decreases
   c.   decreases   decreases   decreases
   d.   decreases   increases   decreases then increases

3.   By changing the Angle of Attack of a wing, the pilot can control the aeroplane's:

   a.   lift and airspeed, but not drag
   b.   lift, gross weight and drag
   c.   lift, airspeed and drag
   d.   lift and drag, but not airspeed

4.   That portion of the aircraft's total drag created by the production of lift is called:

   a.   parasite drag, which is greatly affected by changes in airspeed
   b.   induced drag, which is not affected by changes in airspeed
   c.   induced drag, which is greatly affected by changes in airspeed
   d.   parasite drag, which is inversely proportional to the square of the airspeed

5.   If the Indicated Air Speed of an aircraft is increased from 50 kt to 100 kt, parasite drag will be:

   a.   four times greater
   b.   six times greater
   c.   two times greater
   d.   one quarter as much

6.   Resistance, or skin friction, due to the viscosity of the air as it passes along the surface of a wing, is a type of:

   a.   induced drag
   b.   form drag
   c.   parasite drag
   d.   interference drag

7.   How do Lift and Parasite Drag vary with airspeed?

    a.   lift and Parasite Drag both decrease as the square of the airspeed
    b.   lift decreases as the square of the airspeed while Parasite Drag increases as the square of the airspeed
    c.   lift increases as the square of the airspeed while Parasite Drag decreases as the square of the airspeed
    d.   lift and Parasite Drag both increase as the square of the airspeed

8.   Parasite drag varies with:

    a.   the square of the airspeed
    b. C_{LMAX}
    c.   the airspeed
    d.   the weight of the aircraft, only

9.   Choose one of the four options below to make an accurate statement.

As airspeed increases:

    a.   induced drag increases
    b.   induced drag is unaffected
    c.   form drag decreases
    d.   induced drag decreases

10.   Which of the following is the cause of wing tip vortices?

    a.   air spilling from the top surface to the bottom surface at the wing tip
    b.   air spilling from the bottom surface to the top surface at the wing tip
    c.   the increased form drag at the wing tip
    d.   the increased parasite drag at the wing tip

11.   Wing tip vortices are caused by unequal pressure distribution on the wing which results in airflow from:

    a.   bottom to top round the trailing edge
    b.   top to bottom round the trailing edge
    c.   bottom to top round the wingtip
    d.   top to bottom round the wingtip

12.   Which of the following is the correct formula for drag?

    a. $\frac{1}{2} \rho V^2 C_L S$
    b. $\frac{1}{2} \rho r V (C_D)^2 S$
    c. $\frac{1}{2} \rho^2 V C_D S$
    d. $C_D \frac{1}{2} \rho V^2 S$

13.   Choose the option below which best describes aircraft drag considerations as True Air Speed increases:

      a.   parasite drag decreases and induced drag increases
      b.   parasite drag increases and induced drag increases
      c.   parasite drag decreases and induced drag decreases
      d.   parasite drag increases and induced drag decreases

14.   An aircraft carries out a given journey, on two separate days. On both days, the pilot flies at an indicated airspeed of 120 knots. On the first day, the air density is greater than on the subsequent day. How will the forces of Lift and Drag acting on the aircraft compare on the two days?

      a.   on the first day the Lift will be greater and Drag will be less than on the subsequent day
      b.   the forces of Lift and Drag acting on the aircraft will remain unchanged
      c.   on the first day the Lift will be less and Drag will be greater than on the subsequent day
      d.   on the first day both Lift and Drag will be less than on the subsequent day

Question	1	2	3	4	5	6	7	8	9	10	11	12
Answer												

Question	13	14
Answer		

The answers to these questions can be found at the end of this book.

CHAPTER 6
THE LIFT/DRAG RATIO

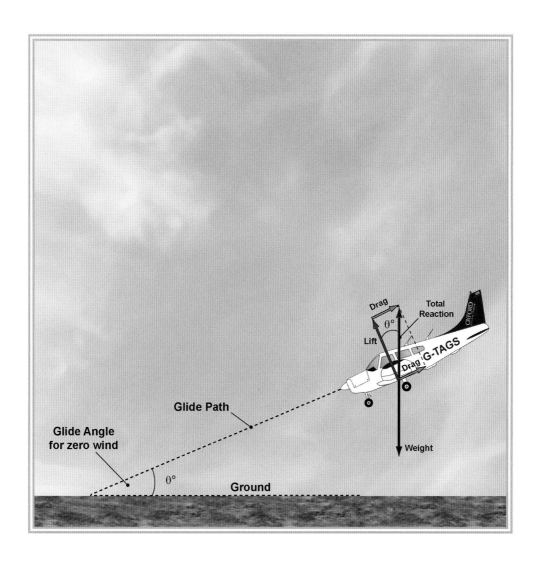

THE RELATIONSHIP BETWEEN LIFT AND DRAG.

Introduction.

Figure 6.1 depicts graphs of the **coefficient of lift**, C_L, and the **coefficient of drag**, C_D, against **angle of attack**, for a particular aerofoil. These graphs are similar to the ones you have already met.

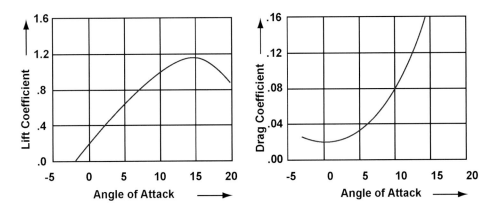

Figure 6.1 Graphs showing C_L and C_D against Angle of Attack.

We have been discussing **lift** and **drag**, at some length, as separate aerodynamic forces acting on an aircraft, in flight. However, in considering aircraft performance and the pilot's control over that performance, you will not be surprised to learn that we must also consider the effects of the forces of both **lift** and **drag**, taken in combination, and the nature of the relationship between **lift** and **drag**.

It is important to keep in mind that C_L and C_D , the **coefficients** of lift and drag are not the same as **lift** and **drag**, and that the graphs showing the variation of C_L and C_D against **angle of attack**, are <u>not</u> graphs illustrating variations in the full **lift** and **drag forces** against **angle of attack**.

You have already met the equations which allow us to calculate the magnitude of the actual **lift** and **drag forces**. They are:

Lift = C_L ½ $\rho v^2 S$

Drag = C_D ½ $\rho v^2 S$

Lift and **drag** are forces, measured in **Newtons**, in standard units, but also often expressed in **pounds** (lbs) or **kilograms** (kg), whereas C_L and C_D are dimensionless values which take account of the shape of the wing's **aerofoil cross-section**, and the wing's **angle of attack** with the relative airflow.

You can see, then, that, to find the **lift** and **drag forces**, themselves, we have to include the values of **air density**, ρ ,**wing area**, **S**, and the aircraft's **true airspeed**, **v**, as well as the coefficients of lift and drag, C_L and C_D.

What the Graphs of C_L and C_D Against Angle Of Attack Teach Us.

The C_L and C_D curves are indicative of changes in the actual **forces** of **lift** and **drag** only if we assume constant airspeed and constant density. (However, even this latter statement is only of mathematical interest to us as, in real life, airspeed is, itself, directly related to angle of attack.)

However, if we bear in mind at all times the true nature of C_L and C_D, the C_L and C_D graphs give us some useful information. So, before we go on to examine the **forces** of **lift** and **drag**, considered in combination, let us take one more look at the C_L and C_D curves, separately, to see what they might have to teach us.

First of all, notice the difference in their shape.

The curve of C_L against **angle of attack (AoA)** is almost a straight line, from a slightly negative **AoA** up to an **AoA** of about 10°. We can see, therefore, that a small increase in **AoA**, say of 1°, from 2° to 3°, has the same effect, in terms of augmenting the **lift** force (at constant airspeed and air density) as does a 1° **AoA** increase from 8° to 9°. C_L continues to rise, less rapidly, beyond 10° **AoA**, reaching a maximum value, called C_{LMAX}, just before the **stalling angle** (sometimes called the **critical angle**) of about 16°, beyond which **lift** decreases abruptly.

However, in terms of C_D, for the same two increases in **AoA**, from 2° to 3° and from 8° to 9°, the effect is markedly different. A 1° increase in **AoA** from 2° to 3° makes no noticeable difference to the **drag** force (at constant airspeed and air density), while the 1° **AoA** increase from 8° to 9° produces a significant increase in drag. The increase in **drag** becomes even more rapid as the **stalling angle** of 16° is approached. C_D continues to rise steeply beyond that angle as the airflow becomes more turbulent and erratic.

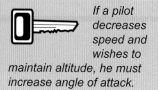

If a pilot increases speed and wishes to maintain altitude, he must decrease angle of attack.

If a pilot decreases speed and wishes to maintain altitude, he must increase angle of attack.

You will become aware of the importance of what these graphs are telling you, at appropriate phases in your flying training.

For instance, if we consider the information from the C_L and C_D graphs against AoA, along with the information that we can extract from the **lift** and **drag equations**, **Lift = C_L ½ $\rho v^2 S$ and Drag = C_D ½ $\rho v^2 S$**, we should easily be able to deduce the following piloting facts:

- If the airspeed, **v**, is increased while the angle of attack C_L or C_D remains constant, the magnitude of both the **lift** and the **drag** forces will increase, and the aircraft will begin to climb. (In fact, because **lift** and **drag** are proportional to v^2, if the airspeed is doubled, the **lift** and **drag** increase fourfold.)

- If the pilot, wishes to increase speed, **v**, in the cruise, and to maintain altitude at the higher speed, he must hold **lift** constant by reducing **angle of attack**, C_L.

- If the pilot, wishes to decrease speed, **v**, in the cruise, and to maintain altitude at the lower speed, he must hold **lift** constant by increasing **angle of attack**, C_L.

- If air density reduces, lift and drag will reduce if true airspeed, **v**, remains constant.

- At constant air density and **angle of attack**, if Fowler Flaps are deployed *(See Figure 10.14 in the Lift Augmentation Chapter)*, wing area, **S**, will increase; therefore, **lift** force (and, thus, altitude) will be able to be maintained at a lower airspeed.

Induced drag is high at low airspeeds and parasite drag is high at high airspeed.

- Similarly, the deployment of an appropriate amount of trailing edge flap will, by increasing C_L, allow altitude to be maintained at a lower airspeed.

What the Lift and Drag Equations Teach Us.

You will have doubtless, by now, worked out for yourself that by memorising the two equations of **lift** and **drag**, and keeping in mind the basic information given by the graphs of C_L and C_D against **angle of attack**, you will be able quite easily to appreciate the relationship between **angle of attack**, **airspeed**, **lift** and **drag**, which is fundamental to basic piloting skill. For instance, you should now be in a position to understand the reasons for the following general piloting issues :

- Low airspeeds are related to high angles of attack.

- High airspeeds require low angles of attack.

- The total drag acting on an aircraft flying at low C_D (say 0° angle of attack), will still be high because although C_D may be low, **v** in the equation **Drag = C_D ½ $\rho v^2 S$** will be high. Of course, drag varies directly, not with **v** but with v^2.

Total drag is high at both very high and very low speeds.

- At a higher, all-up weight, when no flap is selected, an aircraft needs to be flown at a higher angle of attack (higher C_L) to maintain a given airspeed.

C_L and C_D are dimensionless coefficients which takes into account wing shape, configuration and angle of attack.

- The total drag acting on an aircraft flying at very high speeds and very low speeds is **high** in both cases. At high speed (small angle of attack and low C_D), most of the drag will be parasite drag, and, at low speed (large angle of attack and high C_D), most of the drag will be induced drag. *(See Figure 6.2)*.

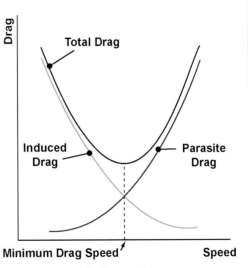

Figure 6.2 The total drag curve.

- C_L and C_D are dimensionless values which take into account **wing shape** and **configuration**, and **angle of attack**; they are not the same as **lift** and **drag force**.

- C_L reduces rapidly beyond an **angle of attack** of 16° : called the **stalling angle of attack**. A conventional, clean wing will always **stall** at this **angle of attack**, and so, <u>in level, cruising flight</u> (at constant air density, ρ, and for a given wing area, **S**), where lift must equal weight, a given aircraft will always stall at the same value of **v**. (**Lift = C_L ½ $\rho v^2 S$**)

- Because the **indicated airspeed** already takes into account the value of ρ, (the **airspeed indicator** (ASI) measures the **dynamic pressure**, $\frac{1}{2}\rho v^2$), an aircraft attempting to maintain steady, level flight at steadily increasing **AoA** will always **stall** at the same ASI reading.

The Lift-Drag Ratio.

In most (but not all) phases of flight, the generation of **lift** by the wing is a distinct benefit, while the generation of **drag** is a distinct disadvantage. When the aircraft is flying very fast at low angles of attack (low C_D), we have seen that **parasite drag** is high, and when the aircraft is flying at low speeds and high angles of attack (high C_D), the **induced drag** is high. *(See Figure 6.2)*. So at neither of these two extremes of **high drag** is the wing working at its most efficient. The wing will be working **most efficiently** when it is generating **maximum lift for minimum drag**.

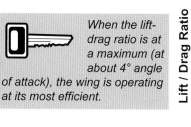
The lift-drag ratio varies with angle of attack and, therefore, also with airspeed.

Consequently, a factor of greater significance to aircraft performance issues than lift and drag considered separately, is the **lift-drag ratio**. The **lift-drag ratio** is commonly expressed, using initial letters, as the **L/D ratio**.

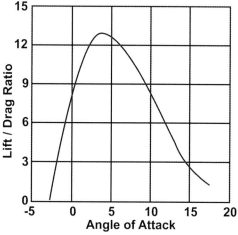

Maximum lift for **minimum drag** occurs at the highest **lift-drag ratio**; that is at the highest value of the **L/D ratio**. From the values available from the two individual graphs of C_L and C_D against **AoA**, we can plot a further graph which shows how the **lift-drag ratio** (**L/D ratio**) varies with **AoA**. Such a graph is depicted in *Figure 6.3*.

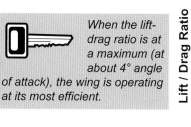
When the lift-drag ratio is at a maximum (at about 4° angle of attack), the wing is operating at its most efficient.

Figure 6.3 Graph showing Lift-Drag (L/D) ratio against Angle of Attack.

You have already learnt that the values of **lift** and **drag** are not the same as the values of C_L and C_D because the actual **lift** and **drag** forces depend on other parameters such as **airspeed**, **air density** and **wing area**. But to obtain information on the **lift to drag ratio**, we may plot either **Lift/Drag** against **AoA** or C_L/C_D against **AoA**. The following mathematical relationship illustrates why this is so.

$$\frac{\text{Lift}}{\text{Drag}} = \frac{C_L \, \frac{1}{2}\rho v^2 S}{C_D \, \frac{1}{2}\rho v^2 S} = \frac{C_L \, \frac{1}{2}\rho v^2 S}{C_D \, \frac{1}{2}\rho v^2 S} = \frac{C_L}{C_D}$$

From *Figure 6.3*, then, you can see that the **L/D ratio** increases rapidly to a maximum value, at an **AoA** of around **4°** and then falls away as **AoA** is increased further. Be aware that this does not mean that lift is greatest at **4° AoA**. As the C_L graph shows, **lift** carries on increasing well beyond an **AoA** of **4°**. But, of course, from the C_D graph you see that the **drag** goes on increasing beyond **4° AoA**, too. Therefore, when we combine the data from the C_L and C_D curves, we see that the **best L/D ratio** (L/D_{MAX}) occurs at **4° AoA**.

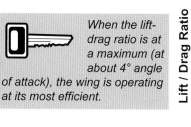
The lift-drag ratio is at a maximum where total drag is at a minimum.

In the chapter on drag, you learnt, that an **AoA** of **4°** is the **AoA** for **minimum drag** (not minimum C_L). So **minimum drag AoA is also the AoA for the** L/D_{MAX}.

Consequently, for the conventional aerofoil wing, greatest efficiency is achieved at an **AoA** of **4°**. This fact explains why the wing's **angle of incidence (rigger's angle of incidence** between the wing chord line and the aircraft's longitudinal axis) is set so that, in level cruising flight, the relative airflow meets an aircraft's wing at about **4°**. Of course, if it is the designer's intention to design an aircraft for speed, the aircraft's wing may meet the relative airflow at an **AoA** of less than **4°**, in the cruise; but if economy and efficiency of operation is the designer's chief concern, the cruising **AoA** will be about **4°**. The aircraft for which the **L/D** graph at *Figure 6.3* was drawn has a maximum **L/D ratio** of **13** at an **AoA** of **4°**. Let us assume that this aircraft is operated in steady cruising flight at an all-up weight of **2125 pounds (lbs)**. Because, **in steady flight, lift** must always equal **weight**, the **lift** generated by the aircraft would also have to be **2125 lbs** (964 kg or about 9457 Newtons). If the aircraft is flown at an airspeed corresponding to the **L/D$_{MAX}$ AoA** of **4°**, the **drag** acting on the aircraft would have the value **163.5 lbs** (74 kg or about 726 Newtons), which, of course, is one thirteenth of **2125 lbs**. This would be the minimum amount of drag generated to provide the lift necessary to support the **weight** of **2125 lbs**. The **weight** <u>could</u> be supported at lower or higher airspeeds, than the speed for **L/D$_{MAX}$**, but, in that case, **AoA** would be higher or lower than the **L/D$_{MAX}$ AoA** of **4°**, and drag would always be greater than **163.5 lbs**.

Even if the aircraft were operated at a higher, or lower, all-up weight, the same **maximum L/D ratio** would be obtained at **4° AoA**. However, as the **lift** and **drag equations** show, if the all-up weight were higher, **lift** would have to be higher and the **maximum L/D ratio** would be obtained at a higher airspeed. Similarly, if the all-up weight were lower, **L/D$_{MAX}$** would be obtained at a lower airspeed.

Performance Criteria Related to Maximum Lift-Drag Ratio (L/D$_{MAX}$).

In steady, level, cruising flight, the **thrust** developed by the propeller must equal **drag**; so, for flight at **L/D$_{MAX}$** (that is, at minimum drag), the thrust required to maintain level flight is also a minimum.

Several important aspects of aircraft performance are related to an aircraft's **maximum achievable Lift-Drag ratio**. The most relevant of these are: **maximum power-off gliding range**, **maximum cruising range**, and **best rate of climb**.

As you have learnt, **L/D$_{MAX}$** corresponds to flight at **4° AoA**, for a conventional aircraft. Whilst light aircraft are not fitted with angle of attack indicators, you learnt in the Chapter on **lift** that, **at a given aircraft weight, a given angle of attack corresponds to a particular airspeed**. Therefore, for a given aircraft, at an assumed normal operating weight, a speed will be published in the **Pilot's Operating Handbook (POH)** for (amongst other performance criteria) **best glide range**, **maximum cruising range** and **best rate of climb**.

The following approximate speeds are given for the **PA-28-161, Warrior** for an assumed maximum gross weight of 2440 lb (1107 kg or 10 860 Newtons):

Maximum range cruising speed = 105 knots.

Maximum rate of climb, without flap, = 75 knots.

Both these speeds will be achieved, with different power settings, of course, at an **AoA** of around **4°**.

The greater the aircraft's weight, the higher the airspeed at which the lift-drag ratio is at a maximum.

For the absolute maximum range, the aircraft should fly at the **AoA** for **L/D$_{MAX}$**, at the airspeed given in the **POH**, and carry the minimum load. If extra payload is carried, the maximum range speed will be higher and the actual range achieved slightly less than for minimum load.

Wind conditions en-route will also have an effect on maximum range speed, as will considerations of propeller and engine efficiency. This situation will be covered in detail in the section on **Aircraft Performance**.

You should also note that maximum range speed considerations for jet aircraft are different for those of piston-engine/propeller powered aircraft. However, those considerations are beyond the scope of this book.

Lift-Drag Ratio and Glide Performance.

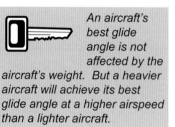

An aircraft's best glide angle is not affected by the aircraft's weight. But a heavier aircraft will achieve its best glide angle at a higher airspeed than a lighter aircraft.

One final point to note is that an aircraft's power-off glide performance expressed as the ratio of **ground distance covered** to **height lost** is the same as the **ratio of Lift to Drag**, assuming zero wind. This situation is depicted in *Figure 6.4*. So, in still air, if an aircraft is gliding at a **Lift-Drag ratio** of, say, **10:1**, it will cover **10 000 feet** (1.65 nautical miles), horizontally, for every **1 000 feet** of height lost.

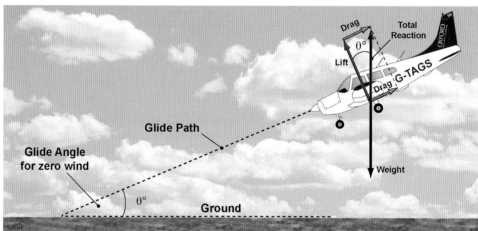

Figure 6.4 In still air, an aircraft's glide performance (distance covered/height lost) is equal to the Lift-Drag ratio.

In the glide, you will notice that there are only three forces acting on the aircraft: **lift**, **weight**, and **drag**. In a steady glide, these three forces are in **equilibrium**, the **weight** of the aircraft being counterbalanced by the **total reaction**: the resultant of the **lift** and **drag** forces.

You can see, then, that an aircraft's **best glide range** (minimum glide angle) is achieved at **L/D$_{MAX}$**. The **angle of attack** (**AoA**) between the wing chord and the relative airflow will be, of course, about **4°**. Without power, and at maximum all-up weight, this **AoA** will be achieved in the **PA28 Warrior**, at an airspeed of about **74 knots**.

An aircraft's **best glide angle** is a function solely of the **lift-drag ratio**, and is not affected by the aircraft's **weight**. However, the greater the **weight**, the higher the **airspeed** at which the **best glide angle** is achieved.

Glide performance will be covered in the **Aircraft Performance** section of this book.

Typical maximum **L/D** ratios for different types of aircraft are shown in the following table:

AIRCRAFT TYPE	TYPICAL L/D $_{MAX}$
Light piston-engine trainer	10 to 15
High-performance sailplane	30 to 50
Jet transport aircraft	15 to 20
Supersonic Fighter	4 to 9 (while subsonic)

Representative PPL - type questions to test your theoretical knowledge of Lift/Drag Ratio.

1. In straight and level flight which of the following is correct?
    (L/D = Lift - Drag ratio)

    a. L/D is maximum at the speed for minimum total drag
    b. L/D decreases with increasing lift
    c. L/D is maximum when lift equals weight
    d. L/D is maximum when lift equals zero

2. If, in level flight, the airspeed decreases below that for maximum Lift / Drag, the effect will be that:

    a. drag decreases because of lower induced drag
    b. drag increases because of increased induced drag
    c. drag increases because of increased parasite drag
    d. drag decreases because of lower parasite drag

3. How does an aircraft's all-up weight affect its best power-off glide angle, in still air?

    a. The best glide angle will be shallower
    b. The best glide angle will be steeper
    c. The best glide angle will not be affected
    d. It is advisable not to carry out a power-off glide at maximum all-up weight

4. An aircraft's glide angle is solely a function of:

    a. Its lift-drag ratio
    b. Its all up weight
    c. The aircraft's state of trim.
    d. The position of the C of G

5. Which of the following light aircraft performance criteria are achieved at L/D_{MAX}?

    a. Endurance will be at a maximum
    b. Angle of climb will be at a maximum
    c. Service ceiling will be highest
    d. Best rate of climb and maximum cruising range will be achieved

Question	1	2	3	4	5
Answer					

The answers to these questions can be found at the end of this book.

CHAPTER 7
WEIGHT

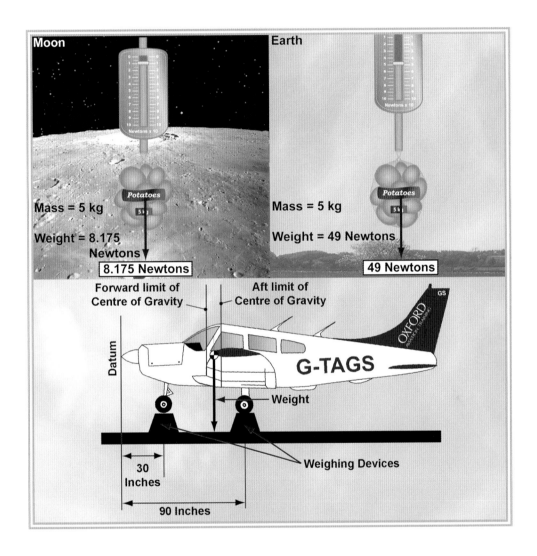

WEIGHT.

Weight and Mass.

We will begin this chapter by differentiating between the concepts of **mass** and **weight**.

Weight and mass are two different concepts. Weight is a force. Mass is a quantity of matter.

Because of the inexact way in which the word **mass** is used in everyday language, it is not uncommon for pilots to confuse the meanings of the terms **mass** and **weight** when they are used in a technical context such as in the study of aviation.

Even in aviation, though, confusion still exists. For many years, **"Weight and Balance"** was the title of a ground school subject in United Kingdom pilot training syllabi. Now, under the influence of the JAA, the subject is called **"Mass and Balance"**. There is a case, however, for the subject to be called "Weight, Mass and Balance" because the **weight** of a body is different from the body's **mass**. However, the subject's title remains **"Mass and Balance"**.

In aircraft operations, the concept of **mass** is of vital importance when considering horizontal accelerations and decelerations, such as during take-off, landing and horizontal, level, turns; whereas, in airborne manoeuvres, where accelerations in planes other than the horizontal are concerned, **weight** as well as **mass** must be taken into account.

The standard unit of mass is the kilogram. The standard unit of weight is the Newton.

What is the difference between weight and mass?

Put simply, **mass is a measure of the amount of matter in a body. Mass** can be measured in **imperial units such pounds (lbs)** or **metric units such as kilograms (kg).** The standard unit of **mass** is the **kg**.

Weight, on the other hand, **is a force.** To be exact, it is the **force** which results from a body of a given **mass**, situated within a **gravitational field**, being subjected to a **gravitational acceleration** as it is attracted to another **mass**. The standard unit of weight is the **Newton (N)**.

On Earth, the weight of a body is the force acting on the body's mass by virtue of the presence of the body within the Earth's gravitational field.

Weight is the name given to the force acting on a mass, and directed to the centre of the gravitational field.

Any body subjected to the Earth's **gravitational field**, which is allowed to fall, will **accelerate** towards the ground (more exactly towards the Earth's centre) at the same **gravitational acceleration** (**9.81 metres/sec^2** or **32 feet/sec^2**), whatever its **mass**.

A body will always possess mass, but if there is no gravity and the body is subjected to no gravitational acceleration, such as may be assumed in deep space, the body will have no weight. *(See Figure 7.1, overleaf.)*

As you can see from *Figure 7.1, overleaf*, mass is a <u>scalar quantity</u>, possessing magnitude only, while weight is a <u>vector quantity</u>, possessing both magnitude and direction.

A body will always possess the same mass, but if there is no force of gravity, the body will have no weight.

In the Earth's **gravitational field**, weight always acts towards the centre of the Earth.

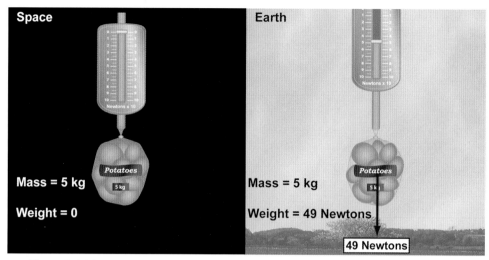

Figure 7.1 A body will always possess mass, but where there is no gravity, there is no weight.

Gravitational Acceleration – The Link Between Mass and Weight.

The linking factor between **mass** and **weight**, then, is **gravitational acceleration**. So,

weight = mass × gravitational acceleration

or, using the symbols, **w** for **weight**, **m** for **mass**, and **g** for the **acceleration due to gravity**,

w = mg

Obviously, if **g = 0**, which we may assume to be the case in deep space, **w = 0**

If we express **mass** in **kg** and **gravitational acceleration** in **metres/sec²**, **weight** will be given in **Newtons**.

Although **gravitational acceleration**, **g**, decreases gradually the further a body is removed from the Earth's surface, as far as aircraft operations are concerned we may consider **g** to be constant at **9.81 metres/sec² (32 feet/sec²)**.

So, for example, the **weight** of a **5 kg** bag of potatoes, on Earth, can be easily found using the formula:

w = mg

w = 5 kg × 9.81 metres/sec² = 49.05 Newtons

In deep space, however, the **5 kg** bag of potatoes will still possess a **mass** of **5 kg**, but its **weight** will be **0**, as depicted in *Figure 7.1*.

On the Moon, where the **force of gravity** is weaker than on Earth (the Moon being less massive than the Earth), **gravitational acceleration** is only ¹/₆ of the Earth's acceleration. So on the Moon, **g = 1.635 metres/sec²**.

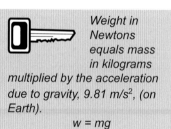

Weight in Newtons equals mass in kilograms multiplied by the acceleration due to gravity, 9.81 m/s², (on Earth).

w = mg

Consequently, although the **mass** of the bag of potatoes that we have been considering will still be **5 kg** on the Moon, its **weight** will be less. The **weight** of the **5 kg** bag of potatoes on the Moon can be calculated as follows:

A body of a given mass will weigh six times less on the Moon than on Earth.

w = mg

w = 5 kg × 1.635 m/sec² = 8.175 Newtons, ($^1/_6$ of its weight on Earth.)

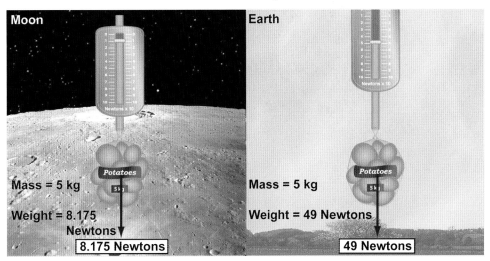

Figure 7.2 On the Moon, the bag of potatoes has the same mass as on Earth, but only $^1/_6$ of the weight.

The bag of potatoes, then, possesses **the same mass, on the Earth <u>and</u> on the** Moon, but, on the Moon, the **weight** of the bag of potatoes is only $^1/_6$ of its **weight** on Earth. *(See Figure 7.2.)*

What Does 1 Newton of Weight Feel Like?

Well, an average sized **apple** weighs around **100 grams** which is **0.1 kg**. 9.81 metres/sec² is almost 10 metres/sec²; therefore, from the equation:

w = mg

we can estimate, without too much inaccuracy, that, on Earth, an apple weighs around 1 Newton (N).

w = mg = 0.1 kg × 10 m/s² = 1 N

By supporting an apple in your hand, then, you can get an idea of the feel of **1 Newton of weight**.

Weight = 1 Newton
Mass = 100g (0.1 kg)

Figure 7.3 An averaged sized apple weighs in the region of 1 Newton.

The General Force Equation. Force in Newtons equals mass in kilograms multiplied by acceleration in m/sec².

The General Equation Linking Force and Acceleration.

Remember, too, that **weight is a force**: the **force** pulling a **mass** to the ground. So, by holding up an apple, you can also get an idea of the magnitude of **1 Newton force**.

In fact, if we re-write the **weight equation**, substituting **force, F,** for **weight, w,** and a general expression for **acceleration, a,** instead of **g** for **gravitational acceleration,** we obtain:

F = ma

F = ma is the **general acceleration formula**, and an expression of **Newton's 2nd Law of Motion** which states that *the acceleration of a body is proportional to the out-of-balance resultant force acting on the body.*

In horizontal acceleration, it is mass which must be considered.

Now, if we wished to accelerate a vehicle of, say, **mass 1000 kg** along a horizontal path, we are not concerned, in the first instance, with the vehicle's **weight**. Provided we ignore friction and rolling resistance, which we must do for this comparison of the concepts of **weight** and **mass, weight** (which acts vertically downwards) can have no affect on the horizontal motion of a **mass** which takes place in a plane **lying perpendicularly** to the line of action of the **weight**.

So, if we also ignore air resistance, it would not matter whether the vehicle of **1000 kg mass** were being accelerated horizontally on the Earth's surface, or on the Moon's surface, where gravity is only $^1/_6$ of the Earth's gravity. If we wished to impart to the vehicle a <u>horizontal</u> acceleration of, say, **2 metres/sec²**, we would have to apply the same force on the Earth as on the Moon. We can calculate this force using the equation:

F = ma

F = 1000 kg × 2 metres/sec² = 2000 Newtons

2000 Newtons, then, would be the force required to impart a horizontal acceleration of **2 metres/sec²** to the vehicle, whether on the Earth or Moon, because, on both celestial bodies, the **mass** of the vehicle is **1000 kg.**

But if we wished to **lift** the same **1000 kg** vehicle, vertically, to load it on a transport device, for instance, the situation between the Earth and the Moon would be very different.

When we lift a body against the force of gravity, it is weight which must be considered.

To **lift** the vehicle, we need to apply an **upwards acting force** which equals the vehicle's **weight**. To calculate that force, we need to use the formula:

w = mg

Now, **g**, the acceleration due to gravity, is, on Earth, **9.81 metres/sec²**, in standard units. We will designate this value by the symbol g_E.

But, **g**, the acceleration due to gravity, on the Moon, is only **1.635 metres/sec²**. We will designate this value by the symbol g_M.

So the **force** required to lift the vehicle of **mass 1000 kg**, on Earth, is given by

w = m g$_E$ = 1000 kg × 9.81 metres/sec^2 = 9810 Newtons

Whereas, the force required to lift the vehicle of **mass 1000 kg**, on the Moon, is given by

w = m g$_M$ = 1000 kg × 1.635 metres/sec^2 = 1635 Newtons

Weight is Different from Mass.
The 1000 kg vehicle, **having the same mass everywhere**, requires the same force to <u>accelerate</u> it horizontally, if we ignore issues like air resistance and friction, whether it is located on the Earth or on the Moon. But, if we wish to <u>lift</u> the vehicle, we have to apply a **force** to overcome the **weight** that the vehicle possesses by virtue of its presence within a particular **gravitational field**. The **lifting force** required to counterbalance the **weight** of the vehicle needs to be **6 times greater on the Earth than on the Moon**.

We can see clearly, then, that a body's **weight** is quite different to its **mass**.

Mass and Weight Applied to Aircraft Operations.

So in considering an aircraft's horizontal acceleration, or deceleration, on a **horizontal** runway, only the **thrust force** developed by the propeller and the aircraft's **mass** are of interest, if we ignore rolling resistance and friction. The scientific consideration in **horizontal accelerations** is the aircraft's **mass**, not its **weight**.

But, as soon as the aircraft gets airborne, the **lift force** generated by the wings has to **counterbalance** the **weight** of the aircraft, if the aircraft is to remain flying. So when we consider the **lift force** that must be generated at take-off, or to carry a given **payload** over a given distance at constant speed, it is concept of **weight** that we are concerned with, not **mass**.

Why the Confusion Between Weight and Mass?
So why do people confuse **mass** and **weight**?

Why, in aviation, do people talk about **mass** to mean both **mass** and **weight**?

And why, in aviation, is the **kg** used to express both **mass** and **weight**, when we know that scientists measure **mass** in **kg** and **weight** in **Newtons**?

Well, the reason why people confuse **mass** and **weight**, in terms of names given to two separate concepts, is that, **in a gravitational field of constant strength, a given mass will always possess the same weight.**

In a **gravitational field** like that of the Earth, as long as we remain near to the Earth's surface (and, in that sense, aircraft, even at 40 000 feet, are always near to the Earth's surface), the **gravitational acceleration, g**, may be regarded as constant at **9.81 metres/sec^2**. So, in the equation, **w = mg**, because **g** is a constant, **w** will always vary in the same proportion as **g**. So if we double the **mass** we double the **weight**, and if we quadruple the **mass** we quadruple the **weight**, and so on.

133

CHAPTER 7: WEIGHT

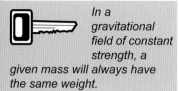

In a gravitational field of constant strength, a given mass will always have the same weight.

Many devices, with which you will be familiar, such as bathroom scales or spring balances, are designed to measure **weight**, because they are measuring the force with which bodies are pulled towards the centre of the Earth. Therefore, scientifically speaking, these weighing devices should be calibrated in **Newtons**. A man should say that he **weighs** about **800 Newtons**, not **80 kilograms** (taking **g** to equal **10 metres/sec²**).

But because, near the surface of the Earth, the <u>relationship</u> between the **weight** of a body and the **mass** of a body can be considered to be a **constant**, **weighing devices** that we use in our every-day life, such as bathroom scales, are calibrated to give their readings in **kilograms, the unit of mass.**

This practice is not scientifically accurate but it is a system that we are used to and, in that part of the Earth's gravitational field in which we live, where **g** is constant at approximately **10 metres/sec²**, it is a system which enables us to talk about **weight in kilograms**, and even to claim that we are measuring **mass**! As long as you understand the difference between **mass** and **weight**, this is a system that will give us useful information and that we can accept. *(See Figure 7.4.)*

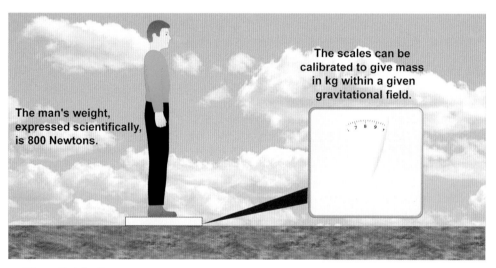

The scales can be calibrated to give mass in kg within a given gravitational field.

The man's weight, expressed scientifically, is 800 Newtons.

Figure 7.4 On Earth, bathroom scales can be calibrated to show mass in kilograms, but these type of scales are, in reality, measuring weight.

Because there is a directly proportional relationship between mass and weight in a gravitational field of constant strength, weighing devices can be calibrated to read mass in kilograms.

But never forget that it is acceptable to use this system of expressing **weight** in kilograms **only** because of the **constant relationship between mass and weight which exists near the Earth's surface**. Given that constraint, it is acceptable to calibrate bathroom scales to tell a man that he weighs **80 kg** instead of **800 Newtons**, and to say that the bathroom scales read **mass** as well as **weight**. However, the same bathroom scales would not give an accurate reading of **mass** on the Moon.

On the Moon, the **80 kg** man, would see only **13.3 kg** displayed on the scales! But as we now know that **mass** is the same everywhere, we can see the error immediately, and understand why the man would be surprised. In order to measure his **mass** on the Moon, the man would have to use a **chemical balance**, and compare himself with a known **mass**. *(See Figure 7.5.)*

134

Figure 7.5 To measure mass accurately, in <u>any</u> gravitational field, the mass to be found is compared with a known mass, using a chemical balance.

Using the **chemical balance**, both **masses** are being acted upon by the same **gravitational field**. **Mass** measurements are straight forward to make in this way.

Of course, if the bathroom scales had been calibrated to read 800 Newtons for the **weight** of the man on Earth, he would not be surprised to learn that he weighed only 133 Newtons on the Moon, knowing that the Moon's gravitational field is only $\frac{1}{6}$ as strong as that of the Earth.

In aviation, you will often hear weight and mass spoken about as if they were the same concept, with both weight and mass measured in kilograms. This system works, as long as we bear in mind the reason why it works.

On the Earth, in a constant gravitational field, we can get away with pretending that **weight** can be called **mass**, and with measuring **weight** in kg, as if it were **mass**. Consequently, in aviation, you will often sometimes meet **weight** and **mass** spoken about as if they were the same concept, and, where the word **weight** is used correctly, you will most often find **weight** measured in kilograms. You are now in a position to understand and to forgive this confusion.

Just remember, though, that when you see a light aircraft with its three wheels standing on **weighing devices** (<u>not</u> "massing" devices"), it is the aircraft's **weight** that is being measured, even though that **weight** is expressed in **kilograms** and might also, sometimes, be expressed as the aircraft's **mass**!

Weight – One of the Forces Acting on an Aircraft in Flight.

Now, having learnt the difference between **weight** and **mass**, and understood why some people sometimes confuse the two, and why **weight** is commonly and unscientifically measured in **kilograms**, we may now look at **weight** as one of the forces which act on an aircraft in flight.

The **weight** of an aircraft is the **force**, exerted by the Earth's gravity, which, acting on the aircraft's mass, acts vertically downwards, through the aircraft's **centre of gravity**, tending to pull the aircraft towards the Earth's centre.

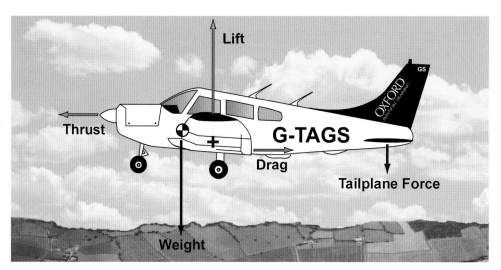

Figure 7.6 The aircraft's weight acts vertically downwards. The total weight of the aircraft is considered as acting through the aircraft's centre of gravity.

Of course, as we perceive **weight**, we should simply say that **weight** is the **force pulling the aircraft towards the ground**. Although each aircraft component will have its own weight, the **total weight** of the aircraft is considered as acting through the aircraft's **centre of gravity**. *(See Figure 7.6.)*

If the aircraft is to fly, the force of **weight** must be opposed by the force of **lift**. In steady, straight and level flight (**level** means **at constant altitude**), **lift**, then, must equal **weight** and must act in the opposite direction to **weight**. If **lift** is greater than **weight**, the aircraft will begin to accelerate upwards; if **weight** is greater than **lift**, the aircraft will begin to accelerate downwards. But that is another story.

In *Figure 7.6*, the **lift force** is shown exactly **counterbalancing** the **weight**, in terms of the size of the forces (magnitude) and their direction. Other flight forces are shown in *Figures 7.6*, but they will not be mentioned in this chapter. On diagrams depicting the flight forces, it is convention to show forces as **arrows**, or **vectors**, where the **length** of the arrow is representative of the **magnitude of the force**, and the **direction** of the arrow shows the **line of action of the force**.

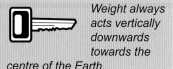

Weight always acts vertically downwards towards the centre of the Earth.

The Centre of Gravity.

The **centre of gravity**, is the point within a body through which all of a body's **weight** is considered to act. If an aircraft were to be suspended by a single force, say a rope, attached to the aircraft's **centre of gravity**, we could place the aircraft with its longitudinal axis horizontal, and the aircraft would remain horizontal in perfect balance, as depicted in *Figure 7.7*.

In fact, if the aircraft were suspended exactly through its **centre of gravity**, we could put the aircraft in any attitude we wished, and it would remain in that attitude, because there could be no out-of-balance force to make it move.

In flight, an aircraft, when manoeuvred, rotates about its **centre of gravity**, but the aircraft's **weight always acts vertically downwards towards the centre of the Earth**. The **magnitude of the weight force** is of considerable importance because of the effect both on aircraft structural integrity and the position of the **centre of gravity**.

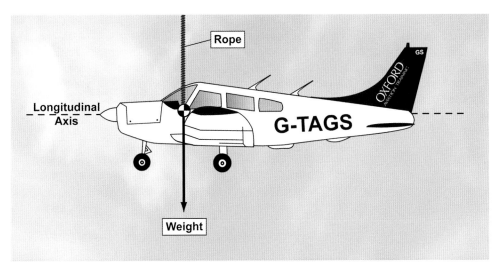

Figure 7.7 If the aircraft were to be suspended through its Centre of Gravity, the aircraft would hang in perfect balance.

All aircraft have published **weights**, such as **Basic Empty Weight, Maximum Gross Weight, Zero Fuel Weight, Maximum Take off Weight, Useful Load, Maximum Landing Weight**, etc. (In JAR-FCL/EASA examinations, you will mostly find the word **mass** substituted for **weight** for reasons we have just discussed.) Furthermore, because, during flight, the aircraft consumes fuel, the **weight** of the aircraft constantly changes. As fuel tanks empty, the distribution of the **weight** throughout the aircraft, and, thus, the position of the aircraft's **centre of gravity**, changes, too.

As you will learn in the **Mass & Balance** section of this series, because **weight** acts through the **centre of gravity**, the position of the **centre of gravity** along the aircraft's longitudinal axis affects the **stability** of the aircraft. Therefore, there are **forward** and **aft limits** *(See Figure 7.8)*, calculated by the aircraft designer, within which the **centre of gravity** must remain throughout a flight. These **centre of gravity limits** are established in order that the pilot may have sufficient elevator authority, in all phases of flight, to control the aircraft in pitch, as he requires. If the **centre of gravity** exceeds the **forward limit**, the aircraft is said to be **nose heavy**. If the **centre of gravity limit** is too far **aft**, the aircraft is said to be **tail heavy**. An aircraft which has its **centre of gravity** outside the **aft limit** may be dangerously **unstable in pitch** and display unfavourable stall and spin characteristics.

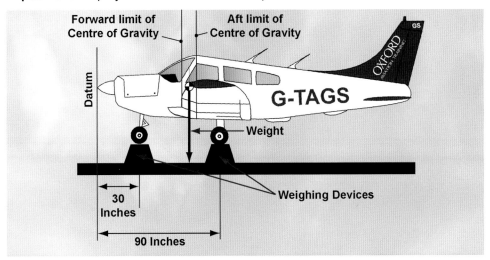

A nose-heavy aircraft is very stable in pitch and will require greater elevator displacement to control in pitch.

An aircraft which is tail heavy may be dangerously unstable in pitch and display unfavourable stall and spin characteristics.

Figure 7.8 Representative fore and aft limits of the centre of gravity for a PA28.

Beware, the centre of gravity may be outside limits, even if the maximum take-off weight (mass) is not exceeded.

A pilot must ensure, before every flight, that the weight (mass) and centre of gravity limitations are not exceeded.

In addition to such **weight** information as **Useful Load**, and **Maximum Take Off Weight (Mass)**, the **Pilot's Operating Handbook (POH)** may contain separate details of the **weight** that may be loaded in the aircraft's baggage compartment. This is a detail that the pilot must not neglect because carrying too much baggage could move the **centre of gravity** too far **aft**, even if the **Maximum Take-Off Weight (Mass)** is not exceeded.

The **POH** may also specify such details as minimum crew weight for solo flight.

Weight, then, although not aerodynamically generated, as are **lift**, **drag** and **propeller thrust**, is a flight force which the pilot must fully understand. **Maximum and minimum weights (or masses)** must be observed in loading an aircraft. **Weight** is a crucial concept, both in itself and in its effect on the position of the **centre of gravity**.

It is one of the pilot's major responsibilities when preparing his aircraft for flight to confirm that the **centre of gravity** is situated **within the limits** stipulated in the Pilot's Operating Handbook.

Representative PPL - type questions to test your theoretical knowledge of Weight.

1. Choose the correct statement option below:

    a. Weight and mass are conceptually the same.
    b. Weight and mass are both forces.
    c. Weight and mass are two different concepts; weight is a force and mass is a quantity of matter.
    d. The weight and mass of a given body will be equal, only in deep space.

2. Choose the correct statement option below.

    a. The scientific unit of mass is the Newton.
    b. The scientific unit of force is the kilogram.
    c. The scientific unit of force is the metre per second^2
    d. The scientific unit of mass is the kilogram.

3. The weight of an aircraft is:

    a. The force acting on the aircraft's mass and directed towards the centre of the Earth.
    b. The same as the aircraft's mass.
    c. The mass of the aircraft when the aircraft is assumed to have zero weight.
    d. The force acting on the aircraft to accelerate it in the horizontal plane.

4. Choose the correct statement option below.

    a. A body always possesses the same mass and weight whatever the strength of the gravitational field.
    b. The mass of a body is dependent on the strength of the gravitational field in which the body is situated.
    c. A body always possesses the same mass but in zero gravity will have no weight.
    d. The weight of a body is independent of the strength of the gravitational field in which the body is situated.

5. Choose the correct equation below.

    a. weight (Newtons) = mass (kg) × linear acceleration (m/s^2)
    b. weight (Newtons) = mass(kg) × acceleration due to gravity (m/s^2)
    c. weight (kg) = force (Newtons) × acceleration (m/s^2)
    d. weight (Newtons) = mass (kg)

6. On Earth:

    a. weight (Newtons) = mass(kg) × linear acceleration (m/s^2)
    b. weight (Newtons) = mass (kg) × 32 m/s^2
    c. weight (Newtons) = mass (kg) × 9.81 m/s^2
    d. weight (Newtons) = mass (kg) × m/s^2

7. On the moon:

    a. the weight of a body will be approximately 1/6 of its weight on the Earth.
    b. the weight of a body will be approximately 6 times its weight on the Earth.
    c. the weight of a body will be the same as its weight on the Earth.
    d. the mass of a body will be approximately 1/6 of its mass on the Earth.

8. When considering the linear acceleration of a body under the action of a given force:

    a. It is the body's weight that will determine the magnitude of the acceleration.
    b. Neither the body's mass nor its weight affects the magnitude of the acceleration.
    c. It is the body's mass that will determine the magnitude of the acceleration.
    d. A force cannot cause a linear acceleration

9. When considering lifting a body in a gravitational field:

    a. It is the body's mass which is crucial to the consideration.
    b. Neither a body's mass nor its weight affects the consideration.
    c. A body of finite weight cannot be lifted in a gravitational field
    d. It is the body's weight which is crucial to the consideration.

10. Despite the difference in concepts between weight and mass, weight may be expressed in kilograms on Earth because:

    a. In a constant gravitational field mass is always equal to weight.
    b. Given that the acceleration due to gravity is constant at 9.81 m/s^2, mass is directly proportional to weight, and, therefore, weighing devices may be calibrated to read mass in kilograms.
    c. In a constant gravitational field there is no difference between mass and weight.
    d. In a constant gravitational field mass and weight have no meaning.

Question	1	2	3	4	5	6	7	8	9	10
Answer										

The answers to these questions can be found at the end of this book.

CHAPTER 8
PROPELLER THRUST

INTRODUCTION.

The technical description of the **propeller** and the engineering aspects of its operation are covered in the book in this series entitled **'Aeroplanes'**. This chapter looks at propellers solely from the point of view of the Principles of Flight.

Figure 8.1. The propeller of a Sopwith Triplane.

A full scientific explanation of the function of a **propeller** is complex, requiring an understanding of quite advanced mathematics, and is, therefore, beyond the scope of this book. Here, we will confine ourselves to the consideration of basic concepts, involving simple equations and, where necessary, simplified mathematics. You will not, however, need to understand the equations or the mathematics to learn from this chapter the principles of operation of the **propeller** that you are required to know, in order to pass your pilot's licence theoretical knowledge examinations.

THRUST.

The force which propels an aircraft through the air is known as **thrust**. As you have learnt, **thrust**, together with **lift**, **drag** and **weight**, is one of the four principal forces which act on an aircraft in flight, *(Figure 8.2)*. At any constant airspeed, **thrust** is equal and opposite to the force of **drag**. If **thrust** is greater than **drag**, for instance, because the pilot, in level flight, has opened the throttle further, the aircraft will accelerate. If **thrust** is less than **drag** the aircraft will decelerate.

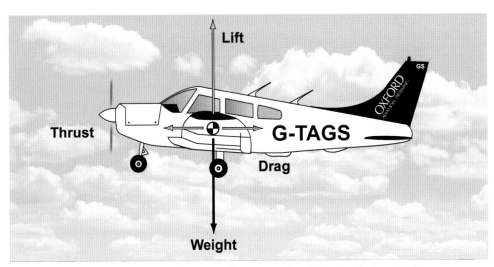

Figure 8.2 The Four forces acting on an aircraft in steady, level flight.

The exact way in which **thrust** is developed by an aircraft's powerplant depends on the type of **propulsion system** fitted to the aircraft. Common types of aircraft **propulsion systems** are: the **Piston Engine/Propeller combination**, the **Pure Turbojet**, the **By-pass Turbojet** and the **Turboprop** *(Figure 8.3)*.

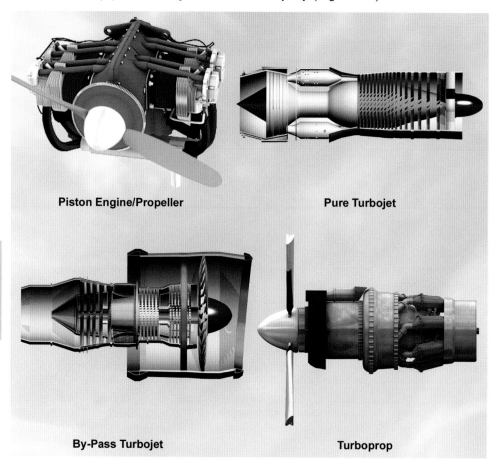

Piston Engine/Propeller

Pure Turbojet

By-Pass Turbojet

Turboprop

Figure 8.3 Common types of aircraft propulsion systems.

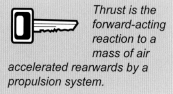

Thrust is the forward-acting reaction to a mass of air accelerated rearwards by a propulsion system.

But, whatever the type of powerplant, **thrust** is always generated by one aspect or another of the application of **Newton's 2nd and 3rd Laws** *(see Page 14)*. For all types of propulsion systems, **a mass of air is accelerated rearwards by the system**, as depicted in *Figure 8.4*, and the **reaction** to this **rearwards acceleration** gives rise to the **thrust force** which drives the aircraft forwards.

Acceleration is, of course, just another name for **change in velocity**. *Figure 8.4* depicts how a given mass **m** of air is accelerated from velocity V_o to velocity V_e, as it passes through a **propulsion system**. V_o is the velocity of the air entering the **propulsion system** and V_e is the increased velocity of the air after it has passed through the **propulsion system**.

In the chapter on **Lift**, you met the Principle of Conservation of Mass which states that, when we consider a closed system such as a **streamtube**, the mass of fluid flowing into the **streamtube** must equal the mass of fluid flowing out of the **streamtube**. Now, a **propulsion system**, such as a jet engine or piston-engine/propeller combination may be considered, for our purposes, to be a **closed system**, so that the mass of air flowing into the engine (through the turbines or propeller disk) is equal to the mass of

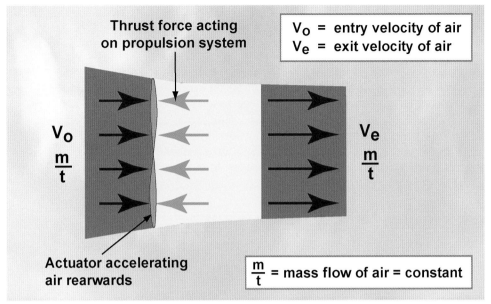

*Figure 8.4 A propulsion system generates forward thrust
by accelerating a mass of air rearwards.*

air flowing out of the engine. In other words, **the mass flow of air is constant**. Furthermore, if we also assume for our purposes that air is an **ideal fluid**, and, therefore, **incompressible** and **inviscid**, the **rate of mass flow of air** into the propulsion system will be equal to the **rate of mass flow of air** out of the system. In other words:

$$\frac{\text{mass}}{\text{time}} = \text{constant}$$

From your science lessons at school, you may recall that **mass × velocity** is called **momentum**, and that **momentum** is a concept which says something about the **quantity of motion** of a **moving mass**. In accelerating the air rearwards, the propulsion system imparts a **rate of change of momentum** to a mass, **m**, of air. In other words, if, in a given time lapse, **t**, the **momentum** of the air is increased from **m V_o** to **m V_e**, **the rate of change of momentum** of the air can be expressed by:

Rate of change of momentum $= \dfrac{(mV_e - mV_o)}{t}$ or $\dfrac{m(V_e - V_o)}{t}$

Now, **Newton's Second Law** states that the **force** acting on a body is equal to the rate of change of momentum of that body, so in the expression:

$$F = \frac{m(V_e - V_o)}{t} \quad \ldots\ldots\ldots\ldots(1)$$

F is the force imparted by the propulsion system to the mass of air in order to accelerate it.

Now $F = \dfrac{m(V_e - V_o)}{t}$ expresses a change in velocity over a given time.

A change of velocity is, of course, an **acceleration**. So we may write:

F   = mass × acceleration ....(2)

Equations **(1)** and **(2)**, then, are expressions of **Newton's 2nd Law** and describe the **force** exerted by the **propulsion system** on the air to accelerate it rearwards. It is at this point that we apply **Newton's 3rd Law** to the situation in order to explain the generation of **forward-acting thrust**. **Newton's 3rd Law** states that **every action has an equal and opposite reaction and act on different bodies.** So the **force** imparted to the air by the **propulsion system** to accelerate it rearwards induces a **reaction force**, equal in magnitude to the accelerating force, and acting on the propulsion system, in the opposite direction (in this case forwards), to give us **thrust**.

We may, therefore, re-write Equations **(1)** and **(2)** as:

$$\text{Thrust} = \frac{m(V_e - V_o)}{t} \quad ....(3)$$

or

Thrust = mass × acceleration............(4)

Finally, looking at Equation **(3)**, and because we are assuming a **constant rate of mass flow** of air, m/t , through the propeller disk, we can see that the **size of the the thrust generated by any aircraft powerplant depends solely on the amount by which the velocity of the rearwards airflow is increased – in other words, accelerated - by the action of the propulsion system.**

$$\text{Thrust} \quad = \quad \frac{m(V_e - V_o)}{t}$$

But mass flow $\dfrac{m}{t}$ = constant

Therefore **Thrust** $\propto$ **(V_e - V_o).** (the symbol $\propto$ means "proportional to".)

Or, stated again, in plain language: **thrust is directly proportional to the increase in velocity imparted by the propulsion system to the air**.

PROPELLERS.

Propeller thrust is proportional to the increase in velocity imparted to the air.

The propulsion system which powers most light aircraft is the **piston engine/ propeller combination***. The **piston engine** causes the **propeller** to rotate, and, by producing **thrust**, the **propeller** acts is such a way as to convert the power developed by the engine into **propulsive power**. As you will discover, the exact nature of the **thrust force** developed by a **propeller** is very complex. As well as accelerating air rearwards, **propeller blades** are also **aerofoils**, and are, therefore, as you learnt in the Chapter on **Lift**, also able to develop **thrust** in the form of a "horizontal lift" force because of the favourable pressure distribution over the blades created by the relative airflow when the propeller is rotating. So do not be surprised if your flying instructors sometimes disagree on what scientific explanation best accounts for the **thrust** developed by a **propeller**.

*   *"engine" from Latin **ingenum** meaning "genius"; "propeller" from Latin **pro** + **pellere** "to drive" meaning "to drive forward."*

DEFINITION OF TERMS.

Before we begin our discussion of the **Principles of Flight** aspects of **propeller theory**, here are some basic illustrations and definitions of **propeller components**, and technical terms describing the function of **propellers**, without which any discussion of propeller theory would be extremely difficult.

Blade Shank (Root).

The **Blade Shank** or **Root** is the section of the blade nearest the **hub** to which the blade is attached. The hub forms the end of the propeller shaft which is turned by the engine.

Blade Tip.

The **Blade Tip** is the outer end of the blade farthest from the **hub**.

Plane of Rotation.

The **Plane of Rotation** is an imaginary plane perpendicular to the propeller shaft. It is the plane which is described when the blades rotate *(see Figure 8.6)*.

Spinner.

The **spinner** is the fairing fitted over the **hub** of the propeller, in order to reduce drag.

Blade Chord Line.

If the propeller blade is viewed end-on, from tip to root, and a cross-section is taken across the blade, it can be seen that the blade is of aerofoil shape. This means that the blade's section has a chord line, just as a wing cross-section does. The **Blade Chord Line** is an imaginary straight line joining the centre of curvature of the leading edge of the propeller blade to the blade's trailing edge.

Figure 8.5 Propeller nomenclature.

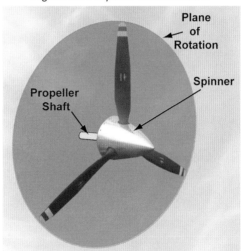

Figure 8.6 Plane of rotation.

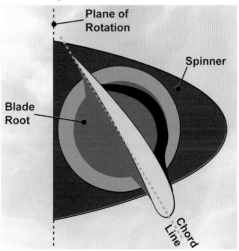

Figure 8.7 Blade cross-section and chord line.

Blade Angle or Blade Pitch.

The **Blade Angle** or **Blade Pitch** is the angle between the **blade chord line** and the **plane of rotation**. The **blade angle** changes along the length of the propeller blade, decreasing from root to tip. This twist in the propeller blade can be seen in *Figure 8.5,* and will be dealt with later in the chapter. The **"mean blade angle"** of a propeller is the blade angle at the **three-quarters blade length position**, measured from **blade root** to **tip**. **Fine-pitch propellers** have a small mean **blade angle**. Propellers with larger mean **blade angles** are called **coarse-pitch propellers**.

Blade Angle of Attack.

The **Blade Angle of Attack** is the angle between the **chord line** of any given blade element and the **relative airflow** which meets the propeller blade when the propeller is rotating. The propeller operates at its most efficient at an **angle of attack** of around **2** to **4 degrees**.

Geometric Pitch.

The **Geometric Pitch** is the distance the propeller would travel forward in one complete revolution, if it were to advance through the air at the **blade angle**, just

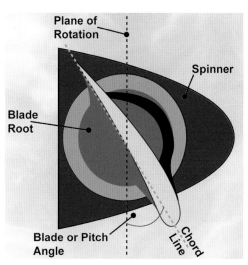

Figure 8.8 Mean blade pitch angle.

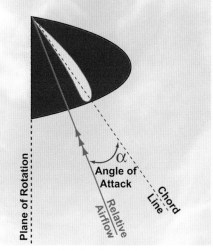

Figure 8.9 Angle of Attack.

as a wood screw penetrates a wooden block with one turn of the screwdriver.

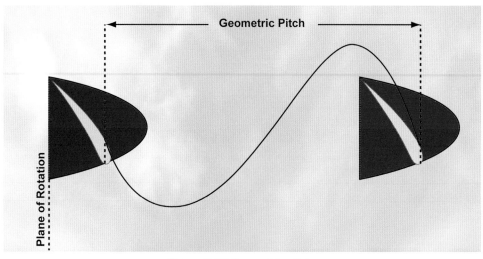

Figure 8.10 Geometric pitch.

Effective Pitch.

In flight, the propeller will hardly ever advance through the air at the **Geometric Pitch**. Air is a fluid, not a solid medium like wood. **Propeller Slip** will almost always be present. The distance that the propeller actually moves forward with one revolution is called the **Effective Pitch.**

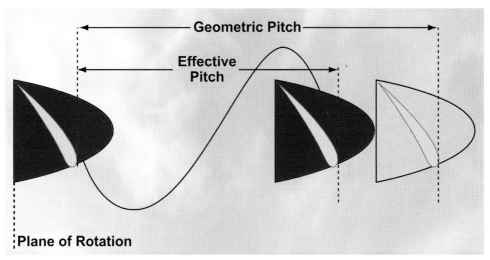

Figure 8.11 Effective pitch.

Propeller Slip.

The difference between **Geometric Pitch** and **Effective Pitch** is called **Propeller Slip**.

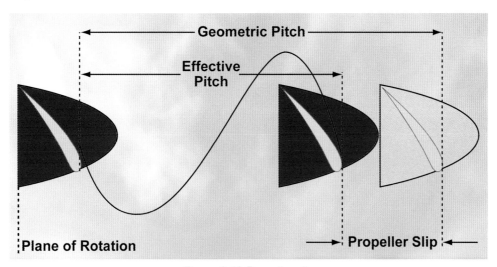

Figure 8.12 Propeller slip.

Helix Angle.

As the propeller rotates and advances through the air (following the line of **Effective Pitch**), the actual path that the blades follow describes a **helix**. The **Helix Angle** is the angle between the **Plane of Rotation** of the propeller and the path of the **Effective Pitch**.

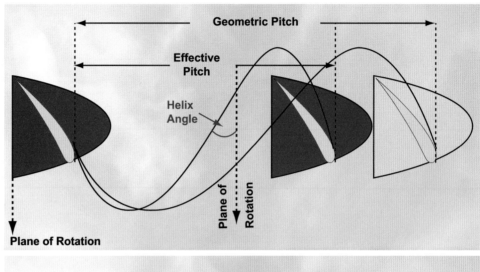

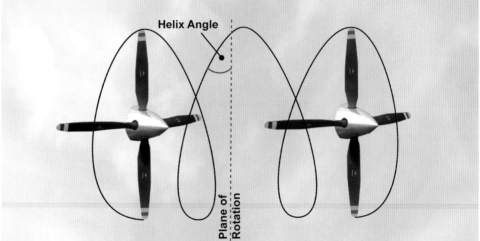

Figure 8.13 (Top) and 8.14 (Bottom) showing the helix angle.

PROPELLER THEORY.

Two Theories of Propeller Thrust?

So far, you have learnt (and, if you have stood behind a propeller-driven aircraft with its engine running, have doubtless experienced) that **a propeller accelerates a large mass of air rearwards**, thus generating **thrust** in accordance with **Newton's 2nd and 3rd Laws**. You have also read in the definitions above that propeller blades are **aerofoils** and are set at a given angle to the plane of rotation and so meet the air at an **angle of attack**. Furthermore, you will recall from an earlier chapter, in this Principles of Flight book, that aerofoils which meet the relative airflow at certain angles of attack generate an aerodynamic force called **lift** by virtue of the **pressure distribution** above and below the **aerofoil**. Rotating propeller blades, then, would seem to be able to generate **thrust** in the form of a **"horizontal lift force"** in accordance with the theories of the Swiss scientist **Bernoulli**, and as illustrated in *Figure 8.16*.

As we have already suggested, there appear to be two theories here which apply to the generation of **thrust** by a **propeller**. We must investigate this situation further.

If we examine a **propeller** from close quarters (remembering to observe appropriate precautions, if the propeller is attached to an aeroplane), perhaps the most obvious feature we observe is that the **propeller blades are twisted** along their length, as shown in *Figure 8.15*. The blade angle, in fact, decreases from hub to tip.

We will learn more about **blade** twist later on, but we can perhaps feel intuitively that the propeller twist may help to explain how air is accelerated rearwards when the propeller rotates, reinforcing the **Newtonian theory of thrust** that we have already read about.

On the other hand, because of the **wing-like, aerofoil structure** of the blades, we are maybe ready to admit, too, that the airflow over the rotating blades produces similar aerodynamic effects to those produced by the airflow over a wing.

Figure 8.15 A propeller blade is twisted along its length with the blade angle decreasing from hub to tip.

Figure 8.16 illustrates the arrangement of forces which likens **propeller thrust** to the **lift force** produced by a wing. We will return to this diagram later.

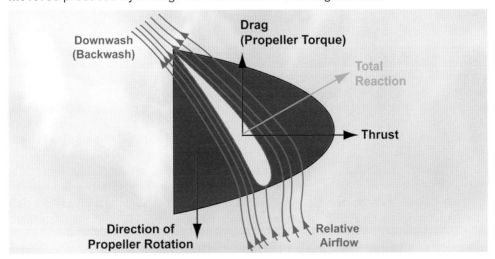

Figure 8.16 The rotating-wing analogy of propeller thrust.

Some books on **elementary propeller theory**, while they may mention that **thrust** is produced by the **reaction to a rearwards acceleration of air**, then go on to examine, in depth, only the **"wing-theory"** explanation of **thrust**. However, because it is difficult for anyone who has spent time around aeroplanes to dismiss the rearwards acceleration of air explanation of **propeller thrust**, no treatment of the subject can be complete unless the **Newtonian** theory is paid serious attention.

Consequently, both the **"rearwards acceleration of air"** theory, and the **"wing theory"** of **thrust** will be covered in this chapter. If you find this state of affairs bewildering, you should draw comfort from the fact that some aerodynamicists defend the view that the two theories ultimately both give rise to a single, identical explanation of **thrust**, and that the two theories really give the same explanation from two slightly different perspectives.

In this chapter, however, for the sake of simplicity, we will consider the concept of **propeller thrust** from the points of view of the two separate theories. First, we will look more closely at the simplified momentum theory of propeller thrust, and, then, we will consider the propeller as a type rotating wing. (the Bernoulli theory).

> *There is both a "Newtonian" and a "Bernoulli" explanation of thrust, which some aerodynamicists regard as being, ultimately, the same explanation from two slightly different perspectives.*

PROPELLER THRUST AND SIMPLIFIED MOMENTUM THEORY.

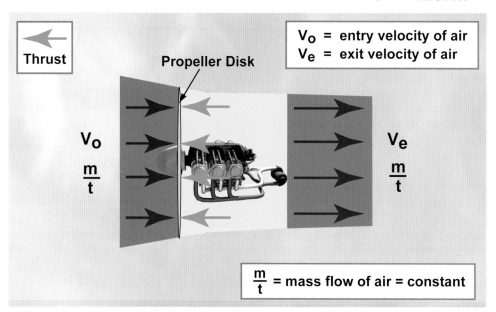

Figure 8.17 Thrust can be explained as a forwards-acting reaction to a rearwards acceleration of air..

Simplified **momentum theory**, as applied to propellers, teaches that a mass of air is accelerated rearwards by the propeller *(Figure 8.17)*, and that the **reaction to this rearwards acceleration of air** at the propeller blades, gives rise to the **thrust force** which drives the aircraft forwards. This explanation of thrust is sometimes known as the **Newtonian explanation** because it explains propeller thrust using **Newton's 2nd and 3rd Laws**. That is, that **"an applied force is proportional to the rate of change of momentum of a body caused by that force"** (Newton's 2nd Law), and **"every action has an equal and opposite reaction and act on different bodies"** (Newton's 3rd law).

The equation: **Thrust** = $\dfrac{m(V_e - V_o)}{t}$ ....(3)

which we met earlier in this chapter, shows us mathematically, that **thrust** is produced by the reaction to the rearwards velocity increase (i.e. acceleration) imparted to a given mass of air flowing through the propulsion system.

As we have already established, if we assume that the mass of air flowing into the propeller disk is equal to the mass of air flowing out of the propeller disk, then we may also assume that the **rate of mass flow $\frac{m}{t}$ is constant.**

Therefore, **thrust** may be considered as being proportional to the increase in velocity ($V_e - V_o$), imparted to the air.

In other words, if: $\frac{m}{t}$ **= constant**

Thrust $\propto (V_e - V_o)$

For a **fixed-pitch propeller** (that is a propeller whose blade angle cannot be varied by the pilot), experiments show that the increase in velocity imparted to the air passing through the **propeller disk**, ($V_e - V_o$), is greatest when the aircraft is stationary, with the propeller blades rotating at maximum revolutions per minute **(RPM)**. Now, it can readily be appreciated that when the aircraft is stationary, V_o, the velocity of the air flowing into the propeller disk, will be very small. However, air is indeed induced, or drawn, into the propeller disk, even though the aircraft is not moving forward. Were it not to be so, there could be no acceleration of air rearwards and the aircraft could not begin to move. In contrast to V_o, however, when the aircraft is stationary and the engine under full power; the velocity of the air <u>leaving</u> the propeller disk, V_e, is <u>very high</u>. Therefore, **velocity difference** of the accelerated air, $V_e - V_o$, is at a maximum when the aircraft is stationary under full power, at maximum RPM. (Provided, that is, that the propeller tips do not approach the speed of sound, a proviso that we shall assume for our explanation of propeller theory.)

For a fixed pitch propeller, thrust is at a maximum when the aircraft is stationary under full power (maximum RPM).

Consequently, from the equation:

$$\text{Thrust} = \frac{m(V_e - V_o)}{t} \quad \dots\dots\dots(3)$$

if ($V_e - V_o$) is a maximum, we can deduce that thrust is <u>also</u> at a maximum.

Thus, we see that the thrust of a fixed-pitch propeller is greatest when a pilot applies full power to begin the take-off run.

Torque.

You should note, too, at this point, that, as well as accelerating air rearwards, the **propeller blades** also give rise to a **drag force** (whose magnitude varies with blade angle of attack and blade velocity), acting in the opposite direction to propeller rotation, **which balances the turning force of the engine** as depicted in *Figure 8.16*. The propeller's **drag force** is often called **"propeller torque"** while the **engine's turning force**, or, more accurately expressed, turning moment, is called **"engine torque"**. The magnitude of the **torque** produced by the propeller enables the propeller to absorb the power of the engine. **Torque is a by-product of thrust**. Without **torque**, there could be no **thrust**, and the propeller would overspeed to the destruction of both it and the engine.

*The propellers's drag force is called **propeller torque**. Propeller torque balances engine torque. Without torque there could be no thrust.*

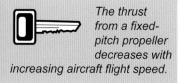

The thrust from a fixed-pitch propeller decreases with increasing aircraft flight speed.

The Variation of Thrust with Speed for a Fixed-Pitch Propeller.

Having established that **propeller thrust** is greatest when the aircraft is stationary under full power, let us see how the **thrust from a fixed-pitch propeller varies with the aircraft's forward velocity**. As aircraft speed increases, V_o increases, too, being equal to the aircraft's forward speed, plus a small value of induced velocity caused by the propeller's rotation. V_e, on the other hand, increases by a much smaller amount with increasing airspeed, because, as we shall see, **increasing airspeed causes the blade's angle of attack to decrease.**

Therefore, with V_o increasing more rapidly than V_e, as the aircraft gathers speed, the value $V_e - V_o$ must decrease, causing the propeller to impart a progressively diminishing acceleration, or velocity increase, to the air passing through its disk.

Consequently, again from Equation **(3)**, we see that the **thrust from a fixed-pitch propeller decreases with increasing aircraft flight speed**. With decreasing **thrust**, caused by a decreasing **angle of attack**, the **propeller torque** which resists the engine's turning moment also decreases, and so **propeller RPM** will increase with increasing aircraft speed. If flight speed could continue to increase indefinitely, the aircraft would eventually reach a speed at which no further increase in velocity could be imparted to the air passing through the propeller disk. At this flight speed, $V_e - V_o$ would equal zero, and **propeller thrust** would also be zero.

The RPM of a fixed-pitch propeller will, at a constant power setting, increase with increasing aircraft flight speed.

In level flight, of course, this zero-thrust speed cannot be reached by the aircraft, because the aircraft's maximum achievable forward speed in level flight is limited to the highest speed at which the propeller can still generate sufficient **thrust** to balance aircraft drag. Also, with zero **thrust**, **propeller torque** would also be zero. There would, thus, be no force to oppose engine torque and the engine RPM would increase to destruction.

It <u>is</u> possible, of course, to increase the forward speed of an aircraft beyond its maximum level-flight speed by entering a dive. In a steep dive, under power, the aircraft does, indeed, approach nearer to the theoretical speed where the propeller produces zero-thrust. As a result, **propeller torque** decreases rapidly, too , and, if the pilot does not throttle back, engine RPM will continue to increase. This is why, with an aircraft powered by a fixed-pitch propeller, it is easy is to exceed maximum permissible engine rotational speed in a dive. In a dive, therefore, pilots must take care not to "red-line" the engine.

PROPELLER POWER AND PROPELLER EFFICIENCY.

You may remember from your Physics lessons at school that **Power** is defined as the **Rate of Doing Work**, and that **Power** may be expressed using the formulae:

$$\text{Power} = \frac{\text{Work Done}}{\text{time taken}}$$

or, because **Work Done = Force × Distance** through which the Force moves,

$$\text{Power} = \frac{\text{Force × Distance}}{\text{time taken}} \quad \dots\dots\dots(5)$$

Let us apply Equation **(5)** to the case of an aircraft in flight. You know that the **Force** which drives an aircraft forward is called **Thrust**. You may also have learned that the term <u>Distance</u> is an expression of **"velocity"**.
    Time

Therefore, the power required to drive an aircraft forward at a given velocity is expressed by:

Power = Thrust × Aircraft Velocity ....(6)

In the specific case of the propeller,

Propeller Power = Thrust × V$_O$ ....(7)

where **V$_O$** is the velocity of air flowing into the propeller disk.

For our **Efficiency** considerations, later on, you must remember that, even when the aircraft is stationary, **V$_O$** has a small positive value when the propeller is turning. Consequently, as we have already discovered, under normal operating conditions, **V$_O$** will always be a little greater than the aircraft's forward velocity.

Let us now examine **propeller power** and **propeller efficiency. Propeller power,** or **propulsive power,** obviously comes ultimately from the engine, and, in order to help it fly efficiently, an aircraft should develop maximum possible **propulsive power** at the expense of the smallest possible power output from the engine. **Propeller efficiency, then, is an expression of what proportion of engine power output is converted into propulsive power.**

$$\text{Propeller Efficiency} = \frac{\text{Propeller Power}}{\text{Engine Power}} \quad ....(8)$$

And, from Equation **(7)**

$$\text{Propeller Efficiency} = \frac{\text{Thrust} \times V_O}{\text{Engine Power}} \quad ....(9)$$

Now, you have already learnt that a propeller develops its **maximum thrust** when it is stationary under full power, at the beginning of its take-off run. You can see, however, from Equation **(9)** that, when the aircraft is stationary, even though the **thrust** is at a maximum, **propeller efficiency** is low, because **V$_O$** is very small.

Of course, **V$_O$** increases as aircraft forward speed increases. You have learnt, too, however, that for a **fixed-pitch propeller, thrust** diminishes as aircraft forward speed increases, and that, at a certain value of forward speed, **thrust** will reduce to zero. What this means for **propeller efficiency**, in practical terms, is that the **efficiency** of a **fixed-pitch propeller** will <u>increase up to a given aircraft speed</u>, but will, thereafter, as aircraft speed increases still further, diminish, eventually approaching zero as the aircraft nears its theoretical zero-thrust speed, and thrust approaches zero. In fact, a fixed-pitch propeller will operate at its optimal efficiency at one value of airspeed, only.

For practical purposes, propeller power is equal to thrust times aircraft velocity.

PROPELLER DIAMETER.

The optimal efficiency of a fixed-pitch propeller is achieved at one value of aircraft airspeed, only.

Though it is beyond the scope of this book, a further relationship between the **power** and **efficiency** of propellers, which is interesting to consider, is that, for a given **power**, both **propeller efficiency** and **thrust** increase as the **diameter** of the propeller increases. This is the reason why man-powered and solar-powered aircraft, which at the end of the 20th Century achieved impressive performances for distance flown, used **large diameter propellers** which turned slowly, imparting a small acceleration to a relatively large mass of air.

Increasing the propeller's **diameter** will also lead to an increase in **propeller torque**, and so large-diameter propellers would theoretically be effective in absorbing the power produced by high-performance piston engines. Unfortunately, though, there are **practical** and **physical limitations** to a propeller's **diameter**.

Firstly, a large **diameter** propeller would make it impossible to achieve ground clearance, unless the aircraft had an impractically long undercarriage.

Secondly, because the rotational velocity of any element of a propeller blade increases with increasing distance from the axis of rotation (the propeller hub), the tips of a propeller blade are moving through the air at a much greater velocity than those parts of the blade nearer to the hub. **The tips of a large-diameter propeller could, therefore, approach the speed of sound**.

Near, or at, the speed of sound, airflow characteristics associated with compression and shock waves would cause propulsive efficiency losses as well as greatly increasing propeller noise.

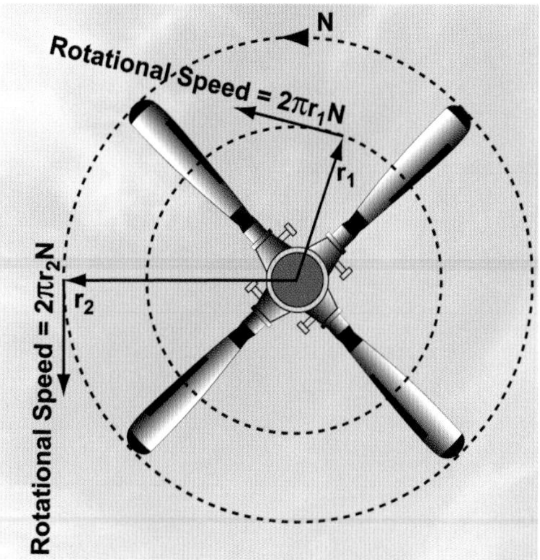

Fig 8.18 The greater the distance of a blade element from the propeller hub, the greater is its rotational speed at any given value of RPM.

Let's look a little further into this latter statement.

The rotational speed of a point moving in a circular path is defined as the linear velocity of that point around the path's circumference.

We can see from *Figure 8.18* that the length of the circumference traced out by a point on a propeller blade increases as the distance of that point from the centre of rotation of the propeller increases. When a propeller is rotating at constant RPM, all points along the length of the blade take the same amount of time to make one revolution. Obviously, though, the elements of the propeller blade furthest from the hub have to travel a greater distance in that time. Therefore, **the greater the distance of a blade element from the hub, the greater its rotational speed, for any given value of propeller RPM**. It can be proven that, at constant angular velocity, **(N)**, measured in revolutions per minute, RPM, the rotational speed of a propeller element, at distance **r** from the axis of rotation of the propeller, is equal to $2 \times \pi \times r \times N$.

Rotational Speed = **2 π r N** ....**(10)**

If **r** is measured in **feet**, Equation **(10)** gives the rotational speed in **feet per minute**. If **r** is measured in **metres**, rotational speed will be in **metres per minute.**

Equation **(10)** also shows us that, for any element of a propeller blade at distance **r** from the hub, rotational velocity increases as **r** increases.

Considering the example of a typical light-aircraft, fixed-pitch propeller of around **6 feet diameter (180 cm)**, at a typical cruise setting of **2 400 RPM**, we can illustrate the type of speed at which propeller tips move. For our example, then, remembering that radius, **r**, is half the diameter:

Rotational Speed of propeller tips = **2 π r N**

= **2 × 3.142 × 3 × 2 400 feet per minute**

= **45 245 feet per minute**

= **514 miles per hour (823 kilometres per hour)**

514 miles per hour is quite a high speed.

The tips of a propeller blade are the fastest moving parts of the propeller. If the blade tips approach the speed of sound, propeller efficiency decreases sharply. Tip speed is a major factor in limiting airspeeds of propeller driven aircraft.

Using the same formula, it is easy to see that the tips of an 8 foot diameter propeller rotating at 3 000 RPM would be moving at 857 miles per hour (1 371 kilometres per hour). This latter speed is, of course, supersonic. It is very difficult to extract satisfactory performance from propellers whose tips are rotating supersonically, and difficult, too, to cater for the stresses, vibrations and noise of transonic operations. These, then, are the main factors which limit the speed of propeller-driven aircraft.

THE PROPELLER AS A ROTATING WING.

Up to now, we have considered, principally, the Newtonian, or simplified momentum theory of **thrust**. But, propeller blades are **aerofoils**. A propeller blade, then, acts like a **rotating wing**, and, like a wing, the propeller blade, in its normal operating range, meets the relative airflow at a certain **angle of attack**.

These **wing-like properties** of the propeller, especially the fact that it cuts through the air at a certain angle of attack, can of course help to explain how air is accelerated rearwards when the propeller rotates, just as a wing induces a downwash to the air flowing over it *(see Figure 8.19)*. But the **propeller blade's aerofoil cross section** also gives us another view on how thrust is produced.

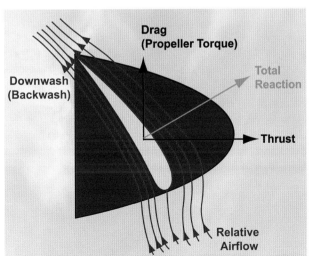

Figure 8.19 The rotating-wing analogy of propeller thrust.

157

Many versions of **propeller theory** offer the explanation that, because a propeller blade is an **aerofoil**, when the propeller rotates and cuts through the air, an **aerodynamic force** is generated by the blade (similar to the **lift** generated by a wing) as a result of **increased pressure behind the blade** and **reduced pressure ahead of the blade**. In the case of the propeller, this **aerodynamic force** acts forwards in the direction of flight and is called **thrust** *(see Figure 8.19)*. So, according to this **"wing-theory"**, the propeller might even be considered as pulling the aircraft through the air. This view is sometimes referred to as the **Bernoulli explanation of thrust**, after the Swiss scientist Daniel Bernoulli who propounded the constant pressure energy theory.

A UNIFIED THEORY OF PROPELLER THRUST.

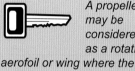

A propeller may be considered as a rotating aerofoil or wing where the reduced pressure in front of the blades and increased pressure behind the blades produce the kind of "horizontal lift force" which helps explain the nature of thrust.

You may find that certain books which contain the **wing-theory**, or **Bernoulli**, explanation, of **thrust** ignore momentum considerations of thrust altogether. And, as we mentioned earlier, other **Principles of Flight** manuals treat the **"wing-theory"** view of **thrust** and the **momentum theory** view of **thrust** as two separate concepts, each of which makes a partial contribution to total propeller **thrust**. Yet other manuals, often the more learned, treat the two concepts as being merely two parts of **one unified concept of thrust, ultimately based on the momentum theory.**

All aerodynamicists seem to agree, however, on two points, which would suggest that both the **Bernoulli** and the **Newtonian** views of thrust both have some validity in explaining the true nature of the **thrust force**.

These two points are:

1.   That a rotating propeller – for example on a simple model aircraft - which is merely an appropriately twisted flat blade, meeting the air at a given angle of attack, will generate thrust by accelerating air rearwards.

2.   That when the propeller has an aerofoil cross section, it is a more efficient producer of thrust than if it were just a twisted flat plate.

We cannot, here, enter into this scientific argument. It is far beyond the scope of this book and, as a student pilot, you are not required to possesses knowledge of **propeller thrust** to that depth in order to pass your theoretical knowledge examinations. You should, however, as a pilot, always be aware that propeller theory is complex and controversial.

PROPELLER ANGLE OF ATTACK.

Both the **rotating wing theory**, which views thrust as horizontal lift, and the **simplified momentum theory**, which explains thrust as a reaction to air accelerated rearwards, require the propeller to operate at an efficient **angle of attack** of around 4 degrees. So, in this section, we will look more closely at the **angle of attack** between a rotating propeller blade and the relative airflow. You will learn that **propeller angle of attack varies with aircraft forward speed and with changing propeller rotational speed**. *(See Figure 8.20)*.

To begin with, we will consider a **single, cross-sectional element** of the blade of a fixed-pitch propeller, taken at approximately mid way between hub and tip. *(See Figure 8.20)* Note that the cross section of the blade that we are considering is an **aerofoil**, and that the **blade angle** is defined as the angle between the chord line of the blade section and the plane of rotation of the propeller.

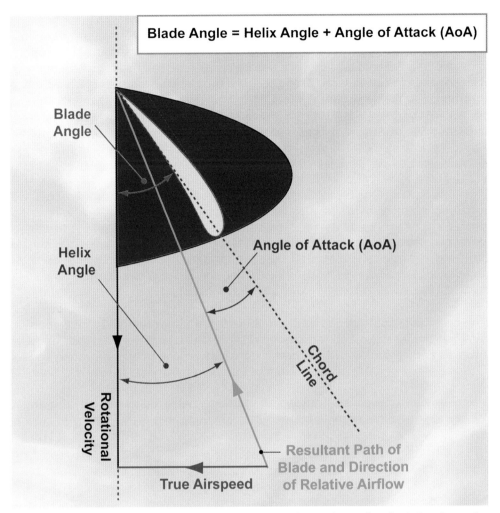

Figure 8.20 Variation of propeller angle of attack with forward speed and rotational speed.

We know, of course, that the propeller blade is twisted, but we'll come back to that later. For the moment, by confining ourselves to the examination of a single element of the blade, we can ignore the twist.

First of all, let us consider a stationary aircraft, just about to start its take-off run, with its propeller rotating at a given RPM. Because the aircraft is stationery the propeller blade is not moving forward and, therefore, there is effectively no helix angle. The rotating blade will meet the air at an angle equal to the **blade angle**, so that, while the aircraft is stationary, the **blade angle** is equal to the **angle of attack**. This would be the situation in *Figure 8.20* if the **"true airspeed" vector** were zero. This initial **angle of attack** will, invariably, be of a positive value, but **less than the stalling angle**, and, so, the propeller will generate **thrust**. After all, if it did not, the aircraft could never begin its take-off role.

But when the aircraft begins to move forwards through the air, the **airflow** over the propeller blade takes on **two components**: one as a result of the **blade's rotation**, and the other as a result of the **blade's forward movement** through the air. On an aircraft in motion, therefore, a rotating blade describes a helical path through the air as shown in *Figure 8.14.* The angle of this helical path, called the helix angle, is represented in *Figure 8.20*.

159

Figure 8.20, depicts the blade cross section with a **triangle of velocities** imposed upon it. Each side of a triangle of velocities is called a **"vector"**, because the length and direction of the line represents both the magnitude and direction of the velocity component it refers to. The **black vector** represents the **rotational velocity of the propeller** around its axis of rotation. The **blue vector** represents the **air mass flowing through the propeller disk**, at right angles to the disk, the magnitude of the blue vector being equal to the **forward speed** of the aircraft (its **true airspeed**), plus the extra velocity of the **induced airflow** into the propeller disk*. The **green vector** represents the **airflow relative to the propeller blade** as it cuts through the air, describing a helix as depicted in *Figure 8.14.*

The **helix angle** for the blade element under consideration is the angle between the **rotational plane** of the blade and the **blade's resultant path along the helix** as the aircraft advances through the air. The blade is shown set at a small positive angle to the **relative airflow**. This is the **angle of attack**. You will remember that if the blade element is to generate an effective aerodynamic force, the size of this **angle of attack** must lie within a particular thrust-producing range (approximately from 1° to 15°), with the most efficient **angle of attack** being around 4°.

If we consider the case of **constant propeller rotational velocity** at **a given engine RPM** (so that the length of the black line is constant), it should be clear that any increase in magnitude of the **aircraft's true airspeed** (i.e. an increase in speed, while maintaining direction) will be represented by an increase in length of the blue vector. This will increase the **helix angle** and decrease the **angle of attack** of the blade element. Conversely, if the aircraft's forward speed decreases, the **helix angle** will decrease and the **angle of attack** will increase.

At any given power setting, the angle of attack of a fixed pitch propeller decreases as aircraft forward speed increases, reducing torque.

Of course, though we are considering constant propeller RPM and, so, an unchanging length for the black propeller rotation vector, in reality, as aircraft forward speed increases, and blade **angle of attack** decreases, propeller **torque** will decrease and the **rotational velocity** of the propeller will increase. All pilots of aircraft powered by **fixed-pitch propellers** will be familiar with the fact that engine (and, therefore, propeller) RPM increases as the aircraft's forward speed increases, despite the fact that the throttle setting has not been touched. However, the percentage increase in propeller RPM is small compared to the percentage increase in forward speed so the principle of the variation of **blade angle of attack** with forward speed, given above, holds good, and, for the purposes of this explanation of **thrust**, we may ignore the increase in rotational speed.

At any given power setting, an increase in forward speed will cause the RPM of a fixed-pitch propeller to increase.

If, then, the aircraft's forward speed increased to the point that the **helix angle** equalled the **blade angle** of our cross-sectional element, the **angle of attack** would be zero and the propeller would be unable to develop any thrust.

At the other extreme, if the aircraft were stationary, such that the **helix angle** were zero, the **angle of attack** of the rotating propeller will be at a maximum. It is, of course, up to the propeller designer to ensure that the **angle of attack** does not exceed the **stalling angle** in this condition, so that sufficient **thrust** can be generated to start the aircraft moving.

Because the **angle of attack** of a fixed pitch propeller **varies** with the aircraft's forward speed, we see again that there can only be a limited range of aircraft speed within which the propeller can do its job efficiently.

* The extra velocity of the induced airflow will be small: very approximately equal to the velocity of airflow into the propeller disk when the aircraft is stationary. Consequently, at high aircraft speeds, the extra velocity of the induced airflow will be negligible, and, so, for convenience, we label the blue vector 'True Airspeed'.

Unfortunately, the situation we have just been considering is far from being the whole story.

The **angle of attack** of a fixed pitch propeller **varies** not only with the **forward speed of the aircraft** but also with the **propellers rotational speed**, by **rotational speed**, you will recall that we mean the **linear velocity** of any blade element around the circumference **described by its rotation**.

At constant aircraft forward speed, the angle of attack of a fixed-pitch propeller will increase with increasing RPM.

Now, for **any given element** of a **propeller blade**, at **a given distance from the propeller hub**, **rotational speed varies both with propeller RPM and with aircraft forward speed**. Referring to diagram *Figure 8.20* let us consider the case of an aircraft flying at constant airspeed but at varying values of propeller RPM. In the diagram, if the **forward speed** of the aircraft remains **constant**, the **length of the blue line** will remain the **same**. In this condition, we can easily see that any **increase in propeller RPM**, which will be represented by an **increase in length of the black vector**, will **decrease the helix angle** and **increase the angle of attack** of the blade element. Conversely, if, at constant forward speed, propeller RPM decreases, the **helix angle** will increase and the **angle of attack** of the blade element will decrease.

Knowing that the **angle of attack** of the propeller blade varies both with **airspeed** and **engine RPM**, and knowing that the blade operates at its most efficient at one given value of **angle of attack** only, it is fairly easy to deduce that a fixed-pitch propeller operates at its most efficient at only one given combination of aircraft forward speed and propeller rotational speed. In all other flight conditions, propeller efficiency will be less than optimal.

The angle of attack of a fixed pitch propeller changes with changing aircraft speed, and changing engine RPM.

Having arrived at this conclusion, you will probably already appreciate why advanced propeller-driven aircraft have powerplants which drive a **variable pitch propeller** at a **constant rotational speed** which can be determined by the pilot. On aircraft fitted with a **variable-pitch, constant speed propeller**, the **angle of attack** of the propeller can be maintained at its optimal value over a wide range of airspeeds and flight conditions. **Variable-pitch, constant speed propellers** are discussed further, below, and are covered in detail in the **Aeroplanes** volume of this series.

WHY IS A PROPELLER BLADE TWISTED?

We have not yet explained why all **propeller blades** are **twisted** from hub to tip in such a way that the **blade angle is smaller at the tip than at the hub**. Let us see why this is. We will begin by looking at the main points we have learned about propeller efficiency.

A fixed pitch propeller operates at optimal efficiency at one combination of aircraft forward speed and propeller rotational speed, only.

1.   A **fixed-pitch propeller** operates at **optimal efficiency** at **one angle of attack** only.

2.   Considering any given propeller blade element of a **fixed-pitch propeller**, at **constant RPM**, the **angle of attack** of that blade element decreases as aircraft forward speed increases and vice versa.

3.   Considering any given blade element of **a fixed-pitch propeller**, at constant forward speed, the **angle of attack** of that blade element increases as its **rotational speed** increases and vice versa. Remember that **"rotational speed"** refers to the **linear speed** of a blade element around the circumference described by the rotating element.

It is Point 3 which helps us to understand why the propeller blade is **twisted**: the **angle of attack** of any **blade element** changes depending on its **rotational speed**. If a propeller maintains a constant RPM at a constant aircraft forward speed, we might think - though we would be wrong - that the **angle of attack** of the propeller would be constant. The **angle of attack** of **any single blade element** will, indeed, remain constant, but considering **all sections of the propeller across the whole length of the propeller blade**, the **rotational velocity** of the **individual blade elements** increases as their distance from the propeller hub increases. We looked at a simple mathematical proof of this fact, earlier in this chapter.

We have already learned that **blade angle of attack increases with propeller rotational speed. Therefore, even at constant propeller RPM, the angle of attack of a blade element of a given blade angle increases with increasing distance from the propeller hub**. So, if the pitch angle of a propeller blade were constant along its length, the **angle of attack** of the different elements of such a blade, at a given propeller RPM, would increase the further the blade elements were located from the hub. Now, **propellers work efficiently at one angle of attack only**, so if every part of a rotating propeller blade presented a different **angle of attack** to the relative airflow, the propeller could never be an efficient provider of **thrust**.

Furthermore, if there were differing angles of attack across the length of the propeller blade, the magnitude of the **thrust** force would also vary along the blade, imposing considerable bending moments on the propeller.

In order to maintain the optimal angle of attack between the blade and the relative airflow, a propeller blade is twisted along its length, decreasing in blade angle from root to tip.

It is, therefore, in order to maintain optimal propeller efficiency (that is, to maintain the most efficient angle of attack) along the whole length of the propeller blade the propeller is twisted such that the blade angle is progressively reduced from root to tip *(see Figure 8.21)*.

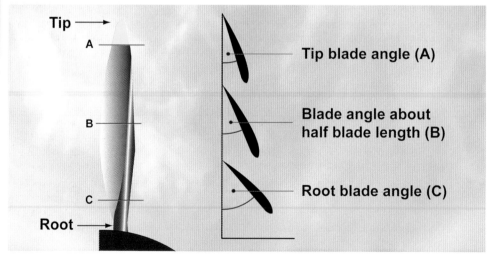

Figure 8.21 Blade angle reduces from root to tip.

Propeller Thrust Explained by the Lift Equation.

Looking at the issue of **propeller twist** from the point of view of the **wing-theory** (Bernoulli) explanation of **thrust** gives another, related perspective on why a propeller blade is twisted. The **wing-theory** treats **thrust** as **horizontal lift**. Now, there is a well known equation which relates **lift force** to **angle of attack** which you learnt about in Chapter 2:

Lift = C$_L$ ½ ρ v² S ....(11)

Similarly, for a propeller producing thrust, in accordance with the wing-theory:

Thrust = C$_L$ ½ ρ v² S ....(12)

Where ρ = air density; **v** = rotational velocity; **S** = surface area of propeller blades, and **C$_L$** = Coefficient of Lift (Here, Coefficient of Thrust).

Now, **C$_L$** is dependent on **aerofoil design** and **angle of attack**. Therefore, since the **aerofoil design** cannot change, **C$_L$** is a variable only because the **angle of attack** can and does change during the propeller's operation.

As ρ and **S** are constants, the only variables in Equation **(12)** are **Thrust**, rotational velocity (**v**) and the **angle of attack**, as represented by **C$_L$**.

We have learnt that in order to maintain efficient propeller operation and to prevent undesirable bending forces acting on the propeller blades, **thrust** should be of a constant value along the whole length of the blade. We also know that, even at constant RPM, the rotational speed, **v**, increases as the distance from the propeller root increases. So, referring to Equation **(12)**, if we want to keep **thrust** constant as **v** is increasing, we must reduce another variable in the equation. But, we have just stated that the only other variable is **C$_L$**, representing the **angle of attack**.

Therefore, in order to keep thrust constant along the whole length of the propeller blade, angle of attack must decrease from root to tip, because rotation velocity, v, increases from root to tip.

In order that the thrust force remains constant along the whole length of the propeller blade, the angle of attack of the blade must decrease from root to tip. This is another reason why a propeller blade is twisted.

For all the reasons stated, then, **the propeller is twisted such that the blade angle is progressively reduced from root to tip**. Obviously, when calculating the **mean blade angle**, the propeller designer is mindful of the principal operating mode of the aircraft for which the propeller is intended. The value of the **mean blade angle** is the angle at the ¾ **position** (measured from root to tip). **Fine pitch propellers** have small **mean blade angles**. **Coarse pitch propellers** have larger **mean blade angles**.

Fine and Coarse Pitch Propellers.
A **glider-tug** aircraft needs **optimal propeller efficiency** at **aerotow speeds** of, say, between 65 and 80 kts, and for **maximum acceleration from standstill** to flying speed for the tug-glider combination. So a **glider-tug** *(see Figure 8.22)* will have a propeller that achieves its **most efficient angle of attack** at **low forward speeds**.

Figure 8.22 A Jodel D140 Glider Tug.

During take-off, there is considerable propeller slip and loss of efficiency, and, in the early stages, the propeller blades are liable to stall. That is why a **glider-tug** aircraft, which needs to accelerate the tug aircraft-glider combination to take-off speed as quickly as possible, while countering the extra drag of the glider it is towing, will be fitted with a **fine-pitch propeller**. However, with its **fine-pitch propeller**, the **glider-tug** will operate at **less than optimal efficiency in the cruise**, on the way, say, to retrieve a sailplane which has landed out, because, at the higher airspeed, its propeller's **angle of attack** will be below the optimal value.

A touring aircraft *(see Figure 8.23)* fitted with a **fixed-pitch propeller** will, on the other hand, have a **coarser pitch propeller** than that of the glider-tug so that the **angle of attack** of the touring aircraft's propeller is **most efficient at the aeroplane's designed cruising speed**.

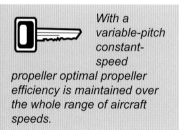

With a variable-pitch constant-speed propeller optimal propeller efficiency is maintained over the whole range of aircraft speeds.

Figure 8.23 The PA-28 Warrior: a typical light training and touring aircraft.

But at low speeds, especially on take off, the **coarse pitch propeller** will be less efficient than a fine-pitch propeller. The blades of the **coarse pitch propeller** will be more likely to stall on the initial take-off roll than those of a fine-pitch propeller, and propeller slip will be more marked.

Put another way, the high drag from the large angle of attack at take off, caused by the combination of **coarse pitch** and very low, or zero, forward speed, will prevent the engine developing full power during initial take-off. This situation will not be a problem for the touring aircraft operating from most licensed airfields, but may mean that its **short-field take-off performance** is poor.

VARIABLE-PITCH CONSTANT-SPEED PROPELLERS.

The significant limitations of the fixed-pitch propeller can be partially overcome by fitting an aircraft with a powerplant which drives a **variable pitch propeller**, at a **constant rotational speed** which can be determined by the pilot.

With a **variable pitch, constant-speed propeller**, a desired propeller rotational speed can be selected by the pilot, and the propeller **blade-angle** will then adjust itself to different flight speeds in order to maintain the **selected rotational speed**. **In this way, optimal propeller efficiency is maintained over a range of aircraft speeds**.

For instance, **blade angle** is coarsened as aircraft speed increases, thus allowing the propeller to maintain a positive acceleration of air rearwards up to a higher aircraft speed than would be possible with a fixed pitch propeller. Conversely, **blade angle** is fined off as aircraft speed decreases.

A variable-pitch, constant-speed propeller can, therefore, achieve both the fine pitch of the glider-tug propeller, at the start of its take-off run, and the coarser pitch of the touring aircraft when it is flying at cruising speed.

The operation of the variable-pitch, constant-speed propeller is described in detail in the **'Aeroplanes'** volume of this series of books.

PROPELLER AIRCRAFT OPERATING ISSUES.

To close this chapter we will take a look at some significant operating issues which affect **propeller-driven aircraft**, and which are most marked during the initial take-off roll. These effects are most apparent in high-powered, piston-engine driven aircraft.

Slipstream Effect.

A rotating propeller will generate a **slipstream** which travels backwards describing a **helical** path around and along the fuselage. If the propeller rotates anti-clockwise, the helical **slipstream** will meet the fin and rudder, producing an **aerodynamic force** at the tail assembly acting to the left, causing the aircraft to yaw to the right. Obviously, if the propeller rotates in the opposite direction, the yaw will also be in the opposite direction. For straight and level flight at the aircraft's cruise speed, any yaw resulting from slip-stream effect is normally eliminated by the manufacturer's rudder trim setting.

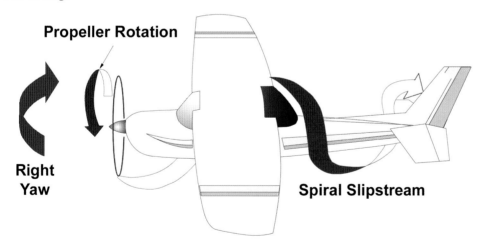

The slipstream effect will cause an aircraft to yaw against the direction of propeller rotation, when power is applied to initiate a climb, and in the direction of propeller rotation when power is reduced to initiate a descent.

Figure 8.24 The slipstream effect.

The **slipstream effect,** however, can cause a marked yaw when full power is applied to begin the take-off roll. In flight, the **slipstream effect** will cause the aircraft to yaw in one direction when power is applied in order, for instance, to make the transition from level flight to the climb, and in the opposite direction when power is reduced prior to levelling-off or descending. When power is applied, the aircraft will yaw against the direction of propeller rotation, and when power is reduced, it will yaw in the direction of propeller rotation. In all these situations, the pilot must prevent yaw by making an appropriate rudder input.

Propeller Torque Effect.

Propeller torque is the propeller's reaction to engine torque. **Propeller torque** enables the propeller to absorb engine power, but it also causes a reaction in the aircraft, itself, causing the aircraft to attempt to rotate about the propeller shaft in the opposite direction to propeller rotation. This aircraft reaction is, of course, resisted by, amongst other things, the undercarriage, which is in contact with the ground.

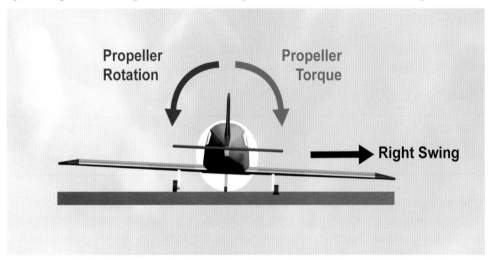

Figure 8.25 Propeller torque effect.

If the propeller is rotating anti-clockwise, as seen by the pilot, the aircraft will, in reaction, attempt to roll to the right. *(See Figure 8.25)* This will apply a downward force on the starboard main wheel thereby increasing its rolling resistance. This situation will cause the aircraft to swing to the right until downward force is removed from the wheels altogether, at lift-off. If the propeller is rotating in a clockwise direction, the tendency to swing will be to the left. Note that swing induced by **propeller torque effect** is in the same direction as swing caused by the slipstream effect. **Propeller torque effect** is most apparent in the early stages of take-off.

The Gyroscopic Effect - Gyroscopic Precession.

Any spinning body, or **gyroscope**, will resist movement when a force is applied to it. If you were to hold the two ends of the axis of a wheel spinning towards you (when viewed from above), you would notice that if you attempted to tilt the axis, by lowering one end, the axis would not move very far in the direction you wished it to, but would instead move in the horizontal plane as if you had tried to push the end of the axis away from you. This phenomenon is known as **gyroscopic precession**. The result of **gyroscopic precession** is that the line of action of any force applied to the spin axis moves through 90° in the direction of spin, before taking effect.

A rotating propeller acts like a **gyroscope**. Therefore, if the pilot of an aircraft pitches the nose downwards, he is, in effect, tilting the axis of rotation of the propeller forwards. **Gyroscopic precession** will cause the effect of the tilting force to take place along a line of action displaced by 90°, in the direction of spin. So, if the propeller is rotating anticlockwise as seen from the pilot's seat, and the pilot pitches the nose downwards, **gyroscopic precession** will cause the aircraft to tend to yaw to starboard (to the right as seen by the pilot). This tendency is especially marked in tail-wheel aircraft, on the take-off run when, under full power (maximum rpm), the pilot lifts the aircraft's tail. **Gyroscopic precession** in a propeller is illustrated in *Figure 8.26*

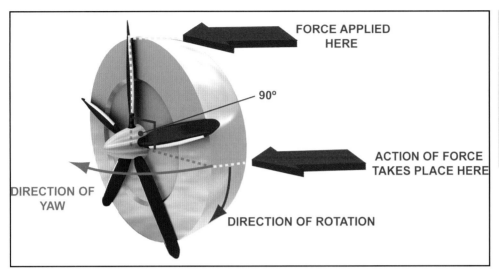

Figure 8.26 Gyroscopic precession in a propeller.

Asymmetric Blade Effect.

Asymmetric blade effect is felt by the aircraft when the axis of rotation of the propeller is inclined upwards to the horizontal path being followed by the aircraft, or, which amounts to the same thing, when the plane of rotation of the propeller is not vertical. This situation arises during the initial take-off run of a tail wheel aircraft, before that part of the take-off run where the pilot raises the tail.

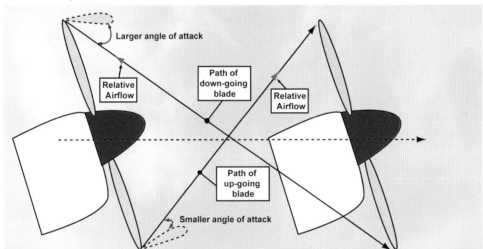

Figure 8.27 The asymmetric blade effect.

As the aircraft accelerates forwards with its tail wheel still in contact with the ground (and considering any half-rotation period of the propeller), the down-going blade will move through a greater linear distance than the up-going blade (*see Figure 8.27*). Consequently, the relative airflow over the down-going blade is of a higher velocity than the up-going blade. From Equation **(12)** you will see that an increase in relative velocity **v** will cause an increase in thrust.

Furthermore, an increase in the velocity of the relative airflow, will cause an increase in blade angle of attack. *(Look back at Figure 8.19 for a graphical illustration of this fact. You will see that for a given propeller rotational speed and a given airspeed, any increase in the relative airflow vector will lead to an increase in blade angle of attack.)*

Therefore, the down-going propeller blade will also have a greater angle of attack (C_L) than the up-going blade. This, too, leads to an increase in thrust on the down going blade, as can be deduced from Equation **(12)**.

Take-off Roll and Type of Undercarriage.

For a tail-wheel aircraft with a propeller rotating anti-clockwise (as seen by the pilot), then, the **Gyroscopic Effect** and the **Asymmetric Blade Effect** will combine to generate more thrust on the left hand side of the propeller than the right hand side of the propeller, causing the aircraft to tend to swing to the right during the initial take-off roll.

Figure 8.28 A " tail - dragger" - the De Havilland Chipmunk, fitted with a tailwheel.

A tail-dragger *(see Figure 8.28)* with a clockwise rotating propeller will, of course, tend to swing to the left.

The **asymmetric effect** will continue until the tail is lifted, thus putting the axis of rotation of the propeller disk at right angles to the path the aircraft is following.

However, **asymmetric blade effect** is dependent on thrust, and is proportional to forward speed, so it is not a significant factor in the initial part of the ground roll for a low-powered, tail-wheel aircraft. But the effect may become increasingly apparent as the ground roll continues, if the aircraft maintains its tail-down attitude.

Asymmetric effect on a tail wheel aircraft is not of any significance during the landing roll when the throttle is closed, as very little thrust is produced by the propeller; in fact it produces mainly drag. However, if the throttle is opened again, smartly, to initiate a go-around, while the tail wheel is still on the ground, **asymmetric effect** may make itself felt (Note that the **asymmetric blade** effect is sometimes referred to as **'P-factor effect**.')

Note, then that during the take-off roll, the **gyroscopic effect** and **asymmetric blade effect**, are experienced by **tail-wheel aircraft** only.

Direction of Swing.

In the case of a propeller rotating **anti-clockwise** as seen by the pilot, **Slipstream Effect**, **Torque Effect**, **Gyroscopic Effect** and **Asymmetric Blade Effect** all induce a **swing to the right**, and **all effects reinforce one another**.

For an aircraft with the propeller rotating **clockwise** when viewed from the pilot's seat, these effects would combine to induce a swing to the left.

So, as a final illustration, imagine you are commencing a take-off in a **tailwheel aircraft** with an **anticlockwise rotating propeller** (as seen from your pilot's seat). You should, then, be prepared for **a possible swing to the right** when you start to roll. If your aircraft has a powerful engine, yaw to the right during the take-off roll, as the tail is lifted into the flying position, will almost certainly be significant.

Consider, then, in this situation, to what extent this **swing to starboard** might be exacerbated by a **cross-wind from the right** which acts on the tail, pushing it even more to the left. The increase in right swing could be considerable. Of course, a cross wind from the left will tend to negate the right swing on take-off. If your aircraft had a **clockwise rotating propeller**, viewed from your seat, it would, of course, tend to **swing to the left on take-off**. A left swing will be amplified by a cross-wind from the left and diminished by a cross-wind from the right.

CONCLUSION.

In this chapter, we have looked at the basic principles of how a **propeller** produces **thrust** from the points of view of both **simplified momentum theory** and the **rotating aerofoil theory**. Both theories appear in specialist text books on **propellers**, and both give a credible explanation of **thrust** generation. Text books for pilots under training, tend to concentrate on the rotating wing-theory, or Bernoulli explanation, of **thrust**, whereas momentum theory is usually found only in more scientifically oriented literature. We have thought it best to mention both theories, so that the reader is aware of how complex, and sometimes controversial, theories of propeller thrust can be.

Several aspects of **propeller theory**, though, are common to both the rotating wing-theory interpretation and the momentum-theory interpretation of **propeller thrust**; these are: **propeller twist**, the **variation of thrust with aircraft forward speed**, and **angle-of-attack considerations**. It is those aspects of **thrust** which are common to both theories of propeller operation which are the ones you need to learn for your pilot examinations. In order to prepare your examinations, be guided by the questions at the end of this chapter and by the key-points in the text margins.

Representative PPL - type questions to test your theoretical knowledge of Propeller Thrust.

1.   A propeller blade is twisted along its length in order to:

   a.   give a progressively increasing blade angle from root to tip
   b.   give a progressively increasing angle of attack from root to tip when the propeller is rotating
   c.   compensate for the decreasing linear speed of the blade from root to tip
   d.   maintain the most efficient angle of attack along the whole length of the propeller blade when the propeller is rotating

2.   Blade angle _____ from the hub to the tip of a propeller blade in order to maintain an optimal _____ from hub to tip during propeller rotation.

   a.   increases   angle of attack
   b.   decreases   geometric pitch
   c.   increases   effective pitch
   d.   decreases   angle of attack

3.   As an aircraft with a variable-pitch, constant-speed propeller accelerates along the runway:

   a.   the angle of attack will decrease and the engine RPM remain constant
   b.   the blade pitch angle increases, maintaining a constant angle of attack and constant RPM
   c.   the angle of attack will remain constant and the engine RPM will increase
   d.   the linear velocity of the propeller tip will gradually decrease

4.   In a dive, with the throttle setting constant, the engine RPM of an aircraft fitted with a fixed-pitch propeller will:

   a.   decrease as the airspeed increases
   b.   remain constant whatever the airspeed
   c.   increase if the airspeed is allowed to increase
   d.   decrease as long as the throttle setting is not changed

5.   In a single-engine, propeller-driven aircraft, the torque reaction of a clockwise rotating propeller (as seen from the pilot's seat) will tend to cause:

   a.   left roll and right yaw during take off
   b.   left roll and left yaw during take off
   c.   right roll and right yaw during take off
   d.   left yaw and right roll during take off

6.   Which of the following combinations will decrease the angle of attack of a fixed pitch propeller blade?

      a.   Increased TAS and increased RPM
      b.   Increased TAS and decreased RPM
      c.   Decreased TAS and increased RPM
      d.   Decreased TAS and decreased RPM

7.   Which of the following combinations will increase the angle of attack of a fixed pitch propeller blade?

      a.   Increased TAS and increased RPM
      b.   Increased TAS and decreased RPM
      c.   Decreased TAS and increased RPM
      d.   Decreased TAS and decreased RPM

8.   The advantage of a constant speed propeller over a fixed pitch propeller is that:

      a.   a greater maximum thrust is available
      b.   a higher maximum efficiency is attained
      c.   more blade surface area is made available
      d.   optimal efficiency is achieved over a wide speed range

9.   The angle of attack of a fixed, coarse-pitch propeller on a touring light aircraft:

      a.   will be lower during the take-off run than in flight
      b.   will be optimal in all flight conditions
      c.   will be most efficient at the cruising speeds published in the pilot's operating manual
      d.   will decrease with decreasing airspeed at constant engine RPM

10.   A propeller blade is twisted from root to tip:

      a.   to provide maximum thrust at the root
      b.   to provide maximum thrust at the tip
      c.   so that propeller efficiency remains high, at any engine RPM
      d.   so that thrust remains approximately constant along the whole length of the propeller blade, at any engine RPM

11.   The angle of attack of a fixed-pitch propeller designed for cruising flight is:

      a.   optimal for steady cruising flight only
      b.   increases with an increase in TAS
      c.   decreases with an increase in RPM
      d.   will always be positive in a power off glide

12. Propeller-blade angle of attack is the angle between the blade chord-line and the:

    a. plane of rotation of the propeller
    b. aeroplane's gradient of climb
    c. the airflow relative to the propeller
    d. helix angle

13. What is the purpose of increasing the number of propeller blades?

    a. To reduce noise
    b. To improve power absorption
    c. To increase the efficiency of the variable pitch mechanism
    d. To enable a longer undercarriage to be fitted

14. What would be the gyroscopic effect of a clockwise rotating propeller (viewed from the pilot's seat) on a single-engine, tail-wheel aircraft as it raises its tail during the take off run?

    a. The aircraft would yaw to the right
    b. The aircraft would yaw to the left
    c. The aircraft would roll to the right
    d. The aircraft would roll to the left

15. During the take-off roll, what effect does torque have on an aircraft with an anti-clockwise rotating propeller, as seen from the pilot's seat?

    a. Weight on left wheel decreased, weight on right wheel increased
    b. Weight on left wheel increased, weight on right wheel remains constant
    c. Weight on left wheel increased, weight on right wheel decreased
    d. Weight on right wheel increased, weight on left wheel remains constant

16. Which of the following definitions of propeller parameters is correct?

    a. Blade Angle is the angle between chord line and the relative airflow
    b. Critical tip speed is the propeller speed at which there is a risk of the flow separating at some part of the propeller
    c. Blade angle of attack is the angle between the blade chord line and propeller's plane of rotation
    d. Geometric pitch is the theoretical distance that the propeller travels forward in one rotation

17. Which of the following gives the most correct explanation of why a propeller's blade angle decreases from root to tip?

    a. To compensate for the change in blade cross section from root to tip
    b. To provide increased thrust at the root
    c. To provide increased thrust at the tip
    d. To compensate for the increase in rotational velocity from root to tip.

18. On take off, why is it that a tail-wheel aircraft displays a greater tendency to swing than a nose-wheel aircraft?

    a. Because the propeller of a tail-wheel aircraft always rotates anticlockwise

    b. Because torque effect in a tail-wheel aircraft counters slipstream effect

    c. Because the tail-wheel aircraft is subject to asymmetric blade effect and gyroscopic effect, in addition to slipstream and torque effect

    d. Because the nose-wheel aircraft is not subject to torque effect and slipstream effect

19. When power is applied, why do aircraft in straight and level flight show a tendency to yaw?

    a. Because of the gyroscopic effect of the propeller

    b. Because of the slipstream effect and torque effect of the propeller

    c. Because most aircraft are fitted with an off-set fin

    d. Because the pilot always applies rudder when increasing power

20. On an aircraft fitted with a fixed pitch propeller, why does a change in airspeed always cause a corresponding change in engine RPM, even though the pilot may not move the throttle lever?

    a. Because a change in airspeed causes a change in inlet manifold pressure which affects engine power output

    b. Because an increase in airspeed causes a decrease in propeller angle of attack , thus reducing propeller torque, while a decrease in airspeed has the opposite effect

    c. Because of the asymmetric blade effect

    d. Because of the slipstream effect

21. Choose the most correct answer from the options below. As a coarse blade pitch is efficient at cruising speeds, why should a pilot ever choose to select fine pitch?

    a. In order to minimise fuel consumption

    b. Because of noise limitations on climbing away from the airfield over built up areas

    c. In order to increase engine RPM to the most fuel efficient level

    d. In order to optimise the aircraft's performance on take-off

22. Which of the answers below is the most correct? What performance advantages does an aircraft possess if it is fitted with a fine pitch propeller?

    a. It will produce maximum thrust at higher cruising speeds

    b. Its engine will be less likely to overheat in a climb, at high RPM and relatively low forward speed

    c. The propeller will give optimal thrust for the take-off and initial climb

    d. It will be able to fly at high speeds without exceeding the maximum permissible engine RPM

23.   What are the advantages of a constant-speed propeller?

      a.   Cruise performance will be improved

      b.   Take off performance will be improved

      c.   The engine can never over-speed whatever the circumstances

      d.   It provides an efficient blade angle of attack over a wide range of airspeeds

24.   What type of aircraft would most-likely be fitted with a fine, fixed-pitch propeller?

      a.   A touring aircraft

      b.   A glider tug

      c.   A high-performance, military, turbo-prop training aircraft

      d.   A turbo-prop passenger aircraft

Question	1	2	3	4	5	6	7	8	9	10	11	12
Answer												

Question	13	14	15	16	17	18	19	20	21	22	23	24
Answer												

The answers to these questions can be found at the end of this book.

CHAPTER 9
THE FOUR FORCES AND
TURNING FLIGHT

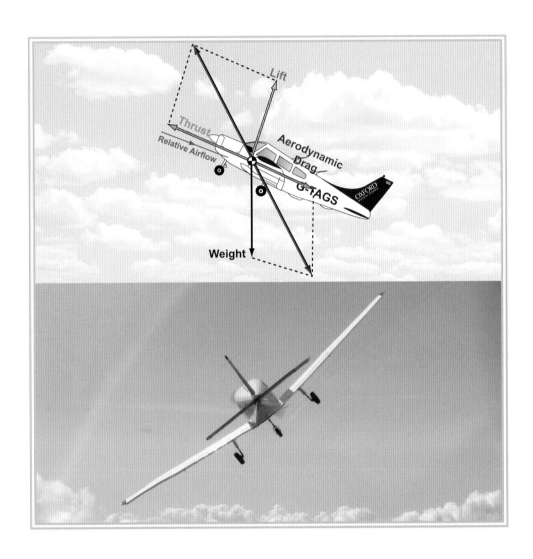

THE PRINCIPAL FLIGHT FORCES.

INTRODUCTION.

You have now studied in some detail the forces acting on an aircraft in flight: **lift**, **drag**, **weight** and **thrust**. In this chapter, we will look at the distribution of and interrelationship between the four flight forces, and how a pilot may control those forces to maintain the forces in balance (equilibrium), in steady, straight flight. We will also examine the role of the principal flight forces in turning flight.

The detailed study of the aircraft's performance during take-off, climb, cruise, descent and landing will be covered in the **Aircraft Performance** section, which you will find later in this book.

We will begin by reminding ourselves that the flight forces act in different directions.

Lift acts at 90° to the relative airflow, and is considered as acting though the **centre of pressure**. If angle of attack is increased, but remains below the stalling angle, the centre of pressure will move forwards along the wing chord. With decreasing angle of attack, the centre of pressure will move rearwards.

When manoeuvring, an aircraft rotates about its centre of gravity.

Weight always acts vertically downwards through the aircraft's **centre of gravity**. During flight, the aircraft consumes fuel, and so the weight of the aircraft constantly changes. As individual fuel tanks empty, the position of the aircraft's **centre of gravity**, may change. Its position must, however, remain within prescribed limits. When the aircraft manoeuvres in pitch, roll and yaw, the aircraft rotates about its **centre of gravity**.

Thrust may be considered to act along the line of the propeller shaft.

Drag may be considered to act parallel to the relative airflow so as to resist the motion of the aircraft. The actual line of action of the total drag is difficult to determine except by experiment, and will vary with changing angle of attack.

As you can deduce from the above descriptions of the lines of action of the flight forces, and from what you have learnt so far, the four flight forces do not act through one point. So, if the designer and pilot require the aircraft to fly in steady straight flight, the interrelationship between the lines of action of the fight forces must be understood.

STRAIGHT FLIGHT AT CONSTANT SPEED.

Equilibrium.
In steady, straight flight, at constant speed, the four forces will be in **equilibrium**. With the four forces all **in equilibrium**, the forces balance each other exactly, either one against one, or two together against the other two together. With the forces in **equilibrium**, the aircraft continues flying in its steady state without any change in attitude or speed. This state of **equilibrium** may be achieved in straight and level flight, a straight climb or a straight descent.

In steady, straight flight, whether maintaining altitude, climbing or descending, all the flight forces acting on the aircraft are in equilibrium.

Figure 9.1 depicts an idealistic case of **equilibrium** for straight and level flight, with lift equal to weight and thrust equal to drag, and with the lines of action of the forces all passing through the same point. As you will learn in this chapter, this idealistic situation of **equilibrium** does not represent reality, but it will serve to illustrate the basic principle of **equilibrium.**

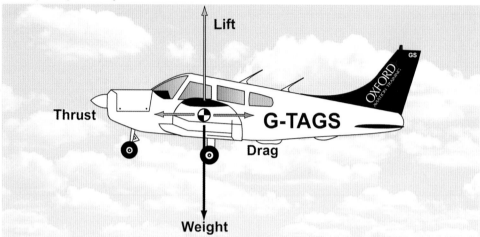

Figure 9.1 An idealistic state of equilibrium of the four main flight forces in straight and level flight.

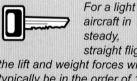

For a light aircraft in steady, straight flight, the lift and weight forces will typically be in the order of 10 times the magnitude of thrust and drag forces.

You should note that, in reality, there is a considerable difference in the magnitude of the two pairs of forces: lift-weight, and thrust-drag. For a light aircraft the lift will typically be in the order of 10 times as great as the drag, giving a **lift-drag ratio** of 10. You have already learnt about the importance of **lift-drag ratio**.

Of course, if the throttle is closed, so that the engine is at idle, the thrust developed by the propeller is negligible and can be ignored. In this, throttled-back situation, with the aircraft in a steady, straight glide, there are only three forces acting on the aircraft. In a straight glide, it is these three forces, **lift**, **weight** and **drag**, which must be in **equilibrium**, as depicted in *Figure 9.2*. We briefly introduced the distribution of forces in the glide, in the chapter dealing with **lift-drag ratio**, and you will meet the glide again, in the En-Route section of **Aircraft Performance**, later in this volume. *Figure 9.2* depicts an idealistic case of **equilibrium** for a straight glide, with the aircraft's weight being balanced by the resultant (i.e. the total reaction) of the lift and drag forces.

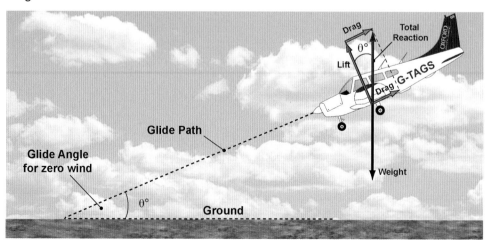

Figure 9.2 An aircraft in a straight glide with three forces in equilibrium and no out-of-balance turning moment.

178

There is one further condition necessary for **equilibrium** in steady, straight flight, in addition to the condition where the lines of action of the flight forces balance one another linearly. The lines of action of the forces must also be so arranged that the aircraft displays no tendency to rotate in the pitching plane. In other words, **the flight forces must produce no out-of-balance turning moment or couple**. **Turning moments and couples** are defined in Chapter 1, and covered in detail in the book of this series containing the subject **Mass & Balance**. The turning moment of a **couple**, where two forces of equal magnitude act as a pair, is illustrated in *Figure 9.3*.

Figure 9.1 and *Figure 9.2, previous page*, as we have emphasised, depict an idealistic condition of **equilibrium** of the flight forces where all the forces act through the same point. When forces act through the <u>same point</u> in this way, there can be no **turning moment**, because there is no **moment arm** or lever arm to give rise to any rotation of the aircraft. In reality, however, this idealistic **equilibrium** condition does not exist.

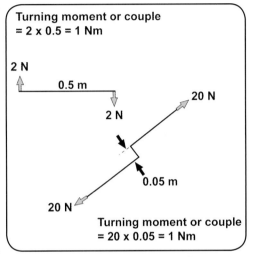

Figure 9.3 The turning moment of a couple depends on the magnitude of the forces and the perpendicular distance between their lines of action.

Disturbance of Flight Equilibrium.

As we have already discussed, the position of the **centre of pressure** changes with angle of attack and the position of the **centre of gravity** changes as fuel is consumed, so, under most conditions of flight, they do not coincide. In reality, too, the lines of action of the thrust and drag forces will not be coincident. *Figure 9.4* depicts a more typical distribution of the lines of action of the main flight forces. It is almost always the case that there is a perpendicular distance between the lines of action of the principal flight forces giving rise to **turning couples** which will cause the aircraft to tend to rotate in the pitching plane.

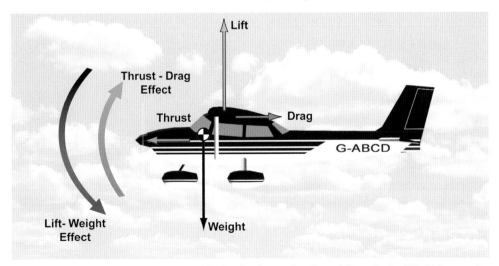

Figure 9.4 Under most conditions of flight, the lines of action of the principal flight forces do not coincide.

Whether the **couple** causes a nose up or nose down movement depends on the position of the **centre of pressure** in relation to the position of the **centre of gravity**, and that will often depend on the aircraft's basic configuration (high-wing, low-wing, monoplane, biplane, etc).

In *Figure 9.4*, the forces of lift and weight, considered as a pair of equal and opposite forces, have their lines of action arranged, so that there is a **moment arm** between them. The lift and weight forces, thus, produce a **couple** which will cause the nose of the aircraft to pitch down. On the other hand, the **couple** formed by the forces of thrust and drag will tend to produce a nose-up pitching movement.

In *Figure 9.4*, then, the two couples oppose each other: the nose-down pitching moment being opposed by the nose-up pitching moment. If we knew the actual magnitude of the forces and the length of their moment arms, we could tell whether or not the two opposing **turning moments** or **couples** balanced and were, thus, in **equilibrium**. It would, however, be most unlikely for the opposing **couples** to balance.

Achieving Balance.

Bur whether the particular **lift-weight** and **thrust-drag couples** depicted in *Figure 9.4* do or do not balance is of little importance, because under no circumstances could the opposing couples from the principal flight forces <u>remain</u> balanced for more than a very short time, probably only seconds. Because of the constant changes in the wing's angle of attack (due to normal atmospheric turbulence), and the corresponding changes in the position of the **centre of pressure**, together with any power variations due to the pilot's use of the throttle, the magnitudes and lines of action of the **lift**, **drag** and **thrust forces** are constantly changing. It follows, then, that, without a **balancing turning moment** which is under the control of the pilot, the four principal forces would very quickly depart from equilibrium, causing an uncontrollable pitching motion which would have disastrous consequences for the aircraft.

Certainly, if the lines of action of the principal flight forces were arranged as depicted in *Figure 9.5*, below, where the **centre of pressure** (CP) is behind the **centre of gravity (CG)**, the **lift-weight** and **thrust drag couples** would reinforce each other to produce a resultant nose-down pitching moment, requiring a **correcting turning moment** to be present from the outset, in order for equilibrium to exist.

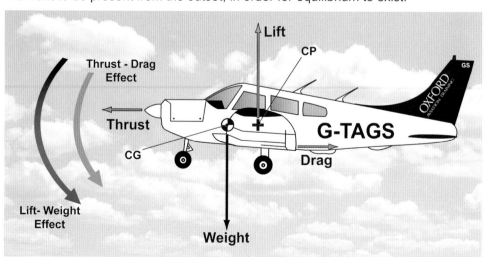

Figure 9.5 Here, the lift-weight and thrust-drag couples are reinforcing each other to produce a nose-down pitching moment.

On an aircraft of conventional design, such as the PA28 Warrior that we depict here, whatever **out-of-balance turning moment** is generated by the principal flight forces, the required **correcting moment** is provided by the aircraft's, tailplane or, in the case of the Warrior, the **stabilator**, (or **all flying tailplane**).

Because the **tailplane** or **stabilator** is situated at a considerable distance from the **centre of gravity**, about which the pitching motion of the aircraft takes place, the force generated by the **tailplane** or **stabilator** need be only small. In the case illustrated by *Figure 9.6*, the stabilator force of the PA 28 would be a downwards force, producing a correcting, nose-up pitching moment about the **centre of gravity**, to balance the **turning moments** generated by the main flight forces.

The out-of-balance turning moments caused by a typical disposition of the thrust/ drag and lift/weight couples are balanced by the tailplane or stabilator force.

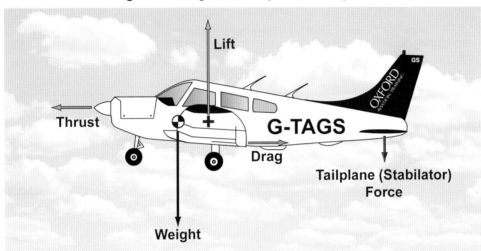

Figure 9.6 With this arrangement of the principal flight forces, equilibrium is achieved because of the balancing moment generated by the stabilator. All forces are in equilibrium, and there is no out-of-balance moment.

The basic function of the **tailplane** or **stabilator**, then, is to stabilise the aircraft in pitch. It does this by supplying the **turning moment** necessary to counter any **out-of-balance moment** in the pitching plane arising from the **lift-weight** and **thrust-drag couples**.

With the centre-of-pressure behind the centre of gravity the balancing tailplane/ stabilator force, typically, acts downwards.

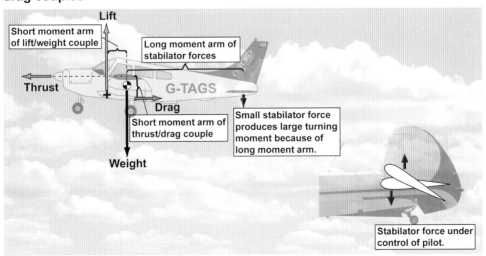

Figure 9.7 Here, the pilot's control over the stabilator allows him to counter any out-of-balance pitching moment of the main flight forces, for all conditions of flight.

The balancing moment produced by a **fixed tailplane, horizontal stabiliser,** or **stabilator** can counter the resultant pitching moment produced by the principal flight forces for only one condition of level flight. However, in practical piloting, a pilot's **control** over the **elevators** or **stabilator** allows him to **modify** that surface's balancing moment in order to counter the resultant pitching moment of the main flight forces, for all conditions of flight. *(See Figure 9.7, previous page)* The student pilot is taught this control principle in his very first flying lesson: fore and aft movements of the control column control the aircraft in pitch through movement of the elevators or stabilator.

More About the Relationship Between the Main Flight Forces - Increasing Power.

We have now seen, then, how the forces acting on an aircraft can be maintained in **equilibrium** by the balancing moment of the tailplane, horizontal stabiliser, or stabilator which is under the control of the pilot through his control of the elevators or stabilator

You have also learnt that a necessary condition for straight and level flight, at constant speed, is that all flight forces should be in **equilibrium**. But in order to maintain straight and level flight at a selection of airspeeds you must understand a little more of how the principal flight forces are interrelated.

Most importantly, you should understand that a change in any one of the forces of **thrust**, **lift** and **drag** will generate a change in the other two.

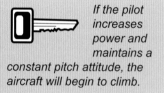

If the pilot increases power and maintains a constant pitch attitude, the aircraft will begin to climb.

Look again at *Figure 9.6*, and let us imagine that, from this straight and level cruising situation, the pilot increases power by opening the throttle a little further. When the pilot increases power, **thrust** is increased. **Thrust** will now be greater than **drag** and the aircraft will accelerate. As the lift formula, **Lift = C_L $\frac{1}{2}$ ρv^2 S**, tells us, the increase in speed will cause an increase in **lift**, which, because it is now greater than **weight**, will cause the aircraft to begin to climb. Furthermore, an increase in power will almost certainly cause a change in pitch attitude. In most cases, the nose will pitch up.

If the nose does pitch up, there will be an increase in angle of attack, and, thus, in C_L , leading to a further increase in **lift**, in addition to the **lift increase** caused by the increase in speed. **Drag** will increase, too, both because of the extra speed (**Drag = C_D $\frac{1}{2}$ ρV^2 S**) and also because of the rise in C_D owing to the increasing angle of attack. **Drag** will go on rising until **thrust** and **drag** balance each other again, and the aircraft stops accelerating. If the pilot does not choose to hold his pitch attitude constant, the increase in the angle of attack induced by the first application of power will reach an angle where C_D and **drag** have increased to such a level that the speed is now lower than when the pilot first increased power. This decrease in speed will, of course, cause the **lift force** to reduce again despite the increase in C_L. The decrease in speed will also decrease the **drag**, and so on and so forth until, eventually, a new equilibrium of the principal flight forces is established, which leaves the aircraft in a steady climb at a constant speed which is a little lower than the initial cruising speed, despite the climb having been initiated by an opening of the throttle.

The **new state of equilibrium** of the four principal flight forces is shown in *Figure 9.8*. Note that in *Figure 9.8*, for simplicity, we have assumed that all the principal forces are acting through the same point, so that there are no turning moments.

As we do not have to consider turning moments, we can ignore the force produced by the tailplane or stabilator.

In the new state of **equilibrium**, then, the flight path has changed from straight and level to a climb. As we have said, the speed will have reduced, and the **lift**, you may be surprised to learn, is also very slightly reduced. But **thrust** and the **drag** have both increased. However, the important point is that the resultant of the **thrust** and **lift** forces is equal and opposite to the resultant of the **drag** and **weight** forces, so **equilibrium** does, indeed, exist and the aircraft is moving at **constant velocity** again, in accordance with **Newton's Second Law**.

An aircraft's weight always acts vertically downwards towards the centre of the Earth.

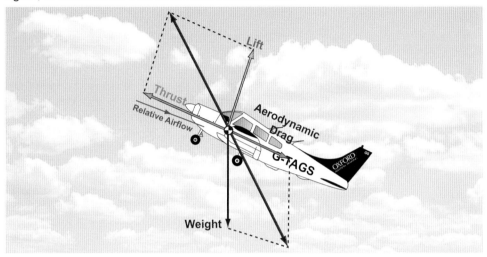

Figure 9.8 Here, the aircraft is climbing with all four principal flight forces in equilibrium. (NB: the assumption here, for simplicity, is that all forces are acting through the same point so that there are no turning moments.)

So the aircraft is in a steady climb, with the **lift force** a little less than when the aircraft was flying level. **In fact, lift is even a little less than weight**. On first consideration, this statement seems as if it cannot be true. But it is, indeed, a fact. In this steady climb, both the **thrust** and the **lift** are contributing to the resultant force which is causing the climb, while the opposing force, which is necessary for equilibrium and, thus, constant velocity, is the resultant of the **drag** and the **weight**.

The **lift** has, indeed, reduced slightly, but it is important to understand that the pilot could not have initiated the climb unless the **lift** had, at first, **increased** as the pilot increased power and speed.

So, in order that an aircraft may begin to climb, the **lift** must always initially increase in order to change the flight path of the aircraft (Newton's 1st Law); but once the aircraft has settled down into a steady climb at constant airspeed, the **lift** reduces and is less than the **weight**. You should know, though, that with the relatively low angles of climb achievable by light aircraft, the reduction in **lift** below the value for **weight** is very small indeed. (This is not the case, however, for high performance fighter aircraft, and, of course, the Harrier can dispense with wing-generated **lift force** altogether.)

In a steady climb, lift is a little less than weight.

The sequence of force changes in establishing the aircraft in the climb may sound a little chaotic, but, in reality, the situation is readily controlled by the pilot. The pilot adjusts his **power setting (RPM)** and **pitch attitude** to achieve the **climbing speed** and **rate of climb** that he desires. A light aircraft will invariably climb with full power, and the pilot will select the pitch attitude to give the speed for either the **best rate-of-climb** or the **best angle-of-climb**. Cruise climbs, though, are also an option for en-route flying. Your flying instructor will teach you all about climbing.

More About the Relationship Between the Main Flight Forces - Increasing Speed in Level Flight.

When a pilot increases power from level flight, it is not always because he wishes to initiate a climb. He will very often want to increase speed in straight and level flight, and to maintain his altitude while simply flying faster.

If a pilot opens the throttle and does not modify his pitch attitude, we know now that the aircraft will climb. But if a pilot does not want to climb but to increase speed, provided he has remembered the lift formula, **Lift = C_L ½ ρV^2 S**, he will know exactly what to do. As he increases power, he will, at the same time, increase forward pressure on the control column to adjust his pitch attitude and so reduce the value of **C_L** by reducing the angle of attack of the wing, thus preventing the increase in airspeed from increasing the **lift**. The pilot continues to reduce the angle of attack as the airspeed increases, until the airspeed ceases to rise.

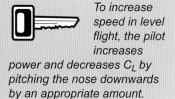

To increase speed in level flight, the pilot increases power and decreases C_L by pitching the nose downwards by an appropriate amount.

The increasing speed will, of course, increase **drag (Drag = C_D ½ ρV^2 S)** and the airspeed will settle down at its new higher value as the **drag force** approaches the value of the newly increased **force of thrust**, and when the flight forces again reach equilibrium, with greater values for **thrust** and **drag**, and slightly different lines of action for all flight forces. This new **equilibrium** situation may be easier to appreciate if we consider the simplified diagram at *Figure 9.9*, showing only the principal flight forces, and with the aircraft at a typical attitude for a light aeroplane flying at a high cruise speed. Again, for simplicity, we have assumed that all the principal forces are acting through the same point, so that there is no turning moment and no need for a tailplane force.

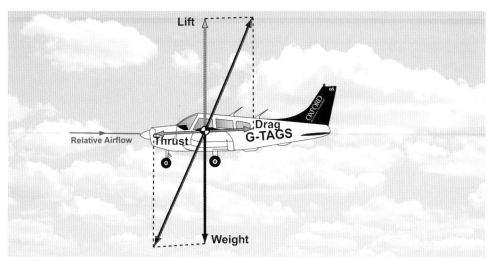

Figure 9.9 Here, the aircraft is flying straight and level in a high cruise-speed attitude, with all four principal flight forces in equilibrium.

You will note that, here, at this high cruise speed, the line of action of the **thrust force** is tilted slightly downwards so that the resultant of the **thrust** and **weight** force balances exactly the resultant of the **lift** and **drag** force. All four main flight forces are in equilibrium, and, in accordance with Newton's 1st Law, the aircraft is, therefore, flying at constant velocity: straight and level, at a new, higher, constant speed.

Obviously, an aircraft cannot increase its level-flight speed indefinitely because, with the throttle fully open, a limiting level flight speed is reached where the resultant of the **thrust** and **weight** forces equals the resultant of the **lift** and **drag** forces, and where no greater **thrust** force is available from the engine. This situation will represent the aircraft's maximum speed in level flight. A higher speed will be possible only if the aircraft descends and harnesses the **force of gravity** to supplement its propeller **thrust**.

But even if an aircraft were to enter a steep dive with the throttle fully open, its speed would not continue to increase indefinitely. Equilibrium of the four flight forces would still eventually be reached, so no further increase in speed would be possible, and, for the case of a vertical dive, a terminal velocity would be achieved. We may talk about such a situation in a book on the **Principles of Flight**, but, obviously, in real life, the magnitude of the aerodynamic forces acting on the aircraft as a result of the increasing speed would cause catastrophic damage to the structure of an aircraft before it reached terminal velocity. That is why your **Pilot's Operating Handbook** contains a very important speed limitation: the **speed never to exceed**, referred to commonly as V_{NE}.

Descending, and Reducing Speed in Level Flight.

It should now be relatively straight forward for you to appreciate that a reduction in propeller **thrust** when the pilot reduces power, in straight and level flight, will either cause the aircraft to descend or, if the pilot wishes, permit the aircraft to maintain attitude at a new lower speed. If power is reduced, **thrust** will for a short time be less than **drag**; the aircraft will, thus, decelerate. The decreasing speed reduces the **lift** and the aircraft will descend. Most aircraft will pitch nose down on reduction of **thrust**, momentarily reducing C_L. **Drag** will reduce, initially, as speed reduces, and with the initial reduction in C_D, but the lowering of the nose will lead to an increase in speed, causing both **lift** and **drag** to rise again. In very much the same way as we described for the increase in power, a reduction in power will lead to a new state of **equilibrium** with the aircraft descending at a new steady speed.

In practice, the descent will be determined by the pilot through his control over pitch attitude and power. Your flying instructor will teach you how to descend at different airspeeds and rates of descent. Of course, if the pilot does not want to descend, as he reduces power, he will raise the nose of the aircraft, thus increasing the angle of attack of the wing, and, consequently, C_L, so that the **lift force** does not reduce with the reduction in airspeed, but allows the aircraft to maintain constant altitude and carry on flying straight and level at a lower speed.

Summary of the Interrelation of the Main Flight Forces in Straight Flight at Constant Speed.

In this chapter, so far, you have learnt two important facts about the flight forces acting on an aircraft.

You have learnt that **all four main flight forces are closely interrelated**. A change, either in the magnitude or line of action, in any one of the three forces: **thrust**, **lift** or **drag**, will induce some kind of change (in magnitude or direction) in the other two. All three forces will then combine with one another, and with **weight** (whose line of action never varies, and whose magnitude may also be assumed to be constant for our present considerations), in order to modify the flight of the aircraft, either in terms of flight path or airspeed, or both.

For instance, when the pilot modifies propeller **thrust** by increasing or decreasing power, following an initial change in airspeed, the flight forces will once again establish themselves in a new state of **equilibrium** with the aircraft either climbing or descending, or maintaining its altitude at a new, constant higher or lower speed. In practice, in straight flight, both the flight path of the aircraft and its speed may be determined by the pilot through his control over pitch attitude and power.

Though we have not considered the situation in this chapter, you will now, probably, readily appreciate that, for straight flight, the initial change in the relationship between the flight forces may be made, not by changing propeller **thrust**, but by modifying **lift** directly through the pilot's selection of a larger or smaller angle of attack. You should be able to work out for yourself what the subsequent changes in the other flight forces might be. In the case of **weight**, remember, it will retain a constant magnitude and direction. As for **thrust**, you will need to consider the case of both fixed-pitch and constant speed propellers.

You have also learnt in this chapter that the four main flight forces, **lift**, **weight**, **thrust**, and **drag** have lines of action that do not pass through the same single point. For instance, the positions of the **centre of pressure** and the **centre of gravity** of an aircraft are variable and hardly ever coincide, and so the force-pairs **lift** and **weight**, on the one hand, and **thrust** and **drag**, on the other, set up turning moments or couples which tend to rotate the aircraft in pitch, about the centre of gravity.

In practice, even if, by some chance, the two couples exactly balanced each other out, such a precarious condition of **equilibrium** would be momentary, probably lasting only seconds. Without a balancing turning moment, under the control of the pilot, the four principal flight forces would very quickly and catastrophically depart from **equilibrium**, causing the aircraft to rotate uncontrollably in the pitching plane. Consequently, conventional aircraft are fitted with a **tailplane (horizontal stabiliser)** and **elevators** (as on the Cessna 152), or a **stabilator** (as on the PA28), both of which provide a balancing turning moment under the control of the pilot.

TURNING FLIGHT.

We will now consider the distribution of flight forces in turning flight. Turning flight is also dealt with, especially in as far as wing loading is concerned, in the chapter dealing with **Flight Limitations**. For the **Principle of Flight** considerations of turning flight, we need only depict, in our diagrams, two of the principal flight forces, **lift** and **weight**, though we shall make mention of **thrust** and **drag**. Consequently, the diagrams associated with the following explanation will show the aircraft viewed from the front.

We have learnt that in steady, straight flight, (straight and level, climb or descent) all the flight forces are in **equilibrium** with no out-of-balance resultant force acting on the aircraft. It is important that we understand that **equilibrium** is a necessary situation for straight flight at constant speed, whether the aircraft is straight and level, or in a straight climb or descent. With the aircraft in a state of **equilibrium**, there may well be resultant forces to consider, as we have seen. But, for equilibrium to exist, if there <u>are</u> resultant forces, they must balance each other out.

Straight flight at constant speed, then, requires **equilibrium**. This situation accords with **Newton's 1st Law** which teaches us that **a body will remain in its state of rest or uniform motion in a straight line unless acted upon by an out-of-balance force**. In straight flight, there is no out-of-balance force acting on the aircraft, and, no matter how high or low the speed at which the aircraft is flying, the pilot feels no force acting on him except his normal **weight**. (**Weight** is, in fact, an acceleration, as you have learnt in the chapter on **Mass and Weight**; that is why we can always feel it; but we will leave that complication aside for the moment.)

But if we want to <u>change</u> the straight flight path (i.e. change direction) or the speed of an aircraft, an out-of-balance force must be applied to the aircraft. (You will remember that we said that although in a straight climb at constant speed the forces are in equilibrium, an <u>initial out-of-balance force</u>, usually an increase in **thrust**, is required to <u>initiate</u> the climb.)

Centripetal Force.

It will be clear to you that when a body is turning in a circular path, it is constantly changing direction. **Consequently, the forces acting on a body which is following a circular path are not in equilibrium.** In circular motion, there must be an out-of-balance resultant force acting towards the centre of the circle, or else the body would be moving in a straight line in accordance with **Newton's 1st Law**. This out-of-balance force is called by scientists a **centripetal force**. *(See Figure 9.10)* **Centripetal** is derived from Latin and means **centre-seeking**.

For an aircraft in turning flight, the **centripetal force** has to be supplied by

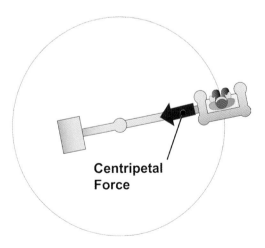

Centripetal Force

Figure 9.10 For a body to travel in a circular path, it must constantly change direction under the influence of an out-of-balance force called "centripetal force".

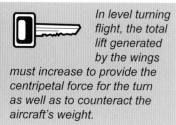

In level turning flight, the total lift generated by the wings must increase to provide the centripetal force for the turn as well as to counteract the aircraft's weight.

the **lift** force being directed towards the centre of the turn. That is why, in order to turn, a pilot must apply bank in the direction of turn. That part of the **lift** force which then provides the **centripetal force** constantly changes the direction of flight of the aircraft, and, because **centripetal force** is an out-of-balance, resultant force, the pilot feels it as an apparent increase in weight. What is actually happening is that the **centripetal force** is accelerating the mass of the aircraft towards the centre of the circle, but because the aircraft's linear velocity (its airspeed) is superimposed on the acceleration towards the centre of the circle, the aircraft does not move towards the centre of the circle but instead describes a circular path at a constant distance, or radius, from the centre. This acceleration, not surprisingly called **centripetal acceleration**, acts on all the individual masses of components, equipment and crew which are part of the aircraft.

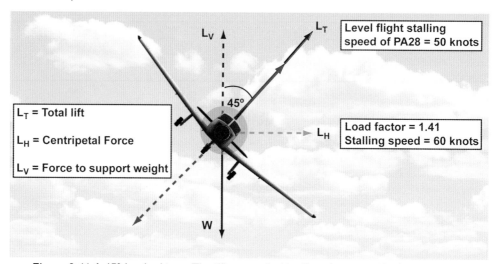

L_V

L_T

Level flight stalling speed of PA28 = 50 knots

45°

L_T = Total lift

L_H = Centripetal Force

L_V = Force to support weight

L_H

Load factor = 1.41
Stalling speed = 60 knots

W

Figure 9.11 A 45° banked turn. The lift generated by the wings must both support the aircraft's weight and provide the turning (centripetal) force.

Now, the only force that a pilot has at his disposal to provide the **centripetal force** for a turn is the **lift** from the wings. That is why, in order to turn, the pilot applies an appropriate amount of bank in the direction in which he wishes to turn. *Figure 9.11* illustrates a 45° banked turn. In your private pilot training, a 45° banked turn is probably the steepest you will be asked to fly.

In the 45°-banked turn illustrated, the **total lift** force, L_T, has to do two jobs. L_T is not only causing the aircraft to turn but is also supporting the **weight** of the aircraft (which continues to act vertically downwards) so as to maintain the aircraft in level flight. To achieve both these objectives, the **total lift** force in the turn needs to be greater than that required for straight and level flight. In *Figure 9.11*, as in the following two diagrams, the blue lift arrow depicts the magnitude of the **lift** required to maintain the aircraft in straight flight, and the red arrow depicts the **extra lift** that the wings must generate to enable the aircraft to turn while maintaining its altitude.

If level flight is to be maintained, as the angle of bank is increased, the angle of attack (and, therefore, C_L) of the wing must also be increased by a progressive backward pressure on the control column. This increases the **lift** force (**Lift = C_L ½ ρv^2 S**) to a value, L_T, such that the vertical component, L_V, of the **total lift** is sufficient to balance the aircraft's **weight** and maintain level flight, while the horizontal component of the **total lift**, L_H, provides the **centripetal force** required to turn the aircraft.

Airspeed in the Turn.

To the pilot, the increase in angle of attack required to generate the **extra lift** for the turn will be apparent as an increase in the back pressure on the control column sufficient to maintain the correct attitude and constant altitude. However, as the back pressure increases, and with it the angle of attack, C_D naturally increases, along with C_L, causing the total **drag** to rise (**Drag** = C_D ½ ρv^2 **S**). The increased **drag** will naturally lead to a reduction in **airspeed**, if **thrust** is not increased. While the reduction in **speed** is small in a medium level turn, up to 30° angle of bank, and may be acceptable, this would not be the case in a 45°-banked turn, or above. In a 45°-banked turn, it is important to increase **thrust** to maintain the entry **speed** because of the increased **stalling speed**. You will learn more about **stalling speed** in turns in the relevant chapters of this book, though, for your interest, we include in the diagrams the **stalling speed** for the angles of bank illustrated. For instance, in a 45°-banked turn, the **stalling speed** of a PA28 Warrior is around 60 knots: 10 knots higher than its straight flight **stalling speed** of 50 knots

An aircraft's stall speed increases during turning flight.

Load Factor.

In a 45°-banked turn, the **lift** force required to generate the necessary **centripetal force** and **centripetal acceleration** for the turn is 1.41 times the magnitude of the aircraft's **weight**. The pilot will clearly sense this increase in force, which is also acting on him, as an **inertial reaction** to the increase in **lift**. In fact, the whole of the aircraft structure will be subjected to the **inertial reaction** to the increase in **lift** generated by the wings, and sense this reaction as an increase in **load factor**. As you will learn in later chapters, it is the increased **wing loading** caused by the higher **load factor** which causes the increase in stalling speed in a turn (the derivation of the value of **load factor** is covered on Page 296).

The inertial reaction to the increased lift force required to maintain a level turn is called the Load Factor.

In a correctly flown turn, the pilot will feel the extra **lift** force as an apparent increase in **weight** pressing him firmly into his seat. In a 60°-banked turn, the **lift** force required for the turn is twice the magnitude of the aircraft's **weight**, and the pilot actually feels that his own **weight** has doubled. *(See Figure 9.12)*.

In a turn, stall speed = straight & level stall speed × $\sqrt{\text{Load Factor.}}$

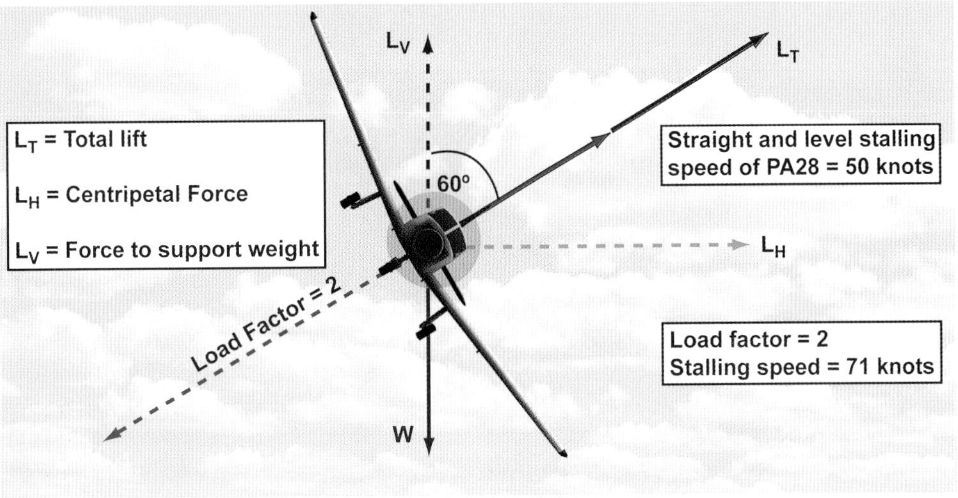

L_T = Total lift

L_H = Centripetal Force

L_V = Force to support weight

Straight and level stalling speed of PA28 = 50 knots

Load factor = 2
Stalling speed = 71 knots

L_V L_T

60°

L_H

Load Factor = 2

W

Figure 9.12 A 60° banked turn. The lift required for the turn is twice its straight flight value. Load Factor is 2, and the stalling speed is 71 knots.

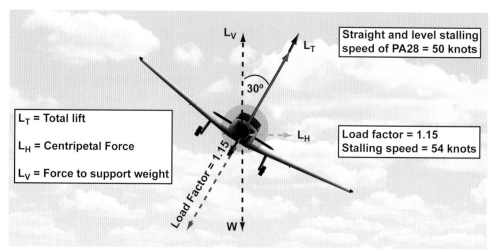

Figure 9.13 A 30° banked turn. The lift required for the turn is 1.15 times its straight flight value; Load Factor is 1.15, and the stalling speed is 54 knots.

In a 30°-banked turn, on the other hand, the **lift** required to produce the **centripetal force** to make the aircraft turn is only 1.15 times the straight-flight lift force. The pilot may not sense this small increase of apparent **weight** at all. *(See Figure 9.13).*

The "Balanced" Turn.
You will learn from your flying instructor how to turn at different angles of bank, and at different airspeeds. During turning exercises, you may well notice, if you do not fly the turn correctly and "keep the ball in the middle", that the out-of-balance force required to make the aircraft turn causes you to slide on your seat either into or out of the turn. If this does happen, your instructor may urge you to fly a "balanced" turn. You may well wish to ask him what he means by "balanced" if the force required to produce the turn, in the first place, is an "out-of-balance" force. The answer will lie in the specialist meaning of "balanced" in the instructor's patter, but the question may make for an interesting conversation in the club house, debriefing room or bar.

Skidding and Slipping Turns.
During turning manoeuvres, uncoordinated use of the aileron and rudder may cause the turn to be unbalanced. In an unbalanced turn, the aircraft will either **slip** or **skid** through the air, while it is turning. *Figure 9.14*, illustrates the difference between

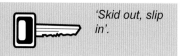
'Skid out, slip in'.

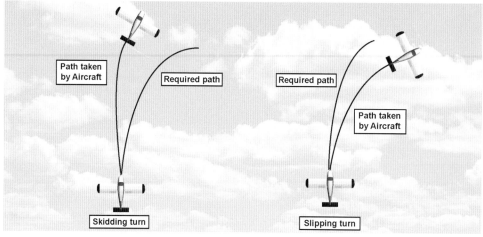

Figure 9.14 The path of a skidding turn and a slipping turn.

slip and **skid**. Basically, for a given radius of turn at a given speed, there is only one correct angle of bank. If an aircraft is overbanked for its turn, or if the pilot has applied too little rudder, the aircraft will **slip** into the turn. On the other hand, if the pilot has applied to small an angle of bank for the turn, or used too much rudder, the aircraft will **skid** out of the turn.

Co-ordination of Turns - Slip and Skid.

Slip and **skid** is displayed by the inclinometer which is the bottom portion of the 'turn co-ordinator', or the 'turn and slip' indicator. *(See Figure 9.15.)* The inclinometer consists of a glass tube filled with liquid, and contains a ball.

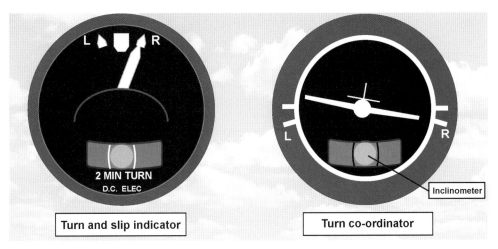

Figure 9.15 The Turn and Slip Indicator and Turn Co-ordinator, showing a balanced rate one turn.

Figure 9.15 indicates a turn to the right. Because the ball is in the middle the pilot sees that his turn is perfectly **balanced,** with no **slip** or **skid** present. If the aircraft were slipping into the turn to the right, as depicted in *Figure 9.16,* the ball would be displaced to the right.

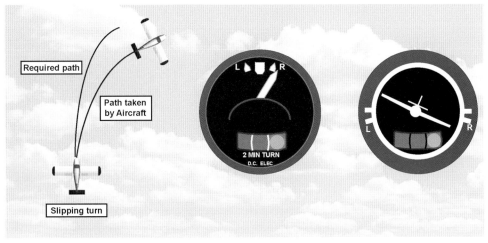

Figure 9.16 The ball indicates a slip in the direction of turn to the right.

The **slip** may have been caused because too much bank or too little rudder has been applied. Therefore, reducing the bank angle could return the aircraft to **balanced flight**. However, the simple rule to "re-balance" the turn, is to 'step on the ball' i.e. apply sufficient right rudder to return the ball to the middle position, between the two vertical lines.

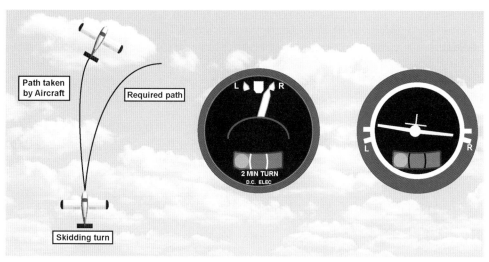

Figure 9.17 The ball indicates a skid away from the direction of turn.

If the aircraft were **skidding** out of the turn to the right, as in *Figure 9.17,* the ball would be displaced to the left. It could be that there is too little bank angle or too much rudder for the rate of turn being flown, but the easiest solution to return the ball to the middle is to apply left rudder. This amounts to the same thing as reducing right rudder. The simple answer, though, as before, is to "step on the ball."

Rate of Turn, Airspeed and Centripetal Force.

The magnitude of the **centripetal force** required to turn an aircraft varies with both **airspeed** and **rate of turn**. (The **rate of turn** is a measure of the time taken to complete a full 360° turn.) If the **rate of turn** is doubled (that is, with half the radius of turn) while maintaining a given **airspeed,** the **centripetal force** required to execute the turn is also doubled. If the **airspeed** were doubled but the **rate of turn** were to remain the same (constant radius), the **centripetal force** would need to be four times as great. The basic mathematical formula behind these statements is shown in *Figure 9.18.* The formula expresses the mathematical relationship between **centripetal force**, F_{CP}, the radius of turn (i.e. **rate of turn**), the mass of the body which is travelling in the circular path, and its linear velocity.

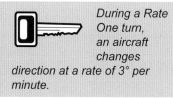
During a Rate One turn, an aircraft changes direction at a rate of 3° per minute.

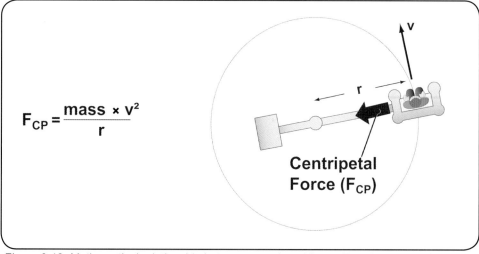

To determine the angle of bank, in degrees, for a Rate One turn, divide the True Airspeed in knots by 10 and add 7.

$$F_{CP} = \frac{mass \times v^2}{r}$$

Figure 9.18 Mathematical relationship between centripetal force, F_{CP}, the radius of turn (i.e. rate of turn), the mass of the body, and the linear velocity, v.

In civilian flying, procedural turns are carried at a rate of 180° per minute, or 3° per second. This **rate of turn** will be indicated on an aircraft's **Turn and Slip Indicator** and termed as a **rate one turn**. At normal light aircraft cruising speeds, a **rate one turn** will not require a **centripetal force** which will cause you any discomfort; a **rate one turn** at 90 knots would require, for instance, only 16° of bank.

The rate at which any aircraft turns is determined by **true airspeed** and **angle of bank**. At a given **true airspeed**, a given **angle of bank** will provide a certain **rate of turn**. A simple way to estimate the **angle of bank** required for a **rate one turn** of 3° per second, at a given **true airspeed**, is to take 10% of the **true airspeed** in knots, and add 7; for example, at 100 knots, a **rate one turn** is achieved with 17° **angle of bank**.

Note, too, the general rule that, in a turn at constant **airspeed**, if the **angle of bank** is increased, the **rate of turn** will increase (i.e. the radius of the turn will also become smaller). If, at constant **angle of bank**, the **airspeed** is decreased, the **rate of turn** will increase (i.e. the radius of the turn will become smaller); if the **airspeed** is increased at constant **angle of bank**, the **rate of turn** will decrease, (i.e. the radius of the turn will get larger). You can figure all this out mathematically, if you wish, from the formula in *Figure 9.18*. Just remember that an increased angle of bank will increase the centripetal force, F_{CP}.

The Pilot's Control of the Turn.

Once established in a turn, at desired airspeed and angle of bank, the pilot can easily control the turn, especially one of low bank angle, using aileron and rudder to maintain angle of bank, and elevator (or stabilator) to control attitude (C_L) and altitude. At steeper angles of bank, throttle must also be used to maintain speed because of the increased drag. But this aspect of your PPL studies belongs properly to flying instruction.

THE PROPELLER SLIPSTREAM.

In addition to the principal flight forces, and the tailplane force, the **propeller slipstream** will also generate an aerodynamic force on the fin (or vertical stabiliser) which acts in the yawing plane. The propeller converts engine power to thrust. It does this by accelerating the air and moving it rearwards. This movement of air is called the propeller's **slipstream** which moves in a helical path behind the propeller.

At constant angle of bank, if airspeed is increased, rate of turn is decreased and vice versa.

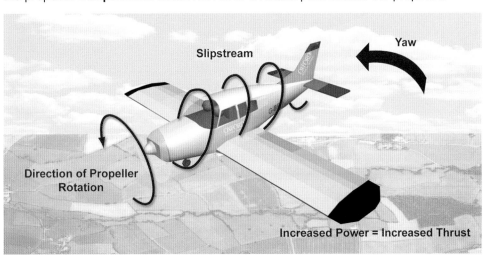

Figure 9.19 With a clockwise rotating propeller (as viewed by the pilot), increasing power will cause the aircraft to yaw to the left.

When the pilot increases power, the aircraft wll tend to yaw in the opposite direction to the propeller rotation. When power is reduced, the yaw will be in the direction of propeller rotation.

When increasing or decreasing power, the pilot must prevent yaw, and maintain balanced flight by applying rudder in the appropriate direction.

The **propeller slipstream** meets the fin (vertical stabiliser) in such a way that it induces a turning moment on the aircraft which is opposite to the direction of rotation of the propeller. Consequently, variations in throttle setting will cause an aircraft to yaw in a direction which depends on the direction of propeller rotation. See *Figure 9.19, previous page.*

If the propeller rotates to the right, or clockwise, when viewed from the cockpit, inducing a yaw to the left, the aircraft will tend to swing to the left if power is increased. Conversely, the aircraft will tend to swing to the right if power is decreased.

The effect of the turning moment can be counteracted by offsetting the fin (vertical stabiliser). This will create an aerodynamic force in opposition to the turning moment caused by the slipstream.

Effect of Power Variations on Yaw.

As we have mentioned, the turning moment caused by the **slipstream** will obviously be affected by increases and decreases of power. So, on increasing and decreasing power, the pilot must apply rudder in the appropriate direction to prevent yaw and maintain balanced flight.

Representative PPL - type questions to test your theoretical knowledge of The Four Forces - Turning Flight.

1. If the throttle is moved to adjust the power in level flight, the resulting change in propeller slipstream will primarily affect:

    a. the aircraft's trim in the pitching and yawing planes
    b. the aircraft's trim in the rolling plane
    c. the longitudinal stability
    d. the lateral stability

2. Which of the four options below most accurately describes the relationship between the forces acting on an aircraft in flight for those forces to be in equilibrium?

    a. Lift equals drag, and thrust equals weight
    b. Lift equals weight, and thrust equals drag
    c. Lift equals thrust plus drag
    d. Lift equals thrust, and weight equals drag

3. An aircraft has a nose down pitching moment due to the lift / weight couple and a nose up pitching moment due to the thrust / drag couple. When power is increased:

    a. it will pitch nose up
    b. it will pitch nose down
    c. the couples both increase in magnitude but remain balanced
    d. the couples both decrease in magnitude but remain balanced

4. In straight and level powered flight the following principal forces act on an aircraft:

    a. thrust, lift, weight
    b. thrust, lift, drag, weight
    c. thrust, lift, drag
    d. lift, drag, weight

5. Considering the forces acting upon an aeroplane, at constant airspeed, which statement is correct?

    a. Weight always acts vertically downwards towards the centre of the Earth
    b. Lift acts perpendicular to the chord line and must always be greater than weight
    c. Thrust acts parallel to the relative airflow and is always greater than drag
    d. The lift force generated by the wings always acts in the opposite direction to the aircraft's weight

6.   The tailplane or horizontal stabilizer usually provides a downwards load in level flight because:

     a.   the main-plane lift is always positive
     b.   the lift/weight and thrust/drag couples combine to give a nose down pitch
     c.   the lift produced is greater than required at high speed
     d.   this configuration gives less interference

7.   Scientifically speaking, an aircraft's mass is a measure of:

     a.   its weight
     b.   how big it is
     c.   how much matter it contains
     d.   its volume

8.   An aircraft rotates about:

     a.   its wings
     b.   its centre of gravity
     c.   its main undercarriage
     d.   its rudder

9.   In a steady gliding descent, assuming zero thrust from the propeller, the three forces acting on the aeroplane are weight, lift and drag. These three forces are in equilibrium, but:

     a.   weight and lift are the same
     b.   weight is greater than lift
     c.   weight is less than lift
     d.   weight and drag are the same

10.   If an aircraft increases speed while maintaining a constant angle of attack with its wings:

     a.   the lift generated by its wings will remain constant but total drag will increase
     b.   the lift generated by its wings will decrease and total drag will increase
     c.   the lift generated by its wings will increase but total drag will remain constant
     d.   both the lift generated by its wings and total drag will increase

11.   Complete the following sentence to make the most correct statement.

In a steady, unaccelerated climb, the four forces acting on the aeroplane (weight, lift, thrust and drag) are in equilibrium, but:

     a.   lift is greater than weight
     b.   lift is equal to weight
     c.   thrust is equal to aerodynamic drag
     d.   lift is less than weight

12. In this diagram, representing an aircraft in a banked attitude during turning flight, which vector represents total lift?

   Use the diagram to answer the question.

   a.   A
   b.   B
   c.   C
   d.   W

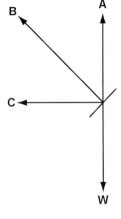

13. Most light aircraft are designed so that, in flight, the centre of pressure is behind the centre of gravity. This means that in order to maintain straight and level flight:

   a.   the tailplane must produce a downwards force
   b.   the tailplane must produce an upwards force
   c.   the tailplane does not need to provide an upwards or a downwards force; it is only used to manoeuvre the aircraft
   d.   the tailplane does not need to produce an upwards or downwards force, the thrust/drag couple balances the forces

14. If the turn coordinator is indicating Rate 1, the aircraft is changing heading at:

   a.   3° per second
   b.   6° per second
   c.   360° per minute
   d.   90° per minute

15. An aircraft performs a steady level turn at 30° Angle of Bank at 80 knots IAS. If the level turn is maintained at the same IAS, but the Angle of Bank is increased to 45°, what will be the effect on the radius and rate of the turn?

   a.   The radius and rate of the turn will be increased
   b.   The radius of the turn will remain unchanged
   c.   The radius of the turn will be smaller, and the rate of the turn will increase.
   d.   For a given radius of turn, the aircraft can have only one airspeed

16. An aircraft's rate of turn is dependent on:

   a.   the angle of bank and power available
   b.   the angle of bank and thrust available
   c.   the true airspeed and angle of bank
   d.   the indicated airspeed and the angle of attack

P.T.O

Question	1	2	3	4	5	6	7	8	9	10	11	12
Answer												

Question	13	14	15	16
Answer				

The answers to these questions can be found at the end of this book.

CHAPTER 10
LIFT AUGMENTATION

LIFT AUGMENTATION.

Take-Off and Landing.

When an aircraft takes off and lands, it is highly desirable that the lift force generated by its wing should be sufficient to support the weight of the aircraft at as low a speed as possible, so that take-off and landing distances will be as short as possible.

This state of affairs could be obtained by fitting a wing whose aerofoil section is thick and highly cambered such as the high-lift aerofoil depicted in *Figure 10.1*. You can see from the graph that this type of aerofoil section produces a higher coefficient of lift, C_L, for any given **angle of attack**.

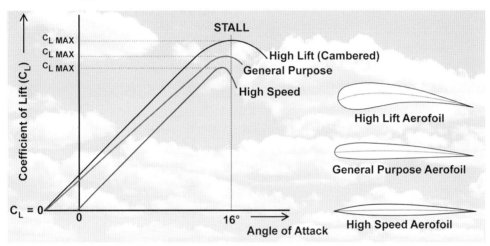

Figure 10.1 $C_{L\ MAX}$ varies according to the type of aerofoil.

As you have learnt, in straight flight, **angle of attack is directly related to airspeed**. For the majority of light aircraft, **16°**, just before the stall, is the angle of attack giving maximum C_L, and that angle is, by definition, achieved at the slowest straight flight speed of which the aircraft is capable.

The speed corresponding to $C_{L\ MAX}$ in straight flight, therefore, is the aircraft's straight flight stalling speed, and the higher the $C_{L\ MAX}$ the slower an aircraft will be able to fly before it stalls.

So a thick, highly-cambered wing would give an aircraft the highest value of lift at the lowest speeds, and provide an aircraft with the shortest take-off and landing run.

The Cruise.

But take-off and landing take up only a small period of time when considering the whole duration of an aircraft's flight. The greater part of flight is spent in the cruise. However, at high cruise speeds, a thickly-cambered wing-section would cause considerable drag and require the aircraft to fly in a pronounced nose down pitch attitude, as depicted in *Figure 10.2 overleaf*.

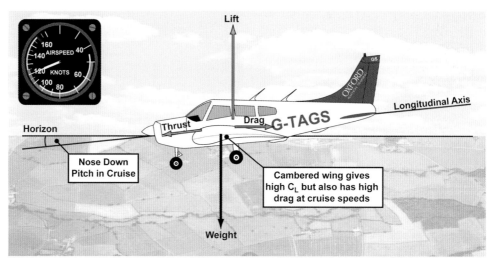

Figure 10.2 A representation of the effect of high-camber wing on the cruise attitude.

It is usual, therefore, for designers to select an aerofoil with a less pronounced camber to optimise the cruise, as in *Figure 10.3*, and then to modify the shape of the aerofoil section by having mechanical, **movable leading and trailing edges**, known collectively as **high-lift devices,** to increase camber and, thus, C_L for any given angle of attack. Using **high-lift devices**, the lift-force generated by an aerofoil can be maintained at the lower speeds of landing and take-off, and so reduce take-off and landing distances. *Figure 10.4* depicts both leading and trailing edge flaps.

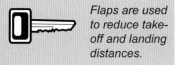

Flaps are used to reduce take-off and landing distances.

Using **high-lift devices**, a pilot may, in effect, convert his wing from a high speed wing to a high lift wing as he wishes.

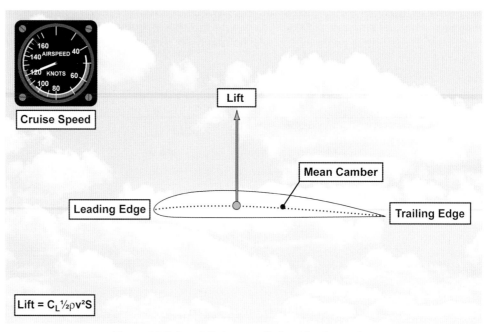

Figure 10.3 Aerofoil shape optimised for the cruise.

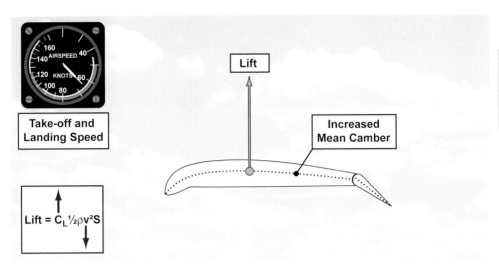

Figure 10.4 High lift devices mechanically alter the camber of an aerofoil to maintain lift at lower speeds.

TRAILING EDGE FLAPS.

The most common of the **high lift devices** used on light aircraft are **trailing edge flaps**. A **flap** is a hinged section of the trailing edge of the wing which can be deflected downwards, and so produce an increase in camber. But as well as increasing C_L through the increase in camber, **trailing edge flaps** will also increase drag.

Figure 10.5 Turning finals with initial flap lowered.

The **flaps** seldom extend the whole length of the trailing edge since the ailerons are also fitted to the extremes of the wing trailing edge. *(See Figure 10.5).*

Operation of the Flaps.

The **flaps** are operated by the pilot in the cockpit. The controlling mechanism can be purely **mechanical** or powered **electrically**, **hydraulically** or **pneumatically**. The **mechanical** system of flap operation provides the pilot with a lever in the cockpit which is connected via rods or cables to the **flaps**.

With **mechanically operated flaps** it is the pilot who provides the force to actuate the system.

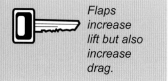

Flaps increase lift but also increase drag.

With a **powered flap system**, the pilot operates a switch in the cockpit in order to deploy the **flaps**. (*See Figure 10.6*).

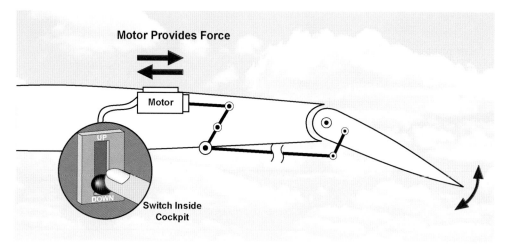

Figure 10.6 Powered operation of the flaps.

Most aircraft have a range of **flap settings** that allow **flap** to be selected in stages. Stages of flap are usually measured in degrees. The Piper PA28 Warrior, allows **flap selection** in stages of 10°, 25° and 40° degrees. Other aircraft may have different settings. The angle of deflection of the **flap** is measured from the chord line of the flap to the chord line of the main aerofoil section, as shown in *Figure 10.7*.

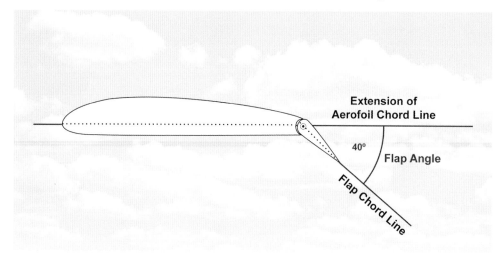

Figure 10.7 Flap angle is measured between the aerofoil and flap chord lines.

Flap Setting Indications.

The pilot needs to have an **indication of the flap setting** selected. *Figure 10.8* shows various arrangements that are commonly in use. There may be markings at the base of the manual flap lever, detents on a switched power system or a gauge indicating flap position

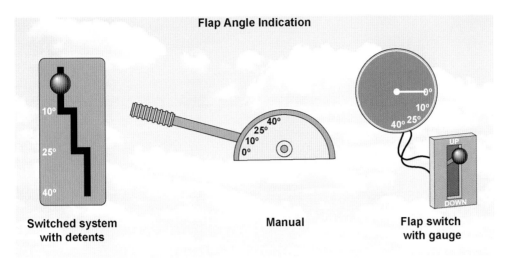

Flap Angle Indication

Switched system with detents **Manual** **Flap switch with gauge**

Figure 10.8 Methods of indicating flap angle.

TYPES OF TRAILING EDGE FLAP.

There are several types of trailing edge flap in use.

The Plain Flap.
The **plain flap**, depicted in *Figure 10.9*, is simple in construction and gives a good increase in C_{LMAX}, but also causes a large increase in **drag**. The **plain flap** is used mainly on low speed aircraft where very short take-off and landing performance is not required.

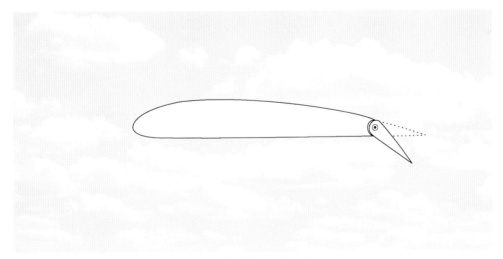

Figure 10.9 The plain flap.

The Split Flap.
The **split flap** forms part of the surface of the lower trailing edge, the upper surface contour being unaffected when the flap is lowered, as can be seen in *Figure 10.10, overleaf*. The **split flap** gives a slightly higher C_{LMAX} than the **plain flap** at higher angles of attack, but drag is also higher since the depth of turbulent air behind the wing is greater, when a **split flap** is deployed.

205

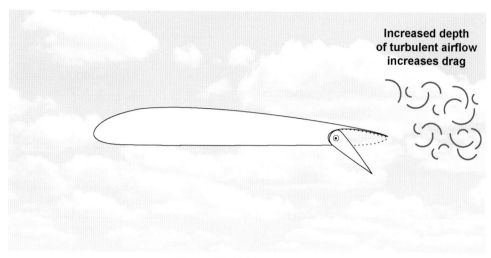

Figure 10.10 The split flap.

The Slotted Flap.

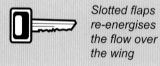

Slotted flaps re-energises the flow over the wing

The **slotted flap** depicted in *Figure 10.11*, is much more complex in construction than either the **plain** or **split flap**. For the same area of **flap**, the **slotted flap** gives a greater increase in C_{LMAX} and produces less drag than both the **plain** and **split flaps**. This is achieved by directing high pressure air from below the wing through the slots formed between the **flap** and the trailing edge. The re-direction of airflow, in this way has the effect of re-energising the **boundary layer** and so **delaying separation**. See *Figure 10.11*.

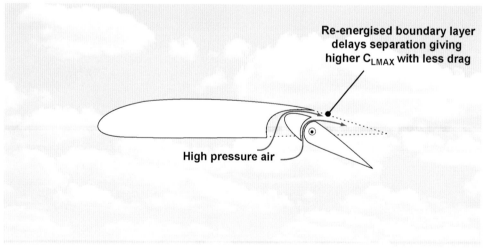

Figure 10.11 The slotted flap.

The Fowler Flap.

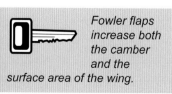

Fowler flaps increase both the camber and the surface area of the wing.

The **Fowler Flap**, depicted in *Figure 10.12*, not only increases camber but also wing area, **S**. You will recall that **S** is a factor in the **lift formula: Lift = C_L ½ ρ v² S**, where **S** is the **surface area of the wing**.

The **Fowler Flap** produces the largest increase in C_{LMAX} of all **flap** types. Because the **Fowler Flap** increases **chord length** as well as wing camber, the **thickness/chord ratio** is reduced, leading to a reduction in **drag**. Larger aircraft usually have slotted **Fowler flaps** which are even more efficient.

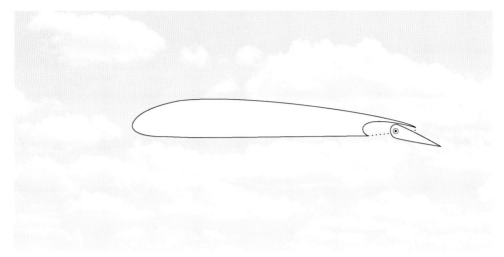

Figure 10.12 The Fowler flap.

COMPARISON OF C_L AND C_{LMAX} FOR DIFFERENT TYPES OF FLAP.

A comparison of the **coefficient of lift, C_L**, and the **coefficient of drag, C_D**, for a basic wing section and for a wing with different types of **flap** deployed, at the same angle of attack, is shown graphically in the right hand graph in *Figure 10.13*.

Compared to the basic wing section, it can be seen that all types of **flap** increase C_L and C_D, at a given angle of attack. Note that the **Fowler Flap** almost doubles C_L, compared to the basic wing section for a modest increase in **drag**.

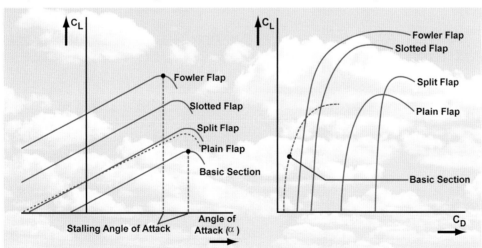

Figure 10.13 Comparison of C_L and C_D for different types of flap.

The Effect of Flap on Stalling Angle of Attack.

Take particular note from the left hand graph in *Figure 10.13*, of what happens to the **stalling angle of attack** for the overall wing when flaps are extended, remembering that C_{LMAX} is reached just before the **stall**. You see that, with flaps extended, the stall occurs at a lower angle of attack than for the basic wing section: the so-called "clean wing".

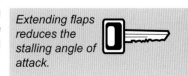

Extending flaps reduces the stalling angle of attack.

Imagine that an aircraft is flying close to the stall with its wing at just below the stalling angle of attack. If flap is now lowered, the mean chord line of the wing will be displaced and the stalling angle of attack will be exceeded. So, to prevent the stall occurring, the angle of attack between the relative airflow and the mean chord line must be reduced, by the pilot selecting a lower nose attitude.

Lowering flaps reduces the **stalling angle of attack** of the wing. As a consequence, when carrying out a stalling exercise from straight and level flight, with flaps extended, the pilot will notice that the aircraft stalls at a lower nose altitude than with the wing clean.

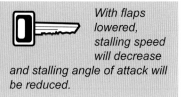

With flaps lowered, stalling speed will decrease and stalling angle of attack will be reduced.

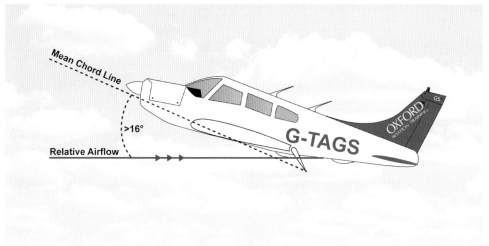

Figure 10.14 When flaps are lowered, the change in the mean chord line changes the angle of attack.

As you will see later, extended flap also reduces the **stalling speed**.

FLAP EXTENSION - EFFECT ON PITCH CHANGE AND NOSE ATTITUDE.

Whatever phase of flight the aircraft is in, whether climbing, descending or in straight and level flight, **at a given speed** the aircraft will always have a more pronounced nose-down attitude with flaps extended than with flaps retracted. *Figure 10.15* depicts an aircraft in straight and level flight with and without flaps extended.

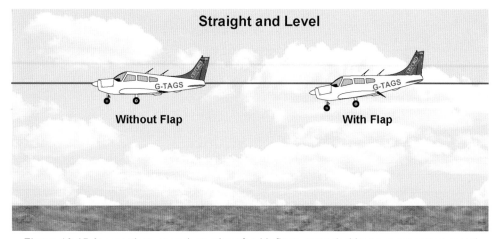

Figure 10.15 At any given speed, an aircraft with flaps extended has a more pronounced nose-down attitude than with flaps raised.

It is possible that the aircraft may adopt a nose-down pitch attitude of its own accord when the pilot extends flaps. This depends on the aircraft type. But whether or not an aircraft initially pitches up or down, on flaps selection, will often depend on whether the aircraft is of a high, low or mid wing design *(see Figure 10.16)*.

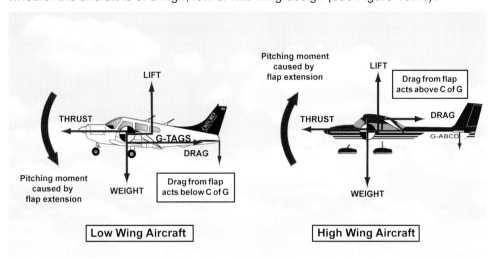

Figure 10.16 The thrust-drag couple either opposes or assists the pitching moment, depending upon the position of the wing.

The **modification of downwash** in the airflow, when **flap** is selected, will also affect an aircraft's reaction, in the pitching plane, to flap selection. Downwash is increased with flaps extended because the airflow will tend to follow the increased camber of the wing's upper surface *(See Figure 10.17)*. The extent to which the increased **downwash** affects the aircraft in the pitching plane will be determined by whether the tailplane or stabilitor is high or low-mounted.

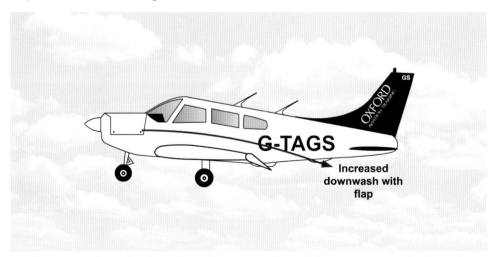

Figure 10.17 Lowering flap will modify downwash and influence an aircraft's trim in the pitching plane.

To sum up, then, the effect of **flap selection** on an aircraft's **longitudinal trim** will differ between aircraft types, depending on the location of the main wing, the position of the tailplane, and the position of the line of action of propeller thrust. All these factors will determine the eventual pitch attitude change of the aircraft when the pilot selects **trailing edge flaps**.

Note that the PA28 Warrior, if trimmed for straight flight, will pitch up when the **flaps** are lowered.

Maximum Lift-Drag Ratio.

As we saw in *Figure 10.13*, the selection of **flaps** increases both **lift** and **drag**, but not in the same proportion. The proportional increase in **drag** is always greater, which means that, **with flaps deployed, the maximum lift/drag ratio is always reduced**, as depicted in *Figure 10.18*.

Lowering flap will always reduce the lift/drag ratio, so glide angle will be steeper and climb angle will be shallower.

As you have learnt, the **lift-drag ratio** is a measure of a wing's **aerodynamic efficiency**, and so, when **flaps** are lowered, the aircraft's **maximum climb angle**, **best glide performance** and **maximum range** are all **reduced**. The greater the angle of flap setting used, the greater will be the reduction in these aspects of aircraft performance.

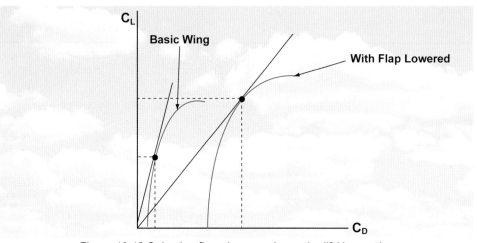

Figure 10.18 Selecting flap always reduces the lift/drag ratio.

Take-Off Flap.

For **take-off**, increasing C_L to its maximum value by selecting a large amount of **flap** would give the lowest minimum flight speed, but **drag** would also be at its maximum which could reduce acceleration to such an extent that the **take-off** distance would be unacceptably long. Consequently, a **smaller flap setting than full flap** is usually used for **take-off**. The Pilot's Operating Handbook, will state the optimum **flap** setting to be used.

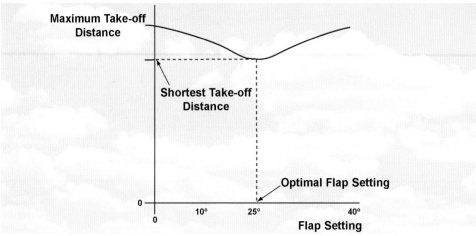

Figure 10.19 Optimum Flap Setting for Take-off.

Figure 10.19 illustrates that, for a representative aircraft, the shortest take-off distance occurs with 25° of flap selected. The take-off distance increases if a lower or greater flap setting is used.

Flap Retraction after Take-Off.

After **take-off** the **flaps** are retracted to improve the climb angle. However, great care must be exercised when raising **flap**. Because of the changes in C_L, **drag** and **pitching moments** which occur on **flap** retraction, the **flaps** should be raised in stages.

Furthermore, to prevent any sudden loss of lift as the **flaps** are retracted, the aircraft must first be accelerated to a safe speed, but not beyond V_{FE} (see overleaf).

The important consideration at this stage of flight is that the aircraft should not be allowed to sink, especially when it is close to the ground.

Landing Flap.

When **landing**, the high drag associated with the use of higher **flap** settings is a benefit to the aircraft. The less favourable **lift - drag ratio** also enables a suitably steep glide path to be flown for the approach, and, after touch-down, the extra drag will help reduce the distance of the landing run. The higher values of C_L produced with flaps lowered will enable the approach to be flown at the lowest possible speeds. The approach speed must remain, however, at least **1.3 times the stalling speed**. During the approach, the **flaps** are lowered in stages to reduce the effects of the changes in **lift**, **drag** and **pitch attitude** on the aircraft.

Figure 10.20 Deployment of landing flap.

Since lift is proportional to the square of the airspeed, as well as directly proportional to C_L, it follows that if **flaps** are selected at too high an airspeed, the large lift force produced could overstress the airframe or flap-operating mechanism. To ensure that neither component is overstressed, **flaps** should not be selected until the aircraft has slowed down to a defined airspeed. This speed is known as V_{FE} which signifies **"Velocity Flaps Extended"**.

Flap should not be selected until the airspeed is within the defined operating range (white arc).

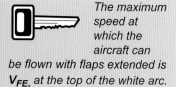

The maximum speed at which the aircraft can be flown with flaps extended is V_{FE}, at the top of the white arc.

The **flaps-extended speed-range** is marked on the **Airspeed Indicator** by a **white arc**, as shown in *Figure 10.21*. The flaps can be safely operated if the aircraft's speed is within this arc. V_{FE} is the airspeed reading at the higher end of the white arc. In *Figure 10.21*, V_{FE} is 104 knots. Bear in mind that not only must the flaps <u>not</u> be lowered until the airspeed has reduced below V_{FE}, but flaps must also be fully retracted <u>before</u> the aircraft accelerates above V_{FE}.

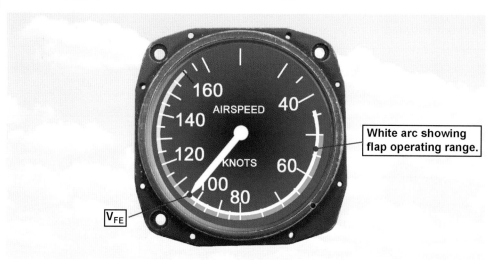

White arc showing flap operating range.

Figure 10.21 The flaps can safely be operated if the aircraft's speed is within the white arc.

Flap Selection for Approach and Landing.

On the approach to land, the pilot gradually slows the aircraft down, progressively selecting more stages of **flap**. Remember that, when selecting **flaps**, it is necessary to pitch the nose of the aircraft down in order to maintain the value of C_L constant by reducing the angle of attack. This action will also improve the pilot's view of the airfield and the runway.

Full **landing flap** is selected only when the pilot is confident of achieving the runway aiming point and has committed himself to land.

LEADING EDGE HIGH-LIFT DEVICES.

There are two types of **leading edge high-lift device**. These are the **slot** and **slat** illustrated in *Figure 10.22*, and the **leading edge flap** shown in *Figure 10.23*.

You should note that the term **slot** is applied to the gap which connects the under-surface and upper-surface of the wing's leading edge. The **slot** can either be fixed, as in the higher of two drawings in *Figure 10.22,* or it can open or close depending on the position of a moveable auxiliary aerofoil known as a **slat**, depicted in the lower drawing at *Figure 10.22*.

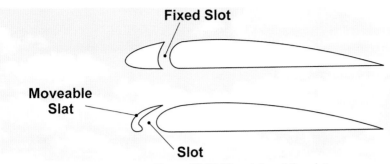

Fixed Slot

Moveable Slat

Slot

Figure 10.22 The slot and the slat.

Leading edge flaps are a complex mechanical flap system, used only on large jet transport aircraft. (*See Figure 10.23*). Those few light aircraft with leading edge high lift devices are more likely to use slots or slats.

Figure 10.23 A typical leading edge flap on a jet transport aircraft.

The main purpose of **leading edge devices** is to delay separation of the airflow from the upper surface of the wing. This **increases the stalling angle of attack** and the corresponding value of C_{LMAX}. (*See Figure 10.24*). Note the difference between **leading edge high-lift devices** and **trailing edge flaps** in this respect. While both devices increase C_{LMAX}, **leading-edge high lift devices** cause the **stalling angle of attack** to **increase, trailing edge flaps cause the** stalling angle of attack **to decrease.**

Leading edge devices increase the stalling angle.

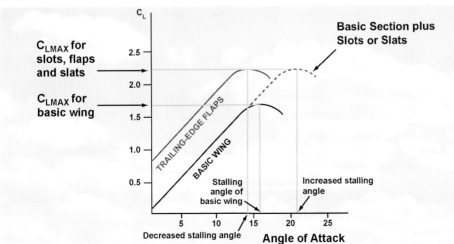

Figure 10.24 Leading edge devices increase the stalling angle of attack whereas trailing edge flaps reduce it.

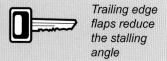

Trailing edge flaps reduce the stalling angle

The Leading Edge Slot.

The **leading edge slot** is a fixed gap between the lower surface and the upper surface of the wing leading edge, stretching from near the wing root to just short of the wing tip.

The **leading edge slot** re-directs high pressure air from below the wing, through the slot, in order to re-energise the boundary layer and so delay separation. *See Figure 10.25.*

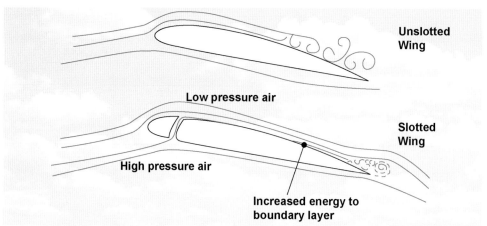

Figure 10.25 The leading edge slot redirects high pressure air from the undersurface of the wing to the upper surface of the wing.

The tailplane is also an aerofoil and may be fitted with slots *See Figure 10.26.*

Figure 10.26 The tailplane is an aerofoil and may be fitted with slots.

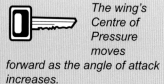

The wing's Centre of Pressure moves forward as the angle of attack increases.

The Principle of Operation of the Leading-Edge Slot.

Consider an un-slotted wing whose angle of attack is increasing towards the stalling angle, as shown in *Figure 10.27.* As the angle of attack increases, the area of lowest pressure on the upper surface of the wing moves forward, and the rate of pressure increase towards the wing's trailing edge increases. Consequently, the boundary-layer is flowing against a continually rising pressure, or **steepening adverse pressure gradient**. (Note that the greater the vertical extent of the pressure distribution envelope on the wing's upper surface, the lower the static pressure)

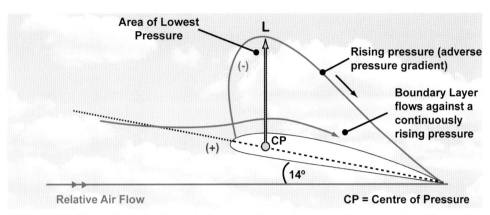

Figure 10.27 At 14° angle of attack the area of lowest pressure has moved well forward.

The further forward the point of lowest pressure the steeper the **adverse pressure gradient** becomes. The airflow in the boundary layer finds it harder and harder to flow against this rising pressure and starts to **separate** from the upper surface. At the point of stall, the large **adverse pressure gradient** has caused the point of separation to move so far forward that there is a marked loss of lift. *(See Figure 10.28).*

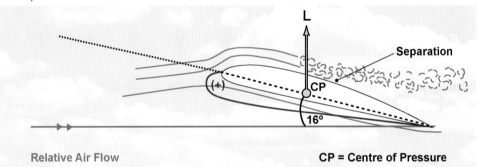

Figure 10.28 At 16°, the stalling angle of attack, the pressure gradient causes the airflow over the upper surface to separate.

But with the **slotted wing**, as depicted in *Figure 10.29*, the **slot** enables the airflow to continue against the **adverse pressure gradient**, at higher angles of attack, without separating, by increasing the energy of the boundary layer. The re-energising of the boundary layer **delays separation** and increases the angle of attack at which the wing stalls.

By re-energising the boundary layer, the slot delays separation and causes the wing to stall at a higher angle of attack.

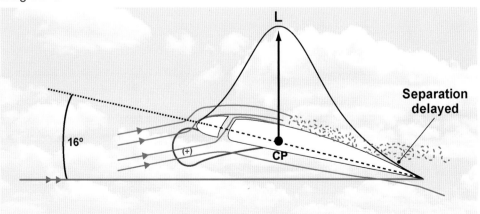

Figure 10.29 The slot re-energises the boundary layer delaying separation and increasing the stalling angle of attack.

The **slot,** of course, will also direct higher pressure air to the upper surface of the wing even at low angles of attack. In this situation, the re-energised airflow thickens the boundary layer causing it to become turbulent (*See Figure 10.30*). This phenomenon increases drag which is not desirable at cruising speed.

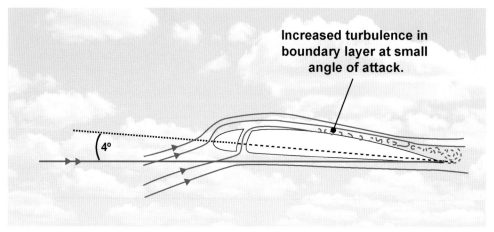

Figure 10.30 At low angles of attack the fixed slot thickens the boundary layer, increasing drag.

The drag problem of the fixed slot can, however, be overcome by making the slot adjustable. This aim is achieved by fitting **slats**.

The Leading-Edge Slat.

A **slat** is a small moveable aerofoil section attached to the leading edge of the wing. When the **slat** deploys by moving away from the leading edge, it forms a **slot**, as depicted in *Figure 10.31.*

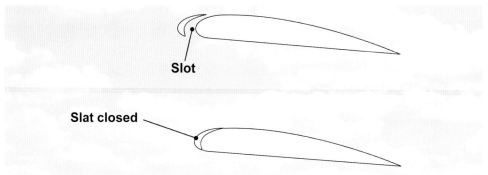

Figure 10.31 Operation of the slat creates an opening which forms a slot.

The **slat** normally operates automatically in response to varying airflow pressures at the leading edge of the wing. At small angles of attack the high pressure at the leading edge holds the **slat** closed, as shown in *Figure 10.32*.

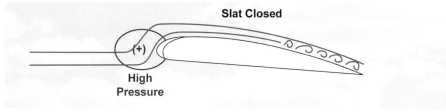

Figure 10.32 High pressure at the leading edge keeps the slat closed at small angles of attack.

216

But as the angle of attack increases, the wing's centre of pressure (CP) moves forward, increasing the pressure differential between the wing's upper and lower surfaces. The resultant aerodynamic force pulls the **slat** open. See *Figure 10.33*.

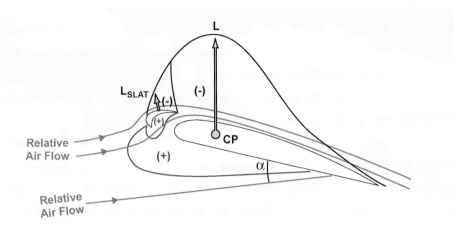

Figure 10.33 At high angles of attack, pressure differential pulls the slat open to create a slot.

In comparison to the pitch change caused by operation of the trailing edge flaps, operation of the **slats** causes only a small change to the pitch attitude of the aircraft. This is because although the **centre of pressure** moves forward to operate the **slats**, it does not move so far forward that the pressure distribution pattern over the wing is modified significantly.

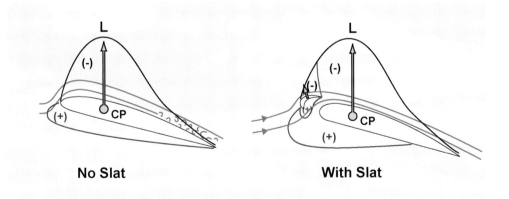

No Slat   **With Slat**

Figure 10.34 When the slat deploys, the change in pitch attitude is small, because the position of the Centre of Pressure alters very little.

Representative PPL - type questions to test your theoretical knowledge of Lift Augmentation.

1.   The leading-edge slot allows flight at higher angles of attack:

      a.   providing an extra lifting surface and hence increase the lift available
      b.   changing the shape and hence the lift characteristics of the wing
      c.   re-energising the airflow over the top of the wing, and delaying separation of the boundary layer
      d.   decreasing lift and hence induced drag

2.   The maximum gliding distance from 6000 feet, in still air, for an aircraft in clean configuration, with a lift/drag ratio of 8:1, is approximately 8 nautical miles. If flaps are deployed:

      a.   the maximum gliding distance will increase
      b.   the maximum gliding distance will be less
      c.   Lift / Drag ratio will be unaffected but will be achieved at a lower airspeed
      d.   the maximum gliding distance will be unaffected

3.   The maximum speed at which the aircraft can be flown with flaps extended is called:

      a. V_{YSE}
      b V_{FE}
      c. V_{NE}
      d. V_{NO}

4.   In which of the following approach scenarios would you normally select full flap?

      a.   When commencing the final approach
      b.   On going around
      c.   When landing into a strong headwind
      d.   In the latter stages of the approach, when satisfied that you can safely touch down in the designated landing area

5.   Which of the following four options describes the consequence of taking off with the manufacturer's recommended take off flap setting selected?

      a.   An increase in the length of the take off run compared to a non-flap take off
      b.   A decrease in the length of the take off run compared to a non-flap take off
      c.   A greater angle of climb
      d.   Easier avoidance of obstacles at the end of a runway

6.   With the flaps lowered, the stalling speed will:

        a.   increase
        b.   decrease
        c.   increase, but occur at a higher angle of attack
        d.   remain the same

7.   When flaps are lowered the stalling angle of attack of the wing:

        a.   remains the same, but C_{LMAX} increases
        b.   increases and C_{LMAX} increases
        c.   decreases, but C_{LMAX} increases
        d.   decreases, but C_{LMAX} remains the same

8.   A pilot lowers the flaps while keeping the airspeed constant. In order to maintain level flight, the nose of the aircraft:

        a.   must be lowered
        b.   must be raised
        c.   must be held at the same attitude but power must be increased
        d.   must be held at the same attitude and power required will be constant

9.   If a landing is to be made without flaps the landing speed will be:

        a.   reduced
        b.   increased
        c.   the same as for a landing with flaps
        d.   the same as for a landing with flaps but with a steeper approach

10.   Lowering the flaps during a landing approach:

        a.   permits approaches at a higher indicated airspeed
        b.   decreases the angle of descent without increasing power
        c.   eliminates floating
        d.   increases the angle of descent without increasing the airspeed

Question	1	2	3	4	5	6	7	8	9	10
Answer										

The answers to these questions can be found at the end of this book.

CHAPTER 11
STABILITY

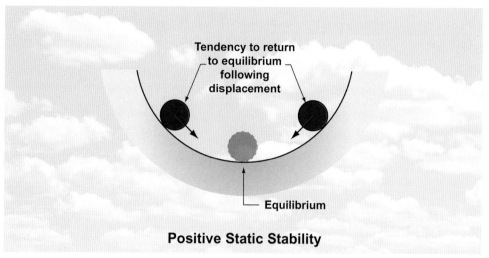

Figure 11.1 Positive Static Stability.

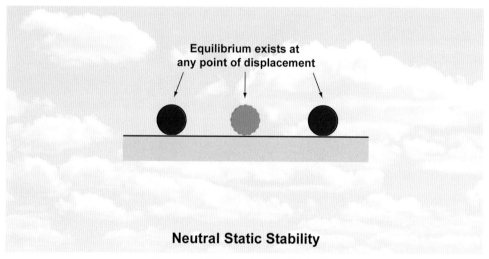

Figure 11.2 Neutral Static Stability.

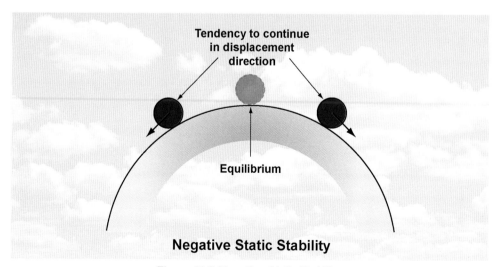

Figure 11.3 Negative Static Stability.

AIRCRAFT STABILITY.

INTRODUCTION.

The dictionary defines **stability** as "firmly fixed"; "established"; "not to be moved"; "not changeable". Applied to an aircraft, the word **stability** means that if the aircraft is flying in a certain direction, at a certain pitch attitude at a certain bank angle, the aircraft will tend to maintain both direction and attitude.

An aircraft which is **stable** will resist any change to its flight path and, if temporarily disturbed from a steady state of flight, will tend to return to its original flight path and attitude without any control input from the pilot. **Stability** is inherent in the aircraft by design and varies, from one aircraft to another, depending on type and role. An aerobatic aircraft, for instance, would normally be less **stable** than an aircraft designed specifically for touring.

A stable aircraft will tend to return to its original flight path and attitude after it has been displaced.

Displacement of an aircraft from its state of steady flight may occur because of pilot input on the controls or a sudden gust of wind. Any force which displaces the aircraft in this way is usually of a temporary nature.

An aircraft possesses two types of **stability**: static and dynamic.

Static and dynamic stability can be positive, neutral or negative, but an aircraft must be statically stable to be dynamically stable.

Static Stability.
Static stability refers to the <u>initial response</u> of an aircraft when disturbed from a given attitude or flight path. **Static stability** can be further subdivided into three different types.

- **Positive static stability**. *(See Figure 11.1).*

- **Neutral static stability**. *(See Figure 11.2).*

- **Negative static stability**. *(See Figure 11.3).*

If an aircraft <u>tends to return</u> to its original state or attitude after it has been displaced, it is said to possess **positive static stability;** put more simply, the aircraft is said to be **stable**. However, if the aircraft tends to remain in the state or attitude that it acquires after a disturbance, it is said to be **neutrally, statically stable**. **Negative static stability** is the tendency for the aircraft, once disturbed, to continue to depart further from its original attitude or flight path. Such an aircraft is said to be **unstable**.

Dynamic Stability.

The word **dynamic** refers to **movement**, and the expression **dynamic stability** refers to the <u>response</u> of an aircraft tending to correct any displacement from its flight path or attitude <u>over a period of time</u>. **Dynamic stability** is subdivided into:

- **Positive dynamic stability**. *(See Figure 11.4a).*

- **Neutral dynamic stability**. *(See Figure 11.4b).*

- **Negative dynamic stability**. *(See Figure 11.4c).*

Let us assume that an aircraft has been disturbed in such a way that its nose pitches up, as depicted in *Figure 11.4*, at Points (a), (b) and (c). In order to return to its original attitude, the aircraft's initial response must be to pitch nose down again. But, of course, as the aircraft attempts to regain its original attitude it is continuing along its flight path.

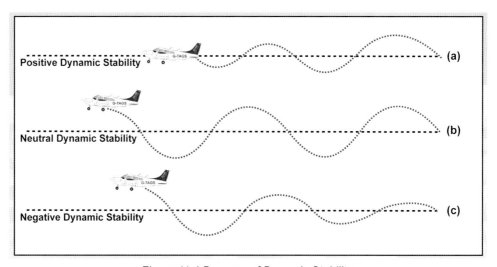

Figure 11.4 Degrees of Dynamic Stability.

If the aircraft possesses **positive dynamic stability** the amplitude of its displacement from its flight path will decrease with passing time *(see Figure 11.4a)* and the aircraft will soon regain its original flight path.

If the aircraft has **neutral dynamic stability** the amplitude of its oscillations about its original flight path remains constant *(see Figure 11.4b)*.

Negative dynamic stability is present when the amplitude of the aircraft's oscillations increases over time, with the aircraft moving further and further away from its original flight path *(see Figure 11.4c.)*.

It should be noted that in all the above situations the aircraft <u>tended</u> to try to regain its original flight path and displayed **positive <u>static</u> stability**, even when it was not **<u>dynamically</u> stable**. An aircraft that has **positive dynamic stability <u>must</u>** possess **positive static stability**.

THE AIRCRAFT'S THREE AXES.

An aircraft has three reference axes about which it rotates in flight, when manoeuvred. They are: the **longitudinal axis**, the **lateral axis** and the **normal axis**. All three axes pass through the **Centre of Gravity (C of G)** of the aircraft as shown in *Figure 11.5*.

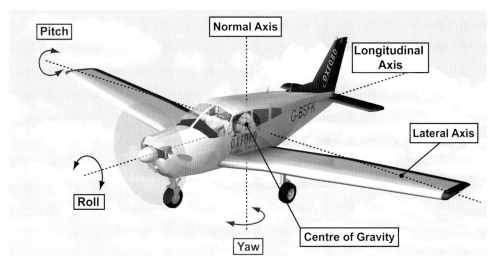

Figure 11.5 The three axes about which an aircraft rotates.

The longitudinal axis runs from nose to tail, passing through the Centre of Gravity.

The **longitudinal axis** runs from nose to tail, passing through the **C of G**. Movement about the **longitudinal axis** is called **roll**. Whenever you consider **stability,** think of the motion about the axis concerned. An aircraft that is **laterally stable,** i.e. stable in roll**, is stable** about its **longitudinal axis.**

The lateral axis runs parallel to a line from wing tip to wing tip and passes through the C of G.

The **lateral axis** runs parallel to a line from wing tip to wing tip and passes through the **C of G**. The aircraft **pitches** about the **lateral axis**. An aircraft which is **stable** in **pitch** is said to be **longitudinally stable**.

The normal axis passes vertically through the C of G at 90° to the longitudinal axis.

The **normal axis** passes vertically through the **C of G** at 90° to the longitudinal axis. Movement about the **normal axis** is called **yaw**. Stability in **yaw** about the **normal axis** is termed **directional stability**.

An aircraft may not be equally **stable** about all three axes. Generally, an aircraft will be designed with pronounced **longitudinal stability**, reduced, but still positive, **directional stability**, and weak to neutral **lateral stability**.

During development and before certification for general use, an aircraft should be able to demonstrate adequate **stability** in order to maintain steady-state flight throughout its speed range, whilst still allowing proper response to the flight controls. In other words, the aircraft must be **stable**, but also **manoeuvrable**. This requirement leads to a "**stability compromise**" whose extent depends on the aircraft's role.

A **very stable** aircraft would offer a large resistance to the pilot's flight-control inputs. This characteristic would reduce an aircraft's **controllability** and **manoeuvrability**, requiring significant physical force from the pilot to move the controls. The opposite situation would prevail if the aircraft were **neutrally stable** or **unstable.** In this case, the aircraft would be very manoeuvrable, and the flight controls very easy to move.

For an aircraft to be **stable**, aerodynamic forces must produce a corrective turning moment to any disturbance which the aircraft may encounter. We will now consider an aircraft's **stability** about each of the three axes.

LONGITUDINAL STABILITY.

Longitudinal stability (in the pitching plane), is **stability about the lateral axis**. An aircraft which is **longitudinally stable** will, following a disturbance in the pitching plane, tend to return to its original pitch attitude.

As you have already learnt, the magnitudes and lines of action of the 4 principal flight forces: **lift**, **weight**, **thrust** and **drag**, are such that, considered on their own, any disturbance of the aircraft from equilibrium would produce an unstable and uncontrollable pitching moment. For this reason, a **tailplane**, or **horizontal stabiliser** is required to generate a balancing moment and give the aircraft **longitudinal stability**.

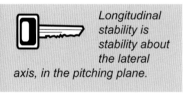

Longitudinal stability is stability about the lateral axis, in the pitching plane.

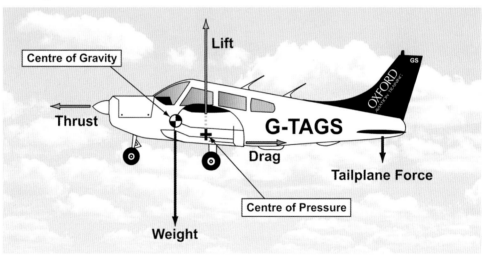

Figure 11.6 The tailplane gives an aircraft longitudinal stability.

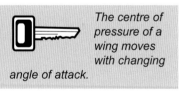

The centre of pressure of a wing moves with changing angle of attack.

A conventional aircraft, then, possesses **positive longitudinal stability** by virtue of its **tailplane**, or **horizontal stabiliser**. Let us now examine **longitudinal stability** a little more closely.

If you think back to what you have learnt about **couples** and **turning moments** and examine *Figure 11.6*, you will see that the degree of **longitudinal stability** that an aircraft possesses depends on, amongst other things, the position of the **Centre of Gravity** (through which the **weight** acts) relative to the position of the **Centre of Pressure** (through which the **lift force** acts)**,** and on the distance of the **tailplane** from the **Centre of Gravity**.

It should be clear that, when considered in isolation, a wing is **dynamically unstable** longitudinally. Look at *Figure 11.7, overleaf*. As the wing begins to pitch up (that is, as angle of attack increases), the **Centre of Pressure** moves forward and the **lift force** increases in magnitude. The wing would have a certain amount of **static stability** if its **Centre of Gravity** were in front of the initial position of the **Centre of Pressure**, but the wing is **highly unstable dynamically** and can not return to **equilibrium** unless a balancing turning moment is applied to it.

Key

L   = Lift
CP   = Centre of Pressure
α   = Angle of Attack

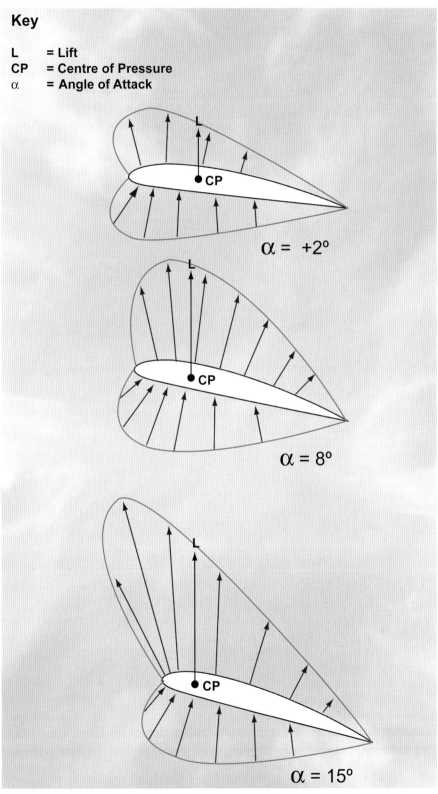

$$\alpha = +2°$$

$$\alpha = 8°$$

$$\alpha = 15°$$

Figure 11.7 Considered in isolation, a wing is dynamically unstable. The Centre of Pressure moves forward as angle of attack increases and the wing cannot return to equilibrium unless a balancing turning moment is applied to it.

The **balancing turning moment,** for an aircraft, is, of course, provided by the **tailplane**, and we are now going to examine how the **tailplane balancing moment** works in flight. If you fell you need to revise the **Principle of Moments** before continuing, refer to Chapter 1, or refer to the appropriate chapter in the **Mass and Balance** section of 'Aeroplanes'.

The **Principle of Moments** states that when a body is in **equilibrium**, or **balance, the sum of the clockwise moments is equal to the sum of the anti-clockwise moments**.

In *Figure 11.8* you can see that although the weights of the two persons are different, the turning moments are equal because of the distance of each person from the pivot. As the turning moments are equal and opposite, the see-saw is in equilibrium.

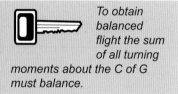

To obtain balanced flight the sum of all turning moments about the C of G must balance.

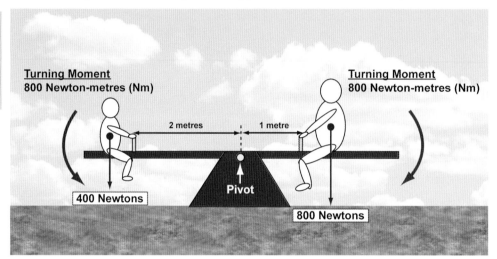

Figure 11.8 Equilibrium is achieved when the anticlockwise moments equal the clockwise moments: (400 × 2)Nm = (800 × 1)Nm.

Now let us consider a wing and tailplane on a conventional aircraft. We depict the wing-tailplane system in *Figure 11.9*; the rest of the aircraft is not shown so that the illustration of the system can be kept as simple as possible.

We have replaced the **Centre of Pressure**, through which the lift force acts, by a point called the **Aerodynamic Centre**. **Lift** from both the wing and the tailplane is shown acting through the **Aerodynamic Centre**. The **Aerodynamic Centre** is defined as the point through which aerodynamic forces act and which remains stationary at 25% of aerofoil chord. The **Aerodynamic Centre** is, for us, simply a convenient concept which prevents our having to think about a moving **Centre of Pressure**.

The **Aerodynamic Centre (AC)** of the wing is depicted at distance x, from the aircraft **Centre of Gravity (C of G)**, and the **AC** of the tailplane is at the greater distance y, from the **C of G**.

The **tailplane** or **horizontal stabilizer** is much smaller than the main wing and, as such, produces a much smaller **lift** force. In the diagrams, the **lift** force produced by the wing is designated, **L**, and the lift from the tailplane L_t. L_t, thought smaller than **L**, is, however, positioned at a greater distance from the aircraft's **C of G** and, so, generates a stabilising moment in pitch.

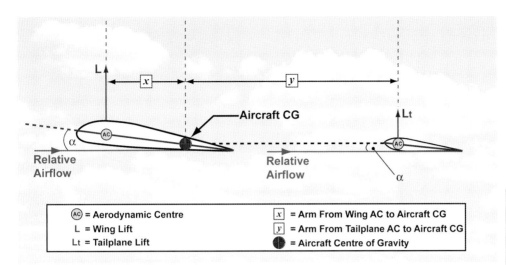

= Aerodynamic Centre $\boxed{x}$ = Arm From Wing AC to Aircraft CG
L = Wing Lift $\boxed{y}$ = Arm From Tailplane AC to Aircraft CG
Lt = Tailplane Lift   = Aircraft Centre of Gravity

Figure 11.9 In level flight the tailplane moment equals the wing moment. $Lx = Lt\,y$

The tailplane or longitudinal stabiliser gives an aircraft longitudinal stability.

In *Figures 11.9 to 11.15,* the aircraft is assumed to be in level, straight flight. The **angle of attack** is α for both **wing** and **tailplane**. The aircraft is in **longitudinal equilibrium** with the wing moment, $\mathbf{L} \times \boldsymbol{x}$, equal and opposite to the tailplane moment $\mathbf{L_t} \times \boldsymbol{y}$, so that the two moments balance.

We will now assume that the **wing** and the **tailplane** experience the same momentary gust. (*See Figure 11.10*). Exposure to this gust causes the **angle of attack,** and hence the **lift**, to increase at both wing and tailplane. The increase in **angle of attack**, in both cases, is taken to be $\Delta\alpha$.

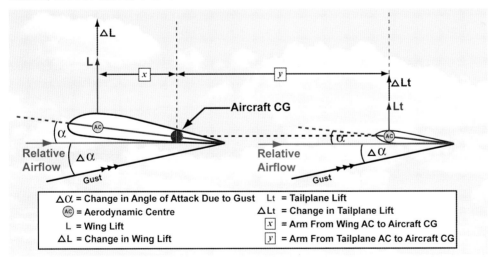

$\Delta\alpha$ = Change in Angle of Attack Due to Gust   Lt = Tailplane Lift
= Aerodynamic Centre ΔLt = Change in Tailplane Lift
L = Wing Lift $\boxed{x}$ = Arm From Wing AC to Aircraft CG
ΔL = Change in Wing Lift $\boxed{y}$ = Arm From Tailplane AC to Aircraft CG

Figure 11.10 The tailplane moment is now greater than the wing moment.

The increase in wing lift $\Delta\mathbf{L}$, will be greater than the increase in tail lift, $\Delta\mathbf{L_t}$, and the aircraft will, therefore, tend to pitch nose-up.

But the stronger **tailplane moment** will rotate the aircraft in the nose-down sense, counterbalancing the nose-up pitching moment caused by the gust. The aircraft will, thus, have demonstrated **positive longitudinal stability**.

In general, then, we may say that an aircraft's **longitudinal stability** depends on the **moments** produced about the **C of G** of the aircraft, as a result of the aerodynamic forces produced at the wing and tailplane, indicated by **L** and **L$_t$** in *Figure 11.10*, and the distance from the **C of G** at which each force acts, indicated by x and y.

The Effects of Centre of Gravity Moment on Longitudinal Stability.

The **C of G** of an aircraft is not fixed but varies according to such changing values as the **weight (or mass)** of the pilot, passengers, baggage and fuel load. It is, of course, not only their **weight** but also their **position** and **distribution** within the aircraft which will affect the **C of G** position. Remember that the **C of G** is the point through which acts the resultant of all the separate weight forces which make up the total weight of the aircraft.

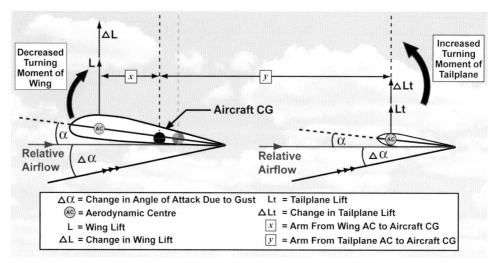

Figure 11.11 Forward movement of the C of G increases static longitudinal stability.

Now consider *Figure 11.11* which depicts the aircraft's **C of G** as having moved forward. This has the effect of reducing the main wing lever arm x, and increasing the tailplane lever arm y. With a forward **C of G**, then, for the same gust and change in angle of attack as before, the **correcting moment from the tailplane** will be even more effective. **Thus, when the C of G moves forward, an aircraft's longitudinal stability increases.**

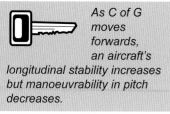

As C of G moves forwards, an aircraft's longitudinal stability increases but manoeuvrability in pitch decreases.

Since increased stability reduces manoeuvrability and increases the force required by the pilot to move the controls, a point must be reached where the forward position of the **C of G** will increase **longitudinal stability** to such an extent that the aircraft may not have enough elevator authority to control the aircraft in pitch. If this were the case, the requirements for certification of the aircraft may no longer be able to be met.

A **limit** will, therefore, be set for the **forward position** of the **C of G**. This **limit** will ensure the minimum requirement for aircraft manoeuvrability, and allow for proper response to the flight controls.

By the same process of reasoning, we may deduce that if the **C of G** is moved **aft**, **longitudinal stability** will **reduce** because the lever arm, y, will decrease in length and the tailplane will decrease in effectiveness.

Consequently, with the **C of G** near its **aft limit**, an aircraft is **less stable longitudinally**. With the **C of G** in this position, an aircraft will be very sensitive in pitch. The pilot would find that even a small displacement of the elevator would cause large pitching movements.

As the **C of G** moves further and further aft it reaches a position where the **turning moment** of the tailplane only just balances the **turning moment** of the **wing**. With the **C of G** in this position, called the **neutral point**, the aircraft would have **neutral static longitudinal stability**. If this were the case, and if any displacement in pitch occurred, the correcting moment of the tailplane would not be great enough to return the aircraft to its original pitch attitude. Because both the wing and tailplane moments would now be equal, the aircraft would remain in its new pitch attitude.

We see, then, that as **stability decreases longitudinally, manoeuvrability increases**, requiring reduced forces from the pilot to move the elevator. Advanced fighter aircraft often display this degree of **manoeuvrability**, with digitally-controlled systems to keep the aircraft stable during straight flight.

With a C of G near the aft limit, an aircraft is less stable longitudinally and, thus, sensitive in pitch.

Centre of Gravity Limits.

If the **C of G** is moved even **further aft than the neutral point**, as depicted in *Figure 11.12*, the aircraft would become **longitudinally unstable**. For this reason an **aft C of G limit**, <u>forward of the neutral point</u>, is established and specified by the aircraft designer, in order to ensure **acceptable positive stability**, and adequate **controllability** and **manoeuvrability**.

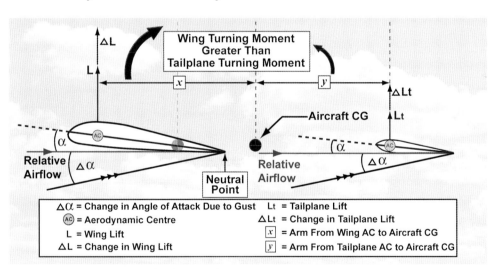

Figure 11.12 With the C of G further aft than the neutral point, the aircraft is longitudinally unstable.

Obviously, then, there will be a **defined range of C of G positions**, between the prescribed **forward and aft C of G limits**, for every aircraft (*See Figure 11.13.*). The **C of G** must lie at a point within this range at <u>all</u> stages of flight. The Pilot-in-Command has a legal responsibility to confirm that the **C of G** position lies **within limits** before every flight.

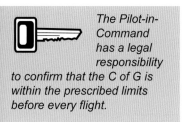

The Pilot-in-Command has a legal responsibility to confirm that the C of G is within the prescribed limits before every flight.

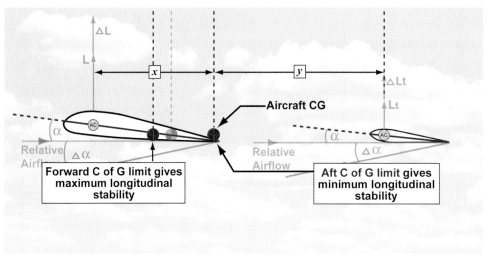

Figure 11.13 The C of G must lie within limits during all stages of flight.

The Effects of Downwash on Longitudinal Stability.

In the take-off and landing configuration longitudinal stability can be reduced due to downwash.

So far in our examination of longitudinal stability, we have assumed that a gust affecting the aircraft in the pitching plane modifies the angle of attack of the wing and the tailplane to the same extent. But any increase in downwash at the wing caused by, say, the lowering of flap or ground effect, will affect the tailplane angle of attack more than the wing angle of attack. As downwash reduces the effective angle of attack (See Chapter 5), the angle of attack at the tail plane is reduced more than the wing angle of attack *(see Figure 11.14)*. This in turn reduces the **tailplane turning moment** opposing the wing turning moment. **Therefore, increased downwash reduces the longitudinal stability of an aircraft.**

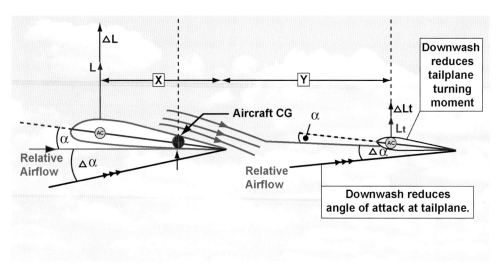

Figure 11.14 Increased downwash reduces longitudinal stability.

LATERAL STABILITY.

Lateral stability is **stability in roll**, **about the longitudinal axis**, which runs from nose to tail through the aircraft's **C of G**, as depicted in *Figure 11.15*.

Figure 11.15 Lateral Stability is stability in roll about the longitudinal axis.

In this section, we will firstly examine **lateral stability** on its own, then we will consider how **lateral stability** and **directional stability** are inter-related.

If an aircraft is displaced in roll and tends to return to its original attitude without pilot input, the aircraft is said to possess **positive lateral stability.**

If an aircraft remains in its displaced position, after being disturbed in **roll**, it has **neutral lateral stability**.

If an aircraft has **negative lateral stability,** it will tend to continue to roll following the initial displacement.

Most light aircraft are designed to be stable in **roll** but not so stable as to cause handling difficulties for the pilot, particularly when manoeuvring close to the ground in gusty crosswinds. As a general rule, good handling qualities are obtained with approximately **neutral lateral static stability**. But most aircraft, if a bank angle is selected but not positively held, will eventually roll into a steeper banked attitude, leading to a spiral dive. This, of course, demonstrates **negative dynamic lateral stability**.

The principal component of the aircraft which contributes to **lateral stability** is the wing. Other components do have an effect but are minor by comparison. To understand how the **lateral stabilising forces** are produced by the wing, we need to look at the changes to the airflow around the wing as the aircraft is displaced in **roll**.

When the aircraft **rolls**, the total lift force is inclined, as depicted in *Figure 11.16*. At any given angle of bank, we see, then, that **lift** no longer directly opposes **weight**. The **resultant** of **weight** and **lift** is a sideways force acting in the direction of the lower wing. The **resultant force**, therefore, causes a **sideslip** which generates a sideways **component** to the **relative airflow** in opposition to the direction of the **sideslip**.

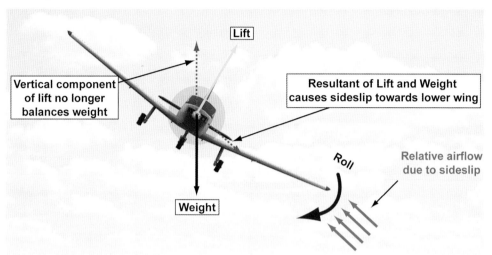

Figure 11.16 With an angle of bank selected, the aircraft will slip towards the lower wing.

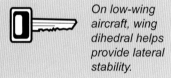

On low-wing aircraft, wing dihedral helps provide lateral stability.

While the **roll** is still taking place, the sideways component to the relative airflow will meet the down-going wing at a slightly greater angle of attack than the up-going wing. This action generates more lift on the down-going wing and tends to counter the **rolling** movement.

Note, however, that a straight wing displays this stability effect, <u>only</u> when the aircraft is rolling. A straight wing, then, does not contribute greatly to **lateral stability** once the side slip is established.

Wing Dihedral.

Greater and longer lasting stabilising moments can be produced if the plane of each wing is angled positively, above a horizontal datum parallel to the lateral axis, as in *Figure 11.17*. This is called **wing dihedral**. The greater the **dihedral**, the greater will be the **lateral stability**.

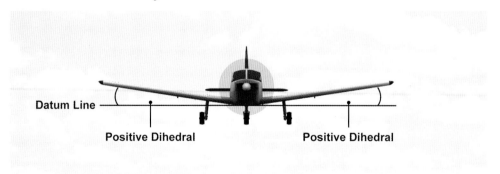

Figure 11.17 Wing dihedral.

In order to examine how dihedral makes an aircraft move stable laterally, let us consider the wing on its own, as depicted in *Figure 11.18*.

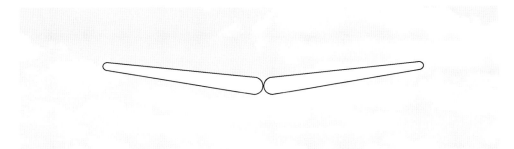

Figure 11.18 A schematic drawing of wing dihedral.

How Wing Dihedral Contributes to Lateral Stability.

When a wing displaying positive **dihedral** is established in a sideslip, the sideways component of the **relative airflow** will meet the lower wing at a greater angle of attack than the upper wing *(see Figure 11.19)*.

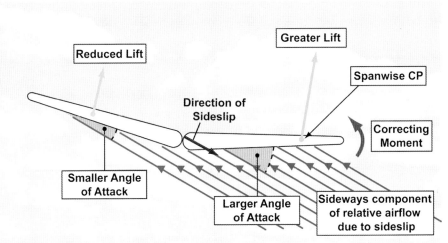

Figure 11.19 With dihedral the lower wing generates more lift in a sideslip.

This fact has two principal consequences, both of which will cause the lower wing to generate greater lift than the upper wing, and so tend to return the aircraft to the wings-level attitude.

- The greater angle of attack at the lower wing **increases** that wing's C_L, and therefore its **lift** force, compared to the **lift** produced by the upper wing.

- The **wing tip** of the **lower wing** effectively becomes **a leading edge**. Consequently, the spanwise **Centre of Pressure (CP)** will now be nearer to the wing tip of the lower wing, causing the lower wing to generate more lift.

Furthermore, depending on the position of the wing in relation to the fuselage, the upper wing will be shielded to some extent from the sideways component of the **relative airflow**. This fact will reduce the lift force on the upper wing, and add further to the aircraft's **lateral stability**.

The Effect of Wing Position on Lateral Stability.

Low-Wing Aircraft.
Certain characteristics of **low-wing** aircraft tend to reduce **lateral stability**.

Because of the position of the low-wing in relation to the fuselage, the sideways component of the **relative airflow** caused by the sideslip flows down around the fuselage at this junction with the lower wing, decreasing its angle of attack, and flows up towards the higher wing increasing its angle of attack, as depicted in *Figure 11.20*.

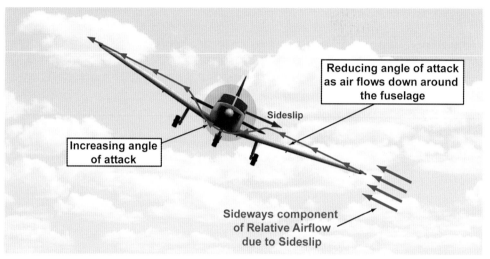

Figure 11.20 Low wing aircraft posess characteristics which reduce lateral stability.

This characteristic of the airflow increases lift on the higher wing and decreases lift on the lower wing.

This phenomenon reduces **lateral stability**. However, other characteristics of low-wing aircraft <u>add</u> to **lateral stability**, even when there is no wing dihedral.

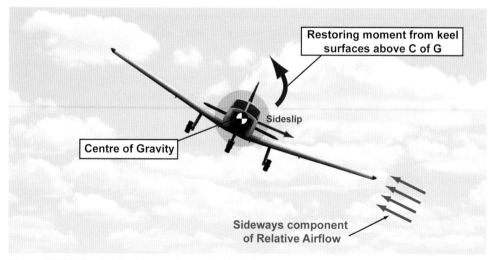

Figure 11.21 The keel surfaces above the C of G set up a restoring moment, adding to lateral stability.

Any **keel surface** (side surface) above the **Centre of Gravity (C of G)**, such as the **fuselage sides** or **fin**, will, during a side slip, set up forces creating a **restoring moment** which will tend to return the aircraft to the wings-level attitude. *(See Figure 11.21)*

Most **low-wing aircraft** possess pronounced **dihedral** to give them **lateral stability.** The **Piper PA28 Warrior** pictured in *Figure 11.22* has a wing of marked **positive dihedral**.

Figure 11.22 Positive dihedral on the Piper PA28 Warrior.

High-Wing Aircraft.
High-wing aircraft have such a degree of **inherent lateral stability** that their **wing dihedral** angle is normally very small. You can see the difference between the dihedral on a high-wing **Cessna 172** and the low wing **Piper PA 28** in *Figure 11.23*.

Figure 11.23 The difference in dihedral between low and high wing aircraft.

With a high-wing aircraft, during a sideslip, the sideways component of the **relative airflow** flows up around the fuselage on the lower wing, increasing its angle of attack and, thus, its lift, and flows down towards the higher wing decreasing its angle of attack and lift. This phenomenon contributes towards **positive lateral stability** *(See Figure 11.24)*.

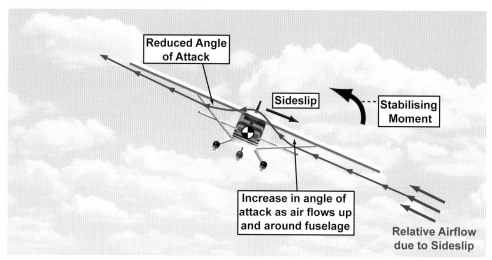

Figure 11.24 Lateral Stability characteristics of a high wing. Relative airflow in a sideslip.

The fuselage and side (or keel) surfaces above the **C of G** also exert a **stabilising** effect.

In addition, high wing aircraft produce a stabilising moment, contributing to their **lateral stability**, as a result of the pendulum effect, as depicted in *Figure 11.25*.

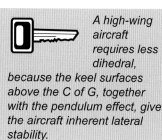

A high-wing aircraft requires less dihedral, because the keel surfaces above the C of G, together with the pendulum effect, give the aircraft inherent lateral stability.

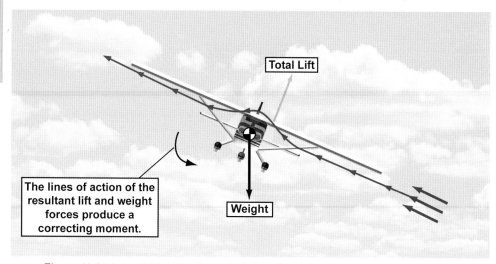

Figure 11.25 Lateral Stability characteristics of a high-wing: the Pendulum Effect.

Swept Back Wings.

The study of high speed flight is not a requirement for the Private Pilot's Licence. However, you should know that **sweepback** also contributes to **positive lateral stability**, because, during a sideslip, the lower wing effectively presents a greater span, and, thus, a greater aspect ratio to the **relative airflow**. The lower wing will therefore generate more lift giving rise to a restoring moment which tends to return the aircraft to the wings-level attitude. *(See Figure 11.26.)*

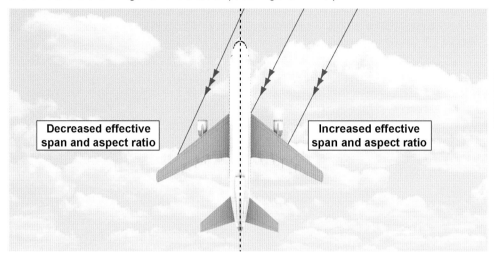

Figure 11.26 Lateral Stability characteristics of a swept-back wing.

Lateral stability is reinforced by sweep-back.

Anhedral.

Jet aircraft with a wing of pronounced sweep-back may actually posses too much **positive lateral stability**. Such aircraft may, consequently have a wing with **anhedral**. **Anhedral** is negative dihedral and reduces **lateral stability.** *(See Figure 11.27).*

Figure 11.27 Anhedral reduces lateral stability.

The Effect of Flaps and Power on Lateral Stability.

You will recall that **flaps** reduce **longitudinal stability** because of their influence on **downwash**. **Lateral stability** is also reduced when **partial span flaps** are deployed.

The deployment of **partial-span flaps** causes the lift on the inboard section of the wing to increase relative to the wing's outer section, as depicted in *Figure 11.28*. This phenomenon, which moves the spanwise **centre of pressure** inboard, reduces the spanwise **moment arm**. Consequently, during a sideslip, any modification of the lift force occurs closer inboard, reducing the correcting moment. The overall effect of deploying **flap**, then, is to **reduce lateral stability**.

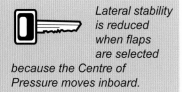

The propeller **slipstream**, at high engine power settings and low aircraft forward speed, also reduces **lateral stability** as the inboard wing sections become more effective than the outer sections in generating lift force because of the energising effect of the slipstream. At low forward speed, of course, the ailerons are less effective.

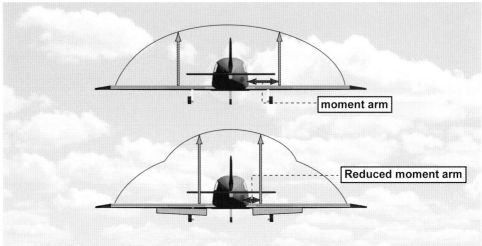

Figure 11.28 The point through which the lift force acts moves inboard with flaps extended.

The reduction in the **lateral stability** is most critical when the effects of **flap, propeller slipstream and low forward speed** are combined. The reduction in **lateral stability** would be conveyed to the pilot as a reduction in the control force required to manoeuvre the aircraft in roll.

Figure 11.29 High power settings at low forward speed reduce lateral stability.

240

DIRECTIONAL STABILITY.

Introduction.
Directional stability is stability about the vertical, or **normal, axis.** Movement about this **axis** is called **yaw,** so **vertical stability** may also be defined as **stability in the yawing plane.** The **tail fin** or **vertical stabiliser** is the surface which contributes most to **directional stability.** *See Figure 11.30.*

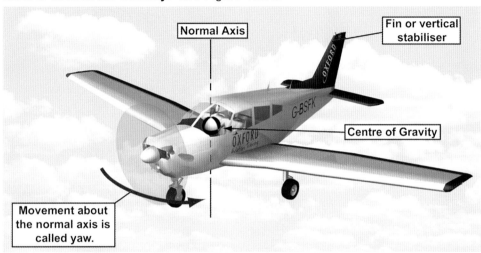

Figure 11.30 Directional stability is stability about the normal axis, in the yawing plane.

An aircraft possesses **positive directional stability** if it tends to recover from a disturbance in the **yawing plane** without any control input from the pilot. Most light aircraft have pronounced **directional stability**, their nose **weathercocking** readily into the **relative airflow**.

Weathercocking is a term which likens the directional stability of an aircraft to the mode of operation of **weathercocks** on church steeples. A **weathercock** swings into the wind because the greater part of its side (keel) surfaces are behind its point of rotation. An aircraft rotates about its **centre of gravity**; therefore, as the greater area of its **keel** surface is behind the **centre of gravity**, the aircraft is **directionally stable**.

The Tail Fin or Vertical Stabiliser.
The **tail fin** is a **symmetrical aerofoil.** Therefore, with a **relative airflow** from straight ahead, the **fin** will be at **0°** angle of attack, as shown in *Figure 11.31*, and no aerodynamic force, except drag, will be produced by the **fin**.

But if the aircraft is disturbed in the **yawing plane,** the angle of attack at the **fin** increases, creating an aerodynamic force opposing the **yaw,** thus providing a **correcting turning moment** about the aircraft's **Centre of Gravity (C of G).** The nose of the aircraft will, therefore, swing back to face the **relative airflow**, and the aircraft will have displayed **positive directional stability**. (See *Figure 11.32*).

Note that when an aircraft is disturbed in the **yawing plane**, it is moving **crabwise** through the air, with the **relative airflow** striking its keel surfaces at an oblique angle. This movement is referred to as **slip** or **skid**. In this flight condition, the **weathercocking** effect will also cause the aircraft to tend to swing back to face the relative airflow.

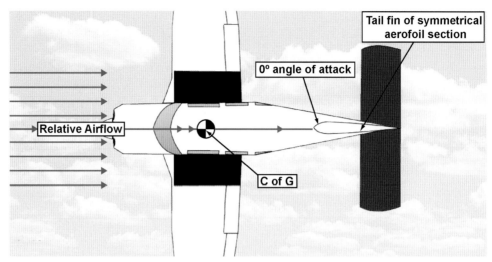

Figure 11.31 The tail fin is a symmetrical aerofoil, exerting no aerodynamic force when the aircraft faces the relative airflow.

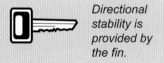

Directional stability is provided by the fin.

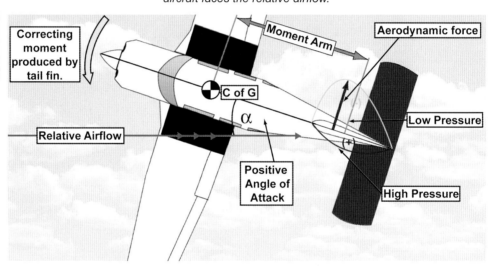

Figure 11.32 The tail fin provides directional stability when the aircraft is disturbed in the yawing plane.

The Effectiveness of the Tail Fin.

The **correcting turning moment** produced by the **tail fin** which gives an aircraft **directional stability** depends on three factors. They are:

• The angle of attack caused by the disturbance in the **yawing plane**.

• The side-surface or area of the **fin,** and efficiency of the **fin's** aerofoil section.

• The length of the **moment arm** between the **fin** and the **C of G.**

A small **fin** at the end of a long fuselage may be just as efficient in giving an aircraft **directional stability** as a large **fin** at the end of a short fuselage.

You may have seen aircraft with more than one **fin**, as depicted in *Figure 11.33*. This feature indicates that the aircraft requires a greater **fin** surface area than a single **fin** can provided.

Figure 11.33 An aeroplane with two tail fins.

The **stabilising action** of the **tail fin** can be supplemented by the use of **dorsal** and **ventral fins**, as illustrated in *Figure 11.34*, **Dorsal** and **ventral fins** are small aerofoil sections positioned above and below the fuselage, respectively, and are used to increase the keel area aft of the aircraft's **C of G**.

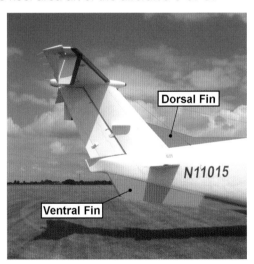

Figure 11.34 Dorsal and Ventral fins.

THE INTERRELATIONSHIP BETWEEN LATERAL AND DIRECTIONAL STABILITY.

Having considered **lateral** and **directional stability** separately, we now need to examine why an aircraft's **lateral** and **directional** rotation about its **C of G** are not independent of each other. There is an important interrelationship between an aircraft's displacement in the **rolling plane** and its displacement in the **yawing plane**. **A displacement in the yawing plane will always influence an aircraft's motion in the rolling plane, and *vice versa*.**

Movements in the rolling and yawing plans are interrelated.

Initial Roll Followed by Yaw.

If a pilot selects an **angle of bank** with ailerons alone, without making any further control movements, the aircraft responds initially by **rolling** about its **longitudinal axis**. The displacement of the ailerons which induces the roll generates increased lift on the up-going wing, while the lift on the down-going wing decreases. As you have learnt in the early chapters of this book, an increase in lift is always accompanied by an increase in drag. Therefore, the up-going wing will be held back relative to the down-going wing, causing the aircraft to **yaw** towards the upper wing. This initial yaw following a roll induced by ailerons alone is, as you will recall, called adverse yaw.

The initial **roll**, therefore, has led to **yaw**. If there is no further control input from the pilot, subsequent developments will be as follows.

An initial roll will be followed by a sideslip towards the lower wing and then yaw in the same direction as roll.

- The aircraft will **slip** towards the lower wing, and the side component of the **relative airflow** will, consequently, strike the aircraft's keel surfaces. In a conventional aircraft, the keel surfaces behind the **centre of gravity (C of G)** are of a greater area than the area of the keel surfaces forward of the **C of G**, and, therefore, because of the **sideslip**, the aircraft will now **yaw** in the direction of the lower wing.

- The **yaw** towards the lower wing naturally causes the higher wing to move forwards while the lower wing moves rearwards. The velocity of the airflow over the higher wing will, thus, be greater than that over the lower wing, further increasing the lift differential between the two wings (**Lift = C$_L$ ½ ρ v² S**) so as to reinforce the **rolling movement**.

- More **roll** will induce more **yaw** which will reinforce the **roll**, and so on.

Thus, the original **roll** first caused yaw against the direction of roll followed by **yaw** in the direction of **roll.** The yaw in the direction of roll **mutually reinforced each other** and, if not halted, by the pilot's intervention, lead to the aircraft entering a **spiral dive**. *(See Figure 11.35)*

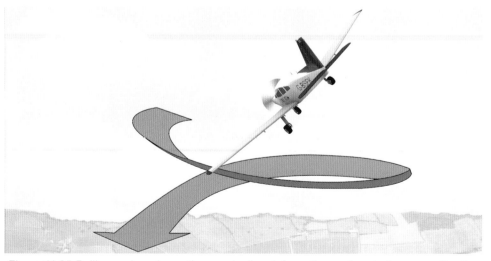

Figure 11.35 Rolling and yawing actions mutually reinforce themselves in the same direction and lead to a spiral dive.

We see, then, that a movement about the longitudinal axis always affects an aircraft's motion about the normal axis. An initial **roll** will, thus, be followed by **yaw**, unless the pilot intervenes by making an appropriate control movement.

An aircraft's degree of **directional stability** compared to its level of **lateral stability** will influence the extent to which a **rolling movement** will induce a **yawing movement**. If the aircraft is very **stable directionally** (as most light aircraft are), with a large **fin** (vertical stabiliser) and **rudder** surface, the tendency for the aircraft to **yaw** in the direction of **slip** will be very marked.

Initial Yaw Followed by Roll.

If the aircraft is displaced in the **yawing plane** (that is, directionally, about its **normal axis**), one wing will move forward relative to the other. Unless the pilot intervenes, the forward moving wing will generate a greater lift force than the rearwards moving wing. The main reason for this is that, during the initial **yaw**, the velocity of the airflow over the forward-moving wing will be greater than that over the rearwards-moving wing, thus increasing lift, (**Lift = C$_L$ ½ ρ v^2 S**).

An initial yaw will be followed by roll in the same direction as yaw.

Consequently, the aircraft will begin to **roll in the direction of yaw**. The **roll** will induce more **yaw**, which in turn will cause more roll, and so on. Again, unless the pilot intervenes, a spiral dive will ensue. An initial yaw, then, will be followed by roll in the same direction as yaw.

The Stability Characteristics of Light Aircraft.

We see, then, that the lateral and directional stability characteristics of an aircraft are inextricable linked to each other.

Light aircraft, generally, posses strong **directional stability**, while having a degree of **lateral stability** that is not much greater than neutral. Paradoxically, therefore, being much **more stable directionally than laterally**, a light aircraft will have a marked tendency to **yaw** into the **sideslip**, causing further **roll**, but have a less marked tendency to correct the **roll**. This sequence of events will, as we have seen, lead to a **spiral dive** if the pilot does not intervene. Thus, **high directional stability** and **weak lateral stability** lead to **spiral divergence**.

A light aircraft is usually more stable directionally than laterally.

However, if **lateral stability** were to be high compared to **directional stability**, the aircraft would display a strong tendency to right itself following a disturbance in the **rolling plane**, while not showing any strong tendency to turn into the direction of any **sideslip**. Such an aircraft may even tend to **yaw** away from the **roll**. An aircraft with these stability characteristics, therefore, may be prone to an oscillatory motion in both the **rolling** and **yawing planes**, known as **dutch roll**.

As we have learnt, the **stability** characteristics of light aircraft are such that **dutch roll** is not a marked feature.

Representative PPL - type questions to test your theoretical knowledge of Stability.

1.   With a forward Centre of Gravity, an aircraft will have:

a.   reduced longitudinal stability
b.   lighter forces for control movements
c.   decreased elevator effectiveness when flaring
d.   shorter take off distances

2.   An aft Centre of Gravity will give:

a.   increased longitudinal stability
b.   heavy forces for control movements
c.   increased elevator effectiveness when flaring
d.   longer take off distances

3.   An aircraft is disturbed from its flight path by a gust of wind. If, over a short period of time, it tends to return to its original flight path without pilot intervention, the aircraft is said to possess:

a.   instability
b.   negative dynamic stability
c.   neutral dynamic stability
d.   positive dynamic stability

4.   An aircraft is disturbed from its flight path by a gust of wind. The aircraft is neutrally stable if, with no intervention from the pilot, it tends to:

a.   return to its original path without further deviation from its original flight path
b.   return to its original path following further deviation from its original flight path
c.   maintain the new flight path
d.   continue to deviate from its original flight path

5.   Complete the following sentence in order to give the most satisfactory definition of stability. An aeroplane which is inherently stable will:

a.   require less effort to control
b.   be difficult to stall
c.   not spin
d.   have a built-in tendency to return to its original state following the removal of any disturbing force

6.   After a disturbance in pitch, an aircraft oscillates in pitch with increasing amplitude. It is:

a.   statically and dynamically unstable
b.   statically stable but dynamically unstable
c.   statically unstable but dynamically stable
d.   statically and dynamically stable

7.   Longitudinal stability is provided by:

        a.   the fin
        b.   the wing dihedral
        c.   the tailplane
        d.   the ailerons

8.   An aircraft wing is constructed with dihedral in order to give:

        a.   lateral stability about the longitudinal axis
        b.   longitudinal stability about the lateral axis
        c.   lateral stability about the normal axis
        d.   directional stability about the normal axis

9.   If the wing Centre of Pressure is forward of the C of G:

        a.   changes in lift produce a wing pitching moment which acts to reduce the change of lift
        b.   changes in lift produce a wing pitching moment which acts to increase the change of lift
        c.   changes in lift give no change in wing pitching moment
        d.   when the aircraft sideslips, the C of G causes the nose to turn into the sideslip thus applying a restoring moment

10.   When the C of G is close to the forward limit:

        a.   small forces are required on the control column to manoeuvre the aircraft in pitch
        b.   longitudinal stability is reduced
        c.   high stick forces are required to manoeuvre the aircraft in pitch because the aircraft is very stable
        d.   stick forces are the same as for an aft C of G

11.   If a disturbing force causes an aircraft to roll and slip towards its lower wing:

        a.   wing dihedral will cause a rolling moment which tends to correct the sideslip
        b.   the fin will cause a yawing moment which reduces the sideslip
        c.   wing dihedral will cause a yawing moment which tends to correct the sideslip
        d.   wing dihedral will cause a nose up pitching moment

12.   Wing dihedral produces a stabilising rolling moment by causing an increase in lift:

        a.   on the up-going wing when the aircraft rolls
        b.   on the up-going wing when the aircraft is sideslipping
        c.   on the lower wing when the aircraft is sideslipping
        d.   on the lower wing whenever the aircraft is in a banked attitude

13. A high wing configuration with no dihedral, compared to a low wing configuration with no dihedral, will have:

   a. greater longitudinal stability
   b. the same degree of longitudinal stability as any other configuration because dihedral gives longitudinal stability
   c. less lateral stability
   d. greater lateral stability

14. If an aircraft with strong lateral stability and weak directional stability suffers a lateral disturbance and enters a sideslip, the aircraft will:

   a. go into a spiral dive
   b. develop simultaneous oscillations in roll and yaw, known as Dutch Roll
   c. develop oscillations in pitch
   d. develop an unchecked roll

15. A wing whose angle of incidence decreases from root to tip is said to have:

   a. washout
   b. taper
   c. sweep
   d. anhedral

16. The lateral axis of an aircraft is a line which:

   a. passes through the wing tips
   b. passes through the Centre of Pressure, at right angles to the direction of the airflow
   c. passes through the quarter-chord point of the wing root, at right angles to the longitudinal axis
   d. passes through the Centre of Gravity, parallel to a line through the wing tips

17. Loading an aircraft so that the C of G exceeds the aft limits could result in:

   a. loss of longitudinal stability
   b. excessive upward force on the tail, and the nose pitching down
   c. excessive load factor in turns
   d. high stick forces

18. Stability about the normal axis:

   a. is increased if the keel surface behind the C of G is increased
   b. is given by the lateral dihedral
   c. depends on the longitudinal dihedral
   d. is greater if the wing has no sweepback

19.   If the Centre of Gravity (C of G) of an aircraft is found to be within limits for take off:

     a.   the C of G will always be within limits for landing
     b.   the C of G limits for landing must be checked, allowing for planned fuel consumption
     c.   the C of G will not change during the flight
     d.   the flight crew will always be certain of being able to adjust the C of G during flight in order to keep it within acceptable limits for landing

20.   An aeroplane is in straight and level flight and a gust causes one wing to drop. If the aeroplane tends to return towards wings level without any intervention from the pilot:

     a.   the aircraft has neutral stability
     b.   the aircraft is stable
     c.   the aircraft is unstable
     d.   the aircraft cannot return to wings level unless the pilot intervenes

21.   The surface that gives an aircraft directional stability is:

     a.   the rudder
     b.   tailplane
     c.   the rudder trim tab
     d.   the fin

22.   Movement of the aircraft about its normal (vertical) axis is known as:

     a.   yawing
     b.   rolling
     c.   pitching
     d.   side slipping

23.   When an aircraft is disturbed from its established flight path by, for example, turbulence, it is said to have positive stability if it subsequently tends to:

     a.   remain on the new flight path
     b.   re-establish its original flight path without any input from the pilot
     c.   become further displaced from its original flight path
     d.   continue to pitch in the disturbed direction until the displacement is resisted by opposing control forces

24.   When an aircraft is disturbed from its trimmed attitude by, for example, turbulence, it is said to have neutral stability if it subsequently:

     a.   oscillates about its original attitude before settling back to that original attitude
     b.   immediately re-establishes its original attitude
     c.   remains in the new attitude
     d.   continues to move in the disturbed direction until the displacement is resisted by opposing control forces

25.   By design, the Centre of Pressure on a particular aircraft remains behind the aircraft's C of G. If the aircraft is longitudinally stable and is displaced in pitch, nose down, by turbulence:

a.   the tailplane will generate an increased upward force
b.   neither an upward nor a downward force will be generated by the tailplane, as the aircraft will already be in equilibrium
c.   the aircraft will maintain its nose-down attitude
d.   the tailplane will generate an increased downward force

26.   The tendency of an aircraft to develop forces which restore it to its original flight situation, when disturbed from a condition of steady flight, is known as:

a.   manoeuvrability
b.   controllability
c.   stability
d.   instability

27.   An aircraft has directional static stability. If it sideslips to the right:

a.   the aircraft will initially tend to roll to the left
b.   the aircraft will initially tend to yaw to the left
c.   the aircraft will initially tend to yaw to the right
d.   the nose will remain pointing forward

28.   Which of the following components provides longitudinal stability?

a.   Engines
b.   Wing
c.   Fuselage
d.   Horizontal stabiliser (tailplane)

29.   To improve lateral stability certain features may be built into an aircraft. Which of the following lists of features would best contribute to an aircraft's overall lateral stability?

a.   High wing, dihedral, high keel surface, sweep back
b.   Dihedral, high keel surface, Frise ailerons
c.   Wash-out, dihedral, Frise ailerons
d.   Slats, dihedral, Fowler flaps

Question	1	2	3	4	5	6	7	8	9	10	11	12
Answer												

Question	13	14	15	16	17	18	19	20	21	22	23	24
Answer												

Question	25	26	27	28	29
Answer					

The answers to these questions can be found at the end of this book.

CHAPTER 12
FLIGHT CONTROLS
AND TRIMMING

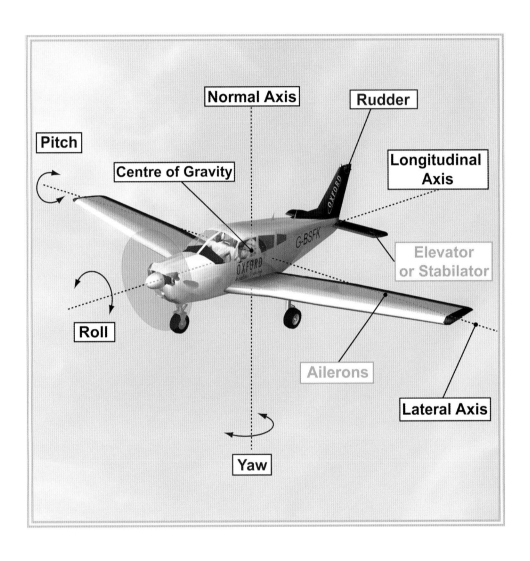

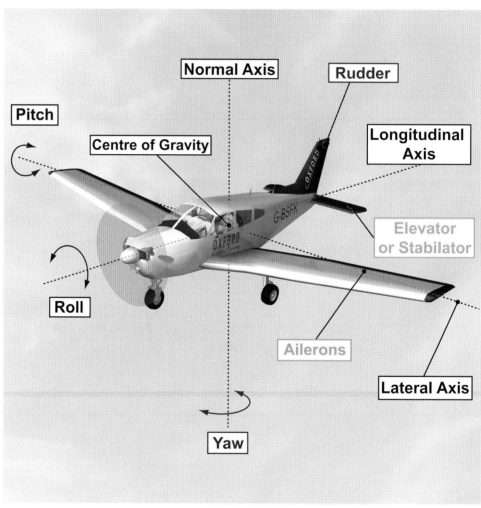

Figure 12.1 The flying control surfaces allow the pilot to manoeuvre the aircraft about its three axes.

FLIGHT CONTROL AND TRIMMING.

INTRODUCTION.

Whatever the degree of stability that an aircraft possesses about its longitudinal, lateral and normal axes, the pilot needs to **control** the aircraft about those axes in order that he may manoeuvre and steer the aircraft as he requires. Then, having selected the aircraft's attitude, a pilot must be able to **trim** the aircraft so that the attitude can be held without his having to apply a constant pressure on the control column or control wheel.

In this chapter, then, you will learn about how an aircraft is **controlled and trimmed**.

We will begin by looking at **control**.

THE FLYING CONTROL SURFACES.

The aerodynamic forces required to manoeuvre an aircraft about its three axes are generated through moveable flap-type **control surfaces** fitted to the main aerofoil sections at the extremities of the wings and fuselage. Sometimes, however, especially in the case of **control** in the pitching plane, the complete aerofoil section will be able to move under the pilot's direction. Because an aircraft rotates about its **Centre of Gravity (C of G)**, in all three planes, the **control surfaces** are positioned at the aircraft's extremities so that the aerodynamic forces they create have as long a moment arm as possible.

The Flying Control Surfaces and their Primary Effects.

An aircraft, generally possess three sets of **flying control surface**s, each of which has an important **primary effect** on the movement of the aircraft about the respective axis.

Yaw is rotation about the aircraft's normal axis and is controlled by the rudder.

- A **rudder** which controls the aircraft in **yaw**, about the **normal axis**. This type of control is called **directional control**.

Pitch is rotation about the aircraft's lateral axis and is controlled by the elevator or stabilator.

- An **elevator** which controls the aircraft in **pitch**, about the **lateral axis**. This type of control is called **longitudinal control**.

- **Ailerons** which control the aircraft in **roll**, about the **longitudinal axis**. This type of control is called **lateral control**.

Roll is rotation about the aircraft's longitudinal axis and is controlled by the ailerons.

Make sure that you learn well the above definitions of the primary effects of the flying control surfaces. These definitions are popular with examiners. Take special care over the words **longitudinal** and **lateral**, and do not confuse the **plane of control** with the **axis** about which control is achieved. For instance, the **elevator** gives **longitudinal control** about the **lateral axis**, and the **ailerons** give **lateral control** about the **longitudinal axis**.

The most common location and arrangement of the **flying control surfaces** on a light aircraft are illustrated in *Figure 12.1*.

Movement in **yaw**, **pitch** and **roll** is generated by the deflection of the respective **control surface**: rudder, elevator or ailerons. The deflection of the control surfaces changes three characteristics of the aerofoil section: its **effective camber**, the orientation of its **mean chord line** and, thus its **angle of attack** with respect to the relative airflow.

The change in the aerofoil's **angle of attack** also modifies the **lift force** produced by that aerofoil, by varying the value of C_L, which, in turn, creates an **out of balance turning moment** about the aircraft's **C of G** which initiates a movement about the corresponding axis. *Figure 12.2* illustrates the principle of how the **mean chord line**, **angle of attack**, and **lift force** of a wing are modified through displacement of the **aileron**.

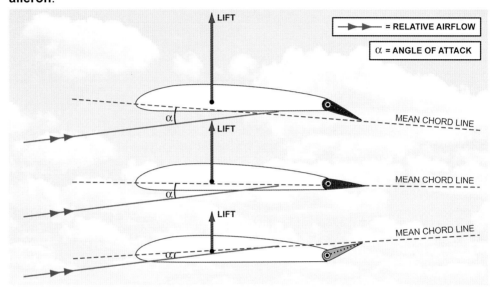

Figure 12.2 Displacement of a control surface modifies the aerodynamic force generated by the aerofoil. Here, aileron displacement is shown changing the lift force produced by a wing.

As we have mentioned, on some aircraft the complete aerofoil section can be displaced by the pilot to modify **angle of attack**. *Figure 12.3* illustrates this type of **horizontal control surface** in the tail assembly, on a PA28 Warrior. This type of control surface is called a **stabilator**, or, in older parlance, **an all-flying tailplane**.

The Planes of Control.

It is important that you should appreciate that the aircraft's **flying controls** cause the aircraft to move about **its own three axes**. The displacement of the **flying controls** alone, by the pilot, does not

Figure 12.3 A stabilator or all-moving (flying) tailplane.

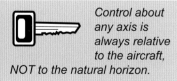

Control about any axis is always relative to the aircraft, NOT to the natural horizon.

manoeuvre the aircraft with reference to the natural horizon or any other line or point on the Earth's surface. Movement of the **flying control surfaces** always has the same primary effect on the aircraft, no matter what **attitude** the aircraft has in relation to the surface of the Earth; (except when the aircraft is at the point of stall). It is only after the pilot has mastered the **effects of controls** that he can go on to use them to change the **attitude** of the aircraft relative to the Earth's surface.

THE FLYING CONTROL SURFACES.

Flying controls are designed to work in the instinctive sense.

Directional Control about the Normal Axis.

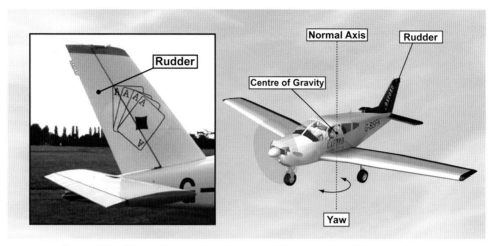

Figure 12.4 The rudder controls the aircraft in yaw, about its normal axis.

The **rudder** is a symmetrically-cambered, hinged aerofoil section, mechanically linked by cables and rods to the **rudder pedals**, which are operated by the pilot's feet. When the **rudder pedals** are central, the **rudder** itself is central. Pushing the right **rudder pedal** forward deflects the **rudder** to the **right**, generating an aerodynamic force which causes the aircraft to **yaw** to the **right** as in *Figure 12.5*.

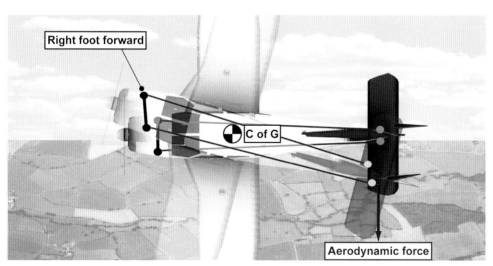

Figure 12.5 Pushing the right rudder pedal forward causes the aircraft to yaw to the right.

If the left **rudder pedal** is pushed forward the aircraft will **yaw** to the left. Because of the positive directional stability created by the fin, the aircraft will tend to return to straight flight when the **rudder pedals** are centralised. The magnitude of the aerodynamic force produced by deflection of the **rudder**, and, therefore, the effectiveness of the **rudder** and the amplitude of the **yawing movement**, is proportional to the amount of deflection of the **control surface**, the airspeed, and the thrust from the propeller; (slipstream effect).

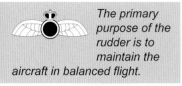

The primary purpose of the rudder is to maintain the aircraft in balanced flight.

Balanced Flight.

You should note that although the rudder is said to give **directional control**, this latter expression can be very misleading. The rudder is <u>not</u> used to turn the aircraft and change direction. A turn is initiated by applying aileron in the direction of the turn to select an angle of bank, the rudder being used to balance the manoeuvre. **The primary use of the rudder, then, is to enable the pilot to maintain the aircraft in balanced flight**, whether in straight or turning flight. In **balanced flight**, the longitudinal axis of the aircraft is approximately parallel to the relative airflow. The aircraft meets the relative airflow head-on, and the ball of the **turn and slip indicator** will be in its central position, between the two vertical markers, as depicted in *Figure 12.6*.

Figure 12.6 The rudder is primarily used to keep the aircraft in balanced flight with the ball "in the middle".

Other uses of the rudder include:

•   The holding of a sideslip in specialist manoeuvres.

•   To balance a coordinated turn, especially to eliminate adverse yaw on entering a turn.

•   To steer the aircraft during taxying.

•   In the recovery from a spin.

•   To overcome asymmetric power effects in the event of engine failure on a multi-engined aircraft.

You have already learnt that directional stability and lateral stability (i.e. stability in the yawing and rolling planes) are inextricably linked. You will not be surprised, then, to learn that pilot-induced yawing movements also have a secondary effect in the rolling plane. This phenomenon is treated below.

Longitudinal Control about the Lateral Axis (Pitch).

The **elevator** or **stabilator (all-flying tailplane)** gives the pilot **longitudinal control** in the **pitching plane** about the **lateral axis** *(See Figure 12.7)*.

Fore and aft movement of the control column or control wheel operate the **elevator** in such a way as to produce a **pitching movement** in the natural and logical sense.

If the pilot moves the **control column aft**, the **elevator** or **stabilator** is deflected **upwards**. This will generate an **aerodynamic force** acting **downwards** at the tailplane which will **pitch** the aircraft's nose up. Likewise, if the **control column is moved forward** an **aerodynamic force** is generated which will **pitch** the aircraft nose **downwards**.

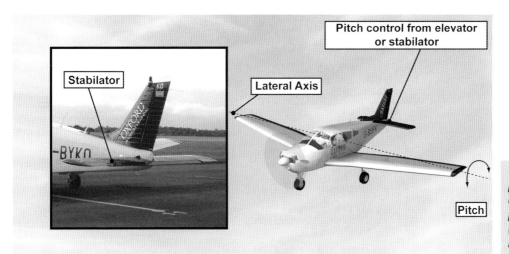

The elevator provides control in the pitching plane (longitudinal control about the lateral axis).

Figure 12.7 The elevator controls the aircraft in pitch.

Fore and aft movements of the control column, then, control the aircraft in **pitch**. In turn, the aircraft's **pitch attitude** will affect **airspeed**. A pilot selects a desired **airspeed** with a combination of **pitch attitude** and **engine power** setting. The effectiveness of the **elevator** or **stabilator** is proportional to the amount of control deflection, the aircraft's speed, and the magnitude of propeller thrust.

Lateral Control about the Longitudinal Axis (Roll).

The **ailerons** give the pilot **lateral control** in the **rolling plane** about the **longitudinal axis**. The **ailerons** are located outboard at the trailing edge of each wing. Control of the **ailerons**, or **roll** control, is achieved by **lateral movements** of the control column or control wheel in the logical and instinctive sense.

To **roll** the aircraft to the **left** requires the **control wheel** to be **rotated anticlockwise** or the **control column to be moved to the left**. Movement of the **control column or control wheel** in the opposite sense will cause the aircraft to **roll** to the **right**.

The **ailerons** are hinged aerofoil sections which move differentially. Movement of the control column either to the left or right will cause one **aileron** to be deflected upwards whilst the other is deflected downwards. In a turn to the right, for instance, as illustrated in *Figure 12.8,* the right (starboard) **aileron** is deflected upwards, and the left (port) **aileron** is deflected downwards.

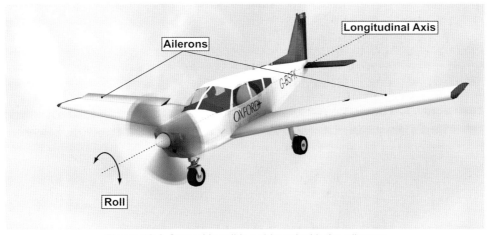

Figure 12.8 Control in roll is achieved with the ailerons.

The aircraft rolls to the right because the lift force has been increased on the left wing and decreased on the right wing.

The roll can be stopped by the pilot centralising the control column at the required angle of bank. This action returns the **ailerons** to their undeflected position, removing the differential in lift generated by the wings.

The effectiveness of the **ailerons** is proportional to the amount of control deflection and to the aircraft's speed through the air. The engine power setting has little or no effect on **aileron** effectiveness, as the **ailerons** lie outside the propeller slipstream.

As the **ailerons** induce a **rolling** movement about the **longitudinal axis**, they will also have an effect on the movement of the aircraft about its **normal axis** for the reasons already examined in the chapter on stability. This **secondary effect of the ailerons** is covered in the next section.

SECONDARY OR FURTHER EFFECT OF CONTROLS.

The **flying control surfaces** have both **primary** and **secondary effects**. You have just learnt about the primary effects of the controls; here, we deal with the **secondary effects**.

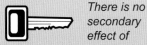

There is no secondary effect of elevator, though a change in the pitch attitude will lead to a change in airspeed.

The Elevator.
There is no **secondary effect** of the **elevator** or **stabilator**, although a change in the aircraft's pitch attitude will induce a change of airspeed.

The Secondary Effect of Rudder.
In the chapter on Stability, you learned that an aircraft's rotation about its normal axis (yaw) and its longitudinal axis (roll) are not independent of each other.

A displacement in the yawing plane will always influence an aircraft's motion in the rolling plane and vice versa.

You have learnt that the **primary effect** of rudder is **yaw**. The **secondary effect** of rudder is **roll in the direction of yaw**.

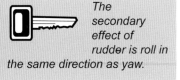

The secondary effect of rudder is roll in the same direction as yaw.

If a pilot initiates a **yaw** with the rudder, one wing will move forward relative to the other. In a **yaw** to the left, for example, the right (starboard) wing will move forwards and the left (port) wing will move rearwards. The velocity of the airflow over the forward-moving right wing will increase, generating a greater lift force than that produced by the rearwards-moving left wing. The aircraft, therefore, will begin to **roll** to the left, in the direction of the **yaw**. Once the **yaw** is established, the wing being held back presents a shorter effective span to the airflow than the forward wing, further increasing the lift on the forward wing, and, thereby, reinforcing the **roll** to the left. The **roll**, will lead to a sideslip which, for the reasons discussed in an earlier chapter, will induce more **yaw**, which, in turn, will lead to further **roll**, and so on, until the aircraft enters a **spiral dive** to the left, if the pilot does not intervene. A **spiral dive** can turn into a dangerous flight manoeuvre becoming an ever-steepening, ever-tightening turn. Your instructor will demonstrate a **spiral dive** to you, and show you how to recover from it, before it becomes dangerous, by first rolling the wings level with coordinated aileron and rudder, and then easing out of the dive.

The secondary effect of rudder, then, is roll in the direction of the initial yaw.

The Secondary Effect of Aileron.

You have learnt that the **primary effect** of **aileron** is **roll**. The **secondary effect** of **aileron** is **yaw** in the direction of **roll**.

If a pilot selects an angle of bank, to the left, say, without making any further control movements, the aircraft will respond by **rolling** to the left, about the **longitudinal axis**. The aircraft, then, will enter a **slip** to the left, towards the lower wing and the side component of the relative airflow will, consequently, strike the aircraft's keel surfaces. Because the keel surface area behind the **C of G** is greater than the area of the keel surfaces forward of the **C of G**, the aircraft will **yaw** in the direction of the lower wing. For the reasons given above, the **yaw** will induce further **roll**, which will lead to further **yaw** and so on, until the aircraft enters a **spiral dive** to the left, if the pilot does not intervene.

The secondary effect of aileron is yaw.

The secondary effect of aileron, then, is yaw in the direction of the initial roll.

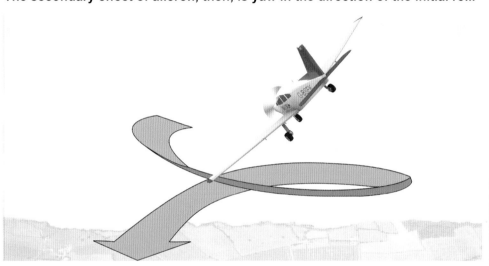

Unless the pilot intervenes, the secondary effect of aileron can lead to a spiral dive.

Figure 12.9 The secondary effects of both rudder and ailerons induce rolling and yawing actions, in the same direction, which mutually reinforce each other and lead to a spiral dive.

Adverse Yaw.

There is yet another effect arising from the interrelationship between control in the rolling and yawing planes that it is vital for you to understand, if you are to become a competent pilot. This effect is called **adverse yaw**. Eliminating **adverse yaw** demands the coordinated use of the ailerons and rudder, which is an ever-present requirement for controlled rolling movements, especially on the entry to turns. A balanced roll requires the use of an appropriate amount of rudder, as well as aileron, applied in the same direction and at the same time.

Adverse yaw arises when the pilot attempts to roll using aileron alone, or with uncoordinated movements of the aileron and rudder. It is convenient to examine **adverse yaw** by considering a pilot attempting to roll his aircraft using aileron alone.

Figure 12.10 Adverse yaw. Here the aircraft is rolling to the left and yawing to the right. Notice the position of the ball showing that the aircraft is out of balance.

If a pilot rolls the aircraft, to the **left**, with aileron alone, aileron deflection will be such that the left (port) wing lowers and the right (starboard) wing rises. During the rolling movement, then, the right wing is generating a greater lift force than the left wing. As you have learnt, the penalty for increased lift is increased drag. Consequently, as the aircraft **rolls** to the **left**, the up-going right wing, generating the greater lift and drag, is held back. So while the aircraft **rolls to the left**, it **yaws to the right**, as shown in *Figure 12.10*.

It is because the **yaw** is in the opposite direction to the **roll** that it is given the name **adverse yaw**. **Adverse yaw** is the aircraft's initial response to the rolling movement. If the pilot were to reverse the **roll**, to the **right**, the aircraft would **yaw** to the **left**. When **adverse yaw** is present, then, the aircraft begins to wallow around, giving the pilot the impression that he does not have the aircraft under control. What is actually happening is that the aircraft is rolling in an **unbalanced** way. Note the position of the ball in *Figure 12.10*. If the aircraft were in balance, the ball would be in the middle. However, the aircraft is rolling to the left but the ball of the **turn and slip indicator** is fully deflected to the left, too, indicating that left rudder is required to bring the aircraft back into balance.

Adverse yaw is counteracted by applying rudder in the same direction of roll.

(Of course, if an angle of bank is selected and held, without any further intervention from the pilot, the aircraft will then slip towards the lower wing and begin to yaw in the direction of roll, eventually entering a spiral dive.)

Adverse yaw then is **yaw** in the opposite direction to the roll. **Adverse yaw** is the **initial reaction** to a roll initiated using aileron alone.

Adverse yaw can be eliminated by using an appropriate amount of **rudder** in the **same direction as aileron** and **at the same time**. By applying **aileron** and **rudder together** in this way, a pilot is said to be using **coordinated control movements**. You will doubtless hear your instructor urge you to use "**coordinated control movements**" several times during your initial training. When you roll with properly coordinated aileron and rudder, the ball of the **turn and slip indicator** will remain firmly in the middle.

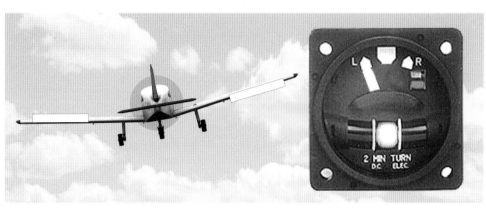

Figure 12.11 Adverse yaw has been eliminated. Here the aircraft is rolling to the left without adverse yaw. The ball's position "in the middle" shows that the aircraft is in balance.

In short wing-span, high-powered aircraft, **adverse yaw** is not very pronounced, but pilots must be ready to balance rolling movements with coordinated aileron and rudder, as required. In long-wing span, low-powered aircraft such as motor-gliders, **adverse yaw** is very pronounced and a high level of aileron and rudder coordination is required, to eliminate **adverse yaw**.

USE OF THE FLYING CONTROLS IN TURNING FLIGHT.

Having learnt what are the primary and secondary effects of controls, this is a convenient point for you to consider how the flying controls are used to enter, maintain and exit a turn. Before continuing, you may wish to read again the section on turning flight in Chapter 9.

You will recall that, in order to turn, the pilot applies an appropriate amount of bank in the direction in which he wishes to turn.

Figure 12.12 A PA28 established in a turn to the left, with the ailerons centralised.

In a level turn, i.e. a turn at constant altitude, the **total lift force, L_T**, depicted in *Figure 12.13,* has to do two jobs: provide the necessary **centripetal force** to turn the aircraft, and also **support the weight of the aircraft** (which continues to act vertically downwards) so as to maintain the aircraft in level flight. **Consequently, in order to achieve both these objectives, the total lift force in the turn needs to be greater than that required for straight and level flight**.

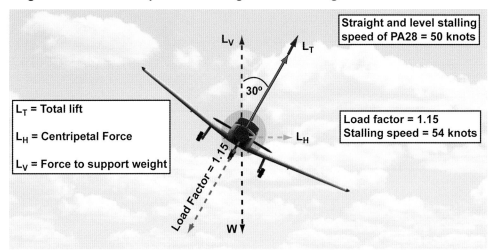

Figure 12.13 In a turn, the lift generated by the wings must continue to support the aircraft's weight while also providing the turning (centripetal) force.

In a medium turn of about 30° angle of bank, the **extra lift for the turn** will be provided by the pilot increasing the back pressure on the control column (thereby increasing the wing's angle of attack and, thus, C_L) sufficiently to maintain the correct pitch attitude and constant altitude. The increase in angle of attack also causes a rise in drag which will lead to a reduction in **airspeed**, if thrust is not increased. The reduction in **speed** is small in a 30°-banked turn, and may be acceptable, but, in steep turns of 45° angle of bank and above, thrust will need to be increased, too, in order to maintain the entry **speed** because of the increased **stalling speed** in the turn. Remember, in a 45°-banked turn, the **stalling speed** of a PA28 Warrior is around 60 knots, 10 knots higher than its straight flight **stalling speed** of 50 knots *(See Figure 12.14)*.

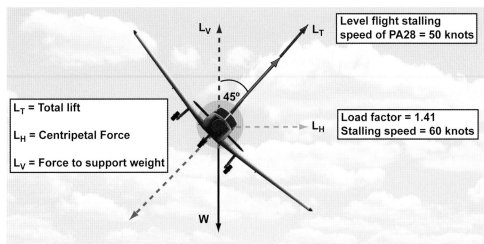

Figure 12.14 A 45°-banked turn. For turns of 45° angle of bank, and above, thrust must be increased to maintain entry speed.

Holding the above facts in mind and recalling what we have just learned about the primary and secondary effects of the controls, we consider below the flying control movements involved in turning flight. Remember, these are considerations to bear in mind in the context of your study of **Principles of Flight**. Your flying instructor will teach you how to **fly the turn**, in your airborne exercises. One of the main teaching points that he will doubtless repeat several times, is the necessity to **keep a good look out in every stage of the turn**.

•   On rolling into the turn, the control column is displaced laterally in the direction of the desired run. Remember, if ailerons are used on their own you will get adverse yaw; therefore, rudder must be applied in the same direction as aileron, in order to maintain balanced flight. The amount of rudder required will depend on the rate of roll and the type of aircraft being flown.

•   As the aircraft is still rolling into the turn, the pilot increases back pressure on the control column sufficiently to increase angle of attack of the wings, through elevator deflection, by the amount necessary to provide the extra lift required to support the weight of the aircraft, while also providing the centripetal force which actually changes the aircraft's direction. The pilot judges the amount of back pressure he needs to apply by holding the correct pitch attitude and maintaining constant altitude

•   For medium turns of up to 30° angle of bank, the small reduction in airspeed resulting from the increased angle of attack, and increased drag, is usually acceptable. This will be about 5 knots in the Warrior for a 30°-banked turn. But for turns of 45° angle of bank, and steeper, the increase in drag is such that thrust must be increased to maintain entry speed.

•   When the required angle of bank is reached, the pilot centralises the ailerons and rudder, although very small rudder pressures may be necessary to maintain balanced flight.

•   The raised wing, which is on the outside of the turn and, therefore, moving faster through the air than the lower wing, will develop more lift. This situation requires the pilot to apply lateral pressure on the control column away from the turn, an action which is called "holding off the turn". However, in the pilot's perception, he needs merely to maintain the required bank-angle with aileron.

•   In the turn, any deviation from the bank angle is corrected with coordinated aileron and rudder movements. In a medium turn, speed is controlled though pitch attitude control, using the elevator. Altitude is also maintained constant with the elevator. The elevator trim may be adjusted appropriately, if the turn is to be prolonged. (See **Trimming**, below.)

•   To exit the turn, the wings are rolled level using **coordinated aileron and rudder**; (control column and rudder pedal inputs at the same time and in the same direction). At the same time, the excess back pressure on the control column, required during the turn, is eased off, to maintain an appropriate pitch attitude and speed.

As mentioned earlier, the above considerations are **Principles of Flight** considerations. Your instructor will teach you how to fly the turn.

Design Features Aimed at Reducing Adverse Yaw.

Differential Ailerons.

The problem faced by designers in terms of **reducing adverse yaw** is to counterbalance the extra drag generated by the wing which produces the greater lift.

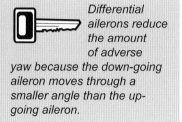

Differential ailerons reduce the amount of adverse yaw because the down-going aileron moves through a smaller angle than the up-going aileron.

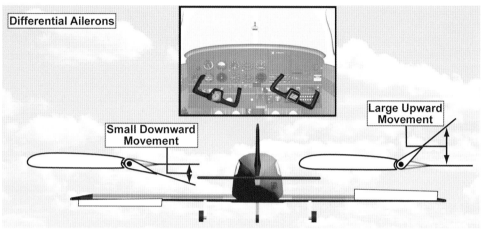

Figure 12.15 Differential Ailerons.

As drag increases with an increasing angle of attack, one way of reducing the drag on the up-going wing is to make the downward deflection of the aileron as small as practically possible. The differential in lift required to induce the roll can still be provided by increasing the upward deflection of the aileron on the downgoing wing. The greater upward deflection of the aileron on the down-going wing also increases the parasite drag on that wing, further reducing **adverse yaw**. With this arrangement, known as **differential ailerons**, **adverse yaw** is reduced, but not eliminated *(See Figure 12.15).*

Frise Ailerons.

Frise ailerons increase parasite drag on the down going wing to counteract adverse yaw.

Another method of reducing **adverse yaw** is for the aircraft designer to concentrate solely on **increasing parasite drag** on the down-going wing in order to balance the drag associated with the increased lift on the up-going wing. This aim is achieved by using a type of aileron hinge which causes the leading edge of the up-going aileron on the down-going wing to protrude into the airflow, thereby **increasing parasite drag**. Conversely, the leading edge of the down-going aileron on the up-going wing remains shrouded. This type of aileron arrangement is known as **Frise Ailerons**. On some aircraft, **Frise Ailerons** and **Differential Ailerons** are combined into one system *(See Figure 12.17).*

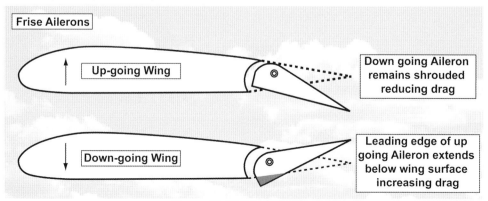

Figure 12.16 Frise Ailerons.

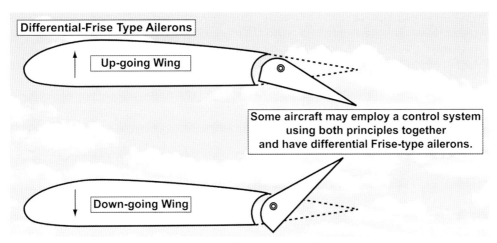

Figure 12.17 Differential-Frise Ailerons.

THE EFFECT OF AIRSPEED ON THE EFFECTIVENESS OF THE FLYING CONTROL SURFACES.

We have already mentioned that the **effectiveness** of the **flying control surfaces increases** with increasing **airspeed**. In this section, we look a little more closely at this aspect of control.

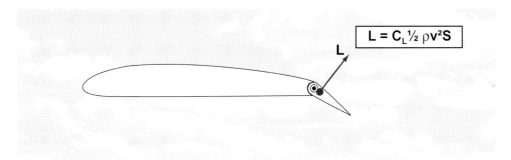

$$L = C_L \tfrac{1}{2} \rho v^2 S$$

Figure 12.18 The increased effectiveness of a control surface is proportional to the square of the airspeed.

You have learnt that movement in **yaw**, **pitch** and **roll** is generated by a deflection of the control surface modifying the effective camber, changing the orientation of the mean chord line and, thus, modifying the angle of attack of the respective aerofoil section. We have explained that this modification of the aerofoil's characteristics also modifies the **lift force** produced by that aerofoil, by varying the value of C_L, creating an out of balance turning moment about the aircraft's **Centre of Gravity** which initiates a movement about the corresponding axis.

However, the modification in **lift force** at the flying control surfaces occurs not only as a result of changing C_L. If we look again at the **lift equation** with which we are now familiar, **Lift** $= C_L \tfrac{1}{2} \rho v^2 S$, we see that **lift** can be increased by increasing **v** as well as by increasing C_L; **v**, of course, is **true airspeed**. But, a closer examination of the **lift formula** shows us that because **lift** increases as the square of the airspeed, v^2, whereas the increase in **lift** with C_L is a simple, direct, linear relationship, the increase in airspeed has a greater proportional influence on **control effectiveness** than the degree of deflection of the control surface which affects C_L only.

The effectiveness of the flying controls is proportional to both airspeed and control deflection.

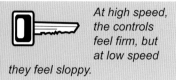

At high speed, the controls feel firm, but at low speed they feel sloppy.

It follows then, that at **low airspeeds**, to obtain the required **control response**, **large movements of the flying controls** are generally required. But, as **airspeed increases** the **control surfaces will become more effective** requiring smaller movements of the control column and rudder pedals to manoeuvre the aircraft.

At low speed, then, the pilot's controls feel quite sloppy and sluggish in response to control inputs. At high airspeed, however, the pilot's controls feel firm and positive and, at very high speeds, can be so effective that it is possible to generate forces beyond those which the aircraft structure was designed to withstand.

THE EFFECT OF PROPELLER SLIPSTREAM ON CONTROLS.

An aircraft on the approach to land, as in *Figure 12.19*, will be flying at relatively low airspeed. It follows, then, that the effectiveness of the controls would normally be reduced compared to cruising flight. But, with flaps deployed and undercarriage lowered, drag will be high requiring appropriately high levels of **thrust** in order to maintain airspeed. The resulting **propeller slipstream** over the tail will help, therefore, to maintain the effectiveness of the rudder and elevator by energising the airflow across those control surfaces. But the ailerons, which are outside the **slipstream**, will not derive this benefit and, so, will be less effective on the approach than in cruising flight.

Figure 12.19 Only the rudder and elevator benefit from the propeller slipstream effect.

Great care, should, therefore, be exercised by the pilot to retain control over the aircraft in roll, when landing in gusty or cross-wind conditions.

CONTROL FORCES.

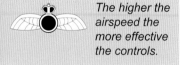

The higher the airspeed the more effective the controls.

The **forces** generated by the **flying control surfaces** are designed to be sufficient to manoeuvre the aircraft, throughout its designed operating envelope.

By the nature of the design of the control surface, the **aerodynamic force**, F, acting from the centre of pressure of the control surface will try to rotate the control surface about its hinge point, in the direction of the **aerodynamic force**, as depicted in *Figure 12.20*. This is called the **hinge moment**. Consequently, in order to move the flying control surface through the required angular displacement and maintain it in that position, the pilot has to overcome and then balance the **hinge moment** by applying a force to the control column or rudder pedals. This is called **'stick force'**. If the **hinge moment** increases the **stick force** applied by the pilot will also need to increase.

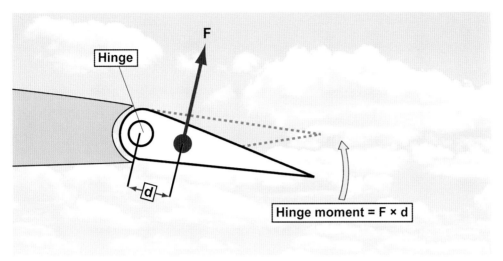

Figure 12.20 The hinge moment at a control surface.

The relationship between **stick force moment** and **hinge moment** provides the pilot with **feel** or feedback information on the **aerodynamic forces** being generated at the control surfaces. At high speed, the **stick force** will be relatively high indicating to the pilot that, if he persists in trying to displace the flying controls to their full deflection, structural damage may occur.

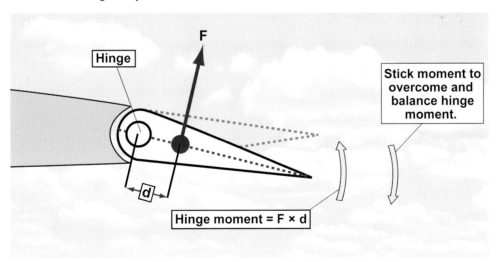

Figure 12.21 The control surface's hinge moment must be balanced by a "stick force moment" applied by the pilot.

Balancing Stick Force.

Large jet transports like the Boeing 747 generate **hinge moments** of great magnitude which would be impossible for the pilot to overcome and balance without the assistance of powered controls and aerodynamic balancing. Powered assistance is usually provided by multiple, engine-driven hydraulic systems.

Figure 12.22 A Boeing 747.

However, light aircraft generally use simple mechanical linkages to operate the flying controls, with the pilot providing the force to operate them *(See Figure 12.23)*.

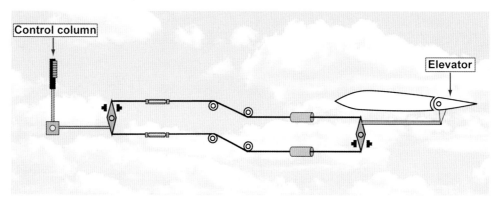

Figure 12.23 A mechanical elevator system in a light aircraft.

AERODYNAMIC BALANCING.

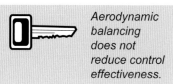

Aerodynamic balancing does not reduce control effectiveness.

Although the forces required from the pilot to move the controls of a light aircraft are generally small, the continuous effort to hold, say, a given pitch altitude can become tiring on a long flight at high cruise speeds, particularly in conditions of persistent turbulence. For this reason, flying control surfaces are often **balanced aerodynamically**. **Aerodynamic balancing** is the most common and simplest form of **balance** on light aircraft. **Aerodynamic balancing** involves using the aerodynamic forces generated by the control surface, itself, and can be achieved without reducing control effectiveness.

The Inset Hinge.
One method of **aerodynamic balancing** is the **inset hinge**. *Figure 12.20* on Page 269 represents the **normal hinge** located near to the leading edge of the control, creating a **large hinge moment**. In *Figure 12.24*, however, the control surface **hinge** has been moved aft closer to the centre of pressure of the control surface so that the **hinge moment** is reduced. In addition, the airflow strikes the control surface in front of the **hinge** at F_1, providing a turning moment which further reduces the **hinge moment**. This arrangement helps the pilot to move the controls by reducing the required stick force.

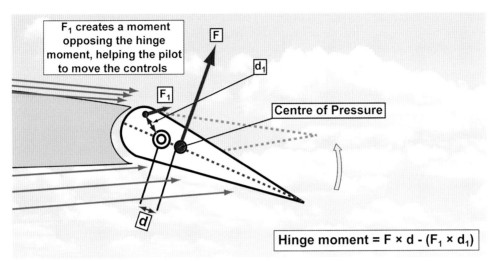

$$\text{Hinge moment} = F \times d - (F_1 \times d_1)$$

Figure 12.24 The inset hinge, produces a smaller hinge moment than the normal hinge.

The Horn Balance.

Similar in operation to the inset hinge is the **horn balance**, shown in *Figure 12.25*. The **horn** is the part of the flying control surface located forward of the **hinge**. In flight, when the control surface is displaced, aerodynamic forces will be generated both forward and aft of the **hinge** line. The moment generated by the aerodynamic force forward of the hinge counters the main control surface **hinge moment**, and assists the pilot to move the control surface. A disadvantage of the **horn balance** is that it produces an increase in overall drag.

In aerodynamic balancing, there is an area of control surface forward of the hinge.

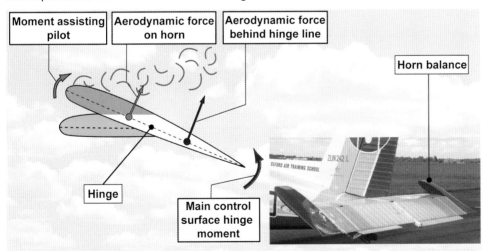

Figure 12.25 A horn balance system on a Zlin.

The Internal Balance.

The same principle as the horn balance is employed, without leading to an increase in drag, in the **internal balance**. The **internal balance** mechanism is enclosed inside the rear of the main aerofoil section, as depicted in *Figure 12.26*. The **internal balance** takes the form of a chamber which senses the same changes in pressure as those produced by the deflection of the control surface, itself. The pressure differential inside the chamber produces **moment** in opposition to the **hinge moment**.

Neither the **internal hinge,** the **horn balance** nor the **internal balance** has any adverse effect upon the principal aerodynamic force produced at the control surface.

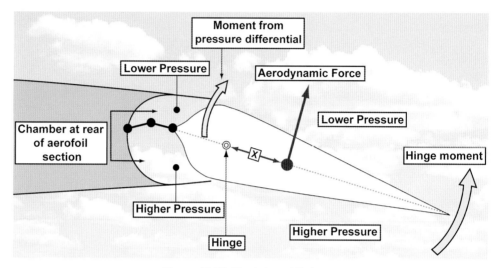

Figure 12.26 The Internal Balance.

TRAILING-EDGE TABS.

The **stick force** required from the pilot to move the flying control surfaces can also be reduced by small aerofoil tabs, known as **trailing-edge tabs**, positioned at the rear of the control surface. Trailing-edge tabs do, however, alter the effectiveness of the flying control concerned.

There are three main types of **trailing-edge tab** device. They are:

* the **balance tab**.

* the **anti-balance tab**.

* the **servo tab**.

These tabs are small aerofoil sections, hinged at the trailing-edge of the flying control surfaces *(See Figure 12.27)*.

Figure 12.27 Trailing edge tabs.

272

The Balance Tab.

The **balance tab** aids the pilot in moving the control surface. With the **balance tab** system, the pilot has no direct control over tab movement. Input to the main flying control is transmitted to a linkage which moves the **balance tab** in the opposite direction to the flying control surface, as depicted in *Figure 12.28*.

Balance tabs move in the opposite direction to the control surface to assist the pilot in moving the control surface.

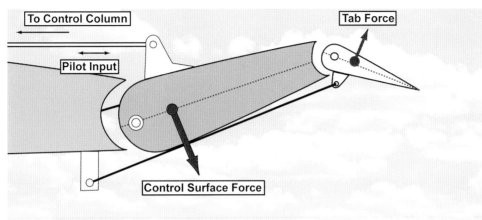

Figure 12.28 A balance tab. The balance tab aids the pilot in moving the control surface.

The pilot moves the control surface through a control rod and, in turn, the control surface movement actuates the **balance tab** movement. The **balance tab** generates a force in the opposite direction to that generated by the main flying control surface. The **balance tab** force reduces the control surface **hinge moment** and, thereby, the stick force required from the pilot. The **balance tab** does, however, cause a slight reduction in control effectiveness.

The Anti-Balance Tab.

Anti-balance tabs increase the stick force required from the pilot in order to provide him with "**feel**". Aircraft fitted with large elevators, and especially aircraft fitted with all-flying tailplanes, are capable of producing very significant aerodynamic forces as a result of their large surface area and their principle of operation. The danger exists, therefore, especially at high speed, that the pilot may over-control and, consequently, over-stress the aircraft. It is, therefore, desirable to increase the stick force and provide the pilot with "**feel**". This objective is achieved by the **anti-balance tab**. *(See Figure 12.29.)* The **anti-balance tab** operates in the <u>same</u> direction as the flying control surface and, thus, increases the stick force required to displace the control surface. This arrangement increases the effectiveness of the control surface itself.

Anti-Balance tabs move in the same direction as the control surface to increase stick force in order to provide the pilot with "feel".

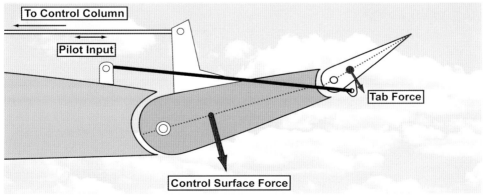

Figure 12.29 The anti-balance tab moves in the same direction as the control surface to increase stick force and provide the pilot with "feel".

*Figure 12.30 **Anti-balance** tabs are most commonly found on aircraft with **all-flying** tailplanes or **stabilators**.*

The Servo Tab.

A servo tab is a pilot-controlled tab which causes the flying control surface to move.

The mechanism of the **servo tab** differs from the other types of tabs in that the pilot's control input is to the **servo tab** and not to the flying control surface. Movement of the **servo tab** creates an aerodynamic force which moves the main flying control surface. For instance, if the pilot selects a nose-up pitch attitude, his input to the control column moves the **servo tab** downwards which, in turn, generates an aerodynamic force which displaces the main flying control upwards.

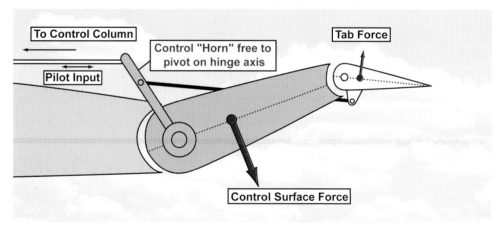

Figure 12.31 The servo tab provides the force which displaces the flying control surface.

MASS BALANCING.

Flutter.

There is one method of balancing which is applied to flying control surfaces but which has nothing to do with alleviating stick force. This is called **mass balancing**. **Mass balancing** is used to prevent control surface **flutter**, a phenomenon which is often associated with high aircraft speeds. **Flutter** is the name given to the oscillation of a flying control surface at high speed, and can cause bending or twisting of the surface. **Flutter** can occur as a result of the **centre of gravity (C of G)** of the control surface being well aft of the hinge.

274

A detailed examination of **flutter** is beyond the scope of this book. Here it is sufficient for us to state that if **flutter** arises and the oscillations remain undamped, structural failure of the control surface can occur.

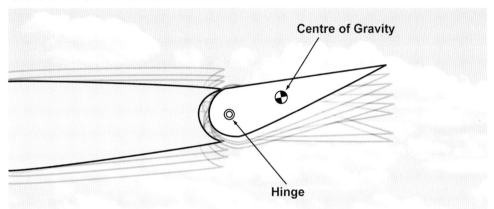

Centre of Gravity

Hinge

Figure 12.32 Flutter can arise if the centre of gravity of the control surface is well aft of the hinge.

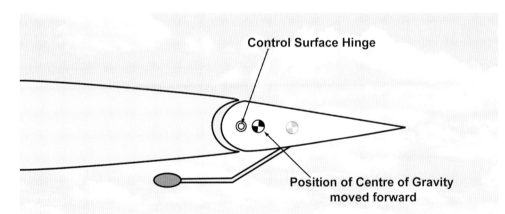

Control Surface Hinge

Position of Centre of Gravity moved forward

Flutter in a control surface reduced by fixing a mass forward of the hinge to move the C of G of the control surface closer to the hinge.

Figure 12.33 Mass balancing moves the C of G position nearer to the hinge and prevents flutter.

Flutter can be prevented by modifying the distribution of the mass of the control surface so that the **C of G** of the control surface lies nearer to the hinge *(See Figures 12.32, 12.33)*. It is because of this method of **redistribution of mass** that this device is called **mass-balancing**. *Figure 12.34* illustrates aileron mass balancing on the Zlin.

Figure 12.34 The mass balance fitted to the ailerons of a Zlin.

TRIMMING.

Introduction.

An aircraft is said to be **trimmed,** or **in trim,** when it is able to maintain its selected attitude without the pilot applying any force to the control column.

When an aircraft is **in trim**, the stick force is zero. Flying **in trim**, therefore, means that the pilot is less susceptible to fatigue and is also free to attend to other required tasks, such as navigation.

Your very first flying lesson will have made you aware of the varying magnitude of the force that you have to apply to the control wheel and rudder pedals in order to select and maintain an attitude, other than the attitude for which the aircraft is trimmed. The design of an aircraft is such that, in still air, at a given airspeed, power setting and configuration, the aircraft will be **trimmed** to adopt **one attitude only**. If the pilot changes power-setting or aircraft configuration (by selecting flap, for instance), or selects and maintains any other attitude, he has, once again, to apply a force to the controls to hold the attitude.

But by using the aircraft's **trimming control system** the pilot can **trim out** the need to apply a force to the control wheel to maintain the new attitude.

Most simple light aircraft can be **trimmed**, in flight, to remove stick force in the pitching plane only **(elevator trim)**, though **directional trim (rudder trim)** is fitted to some light aircraft.

The three most common methods of **trimming** a light aircraft are:

• The fixed **trim tab**.

• The adjustable **trim tab**.

• Spring-bias **trimming**.

A fixed trim tab will trim the aircraft for one airspeed only.

Fixed Trim Tabs.

The most basic method of achieving trimmed flight is with a **fixed trim tab**. The **fixed trim tab** is a narrow metal plate attached to the trailing edge of a control surface, usually the aileron *(See Figure 12.35)*.

Figure 12.35 A fixed trim tab on a aileron.

If, for instance, an aircraft, at cruise speed, requires the pilot to hold the control column slightly to the right in order to maintain wings level, this condition may be corrected by adjusting the **fixed trim tab** on the aircraft's starboard (right) aileron. This type of adjustment should be carried out by a qualified aircraft technician. In this case, the fixed trim tab is bent down slightly, in order to create an aerodynamic force which will deflect the starboard aileron upwards slightly so that the aircraft is trimmed for wings-level flight at cruise speed.

It is not uncommon to find that ailerons have a **fixed trim tab** fitted to one aileron only. Adjustment is naturally a case of trial and error and, so, trim corrections will probably require several flights to achieve.

Fixed trim tabs are generally found on low performance aircraft, only. You should note that there can be only one speed, normally the cruise speed, at which the **fixed trim tab** will hold the aircraft in trim.

The Adjustable Trim Tab.
The greatest changes in stick force with speed tend to occur in **pitch**. The elevator or stabilator is, therefore, invariably fitted with **trim tabs** which can be adjusted in flight. A typical **adjustable elevator trim tab** is shown in *Figure 12.36*.

Figure 12.36 An adjustable trim tab fitted to the elevator of a Cessna.

If, for instance, a pilot were to ease back on the control column to raise the nose of the aircraft *(See Figure 12.37)*.and wished to maintain this new attitude, he would have to continue to apply a **rearwards force** to the control column, unless he **re-trims** the aircraft.

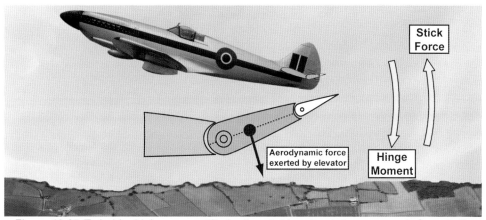

Figure 12.37 To hold a higher nose attitude, the pilot has to apply a rearwards force to the control column, until he re-trims.

In order to remove the **stick force**, the pilot must **re-trim** the aircraft for the higher nose attitude. The trimming system is so designed that the pilot moves the cockpit trim controls in the instinctive sense: rearwards to trim for a nose-high altitude, and forwards to trim for a lower nose altitude *(See Figure 12.38)*.

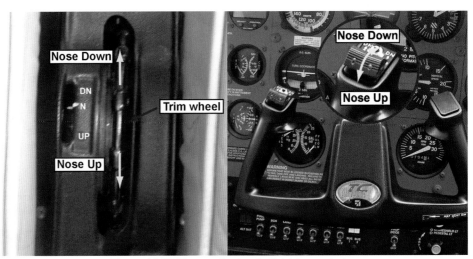

Figure 12.38 Two methods of pilot trim control.

In this case, by moving his cockpit trim control rearwards, the pilot causes the adjustable **trim tab** to move in the opposite direction to the direction of elevator displacement *(See Figure 12.39)*, thus creating a balancing force which holds the elevator in its new position and maintains the new nose-high altitude, without the pilot having to apply any further force to the control column.

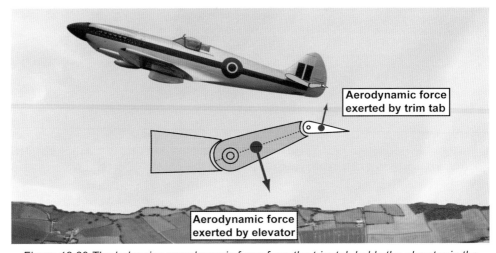

Figure 12.39 The balancing aerodynamic force from the trim tab holds the elevator in the new position. The aircraft is now trimmed for the new nose-high altitude.

The simple trim tab will retain its fixed position relative to the control surface, whatever the control surface movement.

Once the aircraft has been trimmed for a given flight attitude, the position of the simple trim tab relative to the control surface will remain fixed, whatever the subsequent displacement of the control surface. However, some **adjustable trim tabs** also serve as **balance tabs**, in which case the **adjustable trim tab** will move about the mean trimmed position as the control surface moves.

Disadvantages of Trim Tabs.

There are three principal disadvantages to using a tab type control to trim an aircraft. Firstly, there is a slight reduction in control effectiveness due to the tab force being in opposition to the force generated by the main flying control surface. Secondly, the deflection of the tab will increase drag. Thirdly, **trim tabs** can reduce the effective range of the control surface.

The Spring Bias Trimming System.

The **spring bias trimming system** works on the principle of an adjustable spring force opposing and, thus, decreasing the stick force applied by the pilot. **Spring bias trimming** has none of the disadvantages associated with the **trim tab system**.

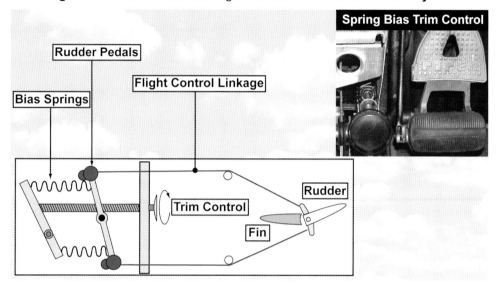

Figure 12.40 The spring bias system.

The **spring bias system** differs from the **trim tab system** in that the trim control system is not linked to the flying control surface but to the associated control linkage. As illustrated in *Figure 12.40*, in the **spring bias system**, the trim control applies a force to the control linkage, to remove **stick force**.

The Variable Incidence Tailplane.

A further method of achieving trim in pitch is the **variable incidence tailplane**. This system, because it adjusts the angle of incidence of the complete tailplane, is very powerful and has the ability to trim for large changes in speed, aircraft configuration and centre of gravity position, while keeping trim drag to a minimum.

Figure 12.41 A variable incidence tailplane.

Representative PPL - type questions to test your theoretical knowledge of Flight Controls and Trimming.

1.   Which of the following provides aerodynamic balance?

    a.   A weight on an arm which protrudes forward of it
    b.   An area of control surface forward of its hinge line
    c.   A fixed trim tab
    d.   A simple, adjustable trim tab

2.   Which flying control surface(s) give(s) control about the aircraft's normal axis?

    a.   The rudder
    b.   The ailerons
    c.   The elevator
    d.   The flaps

3.   A control surface may have a mass balance fitted to it, in order to:

    a.   help prevent a rapid and uncontrolled oscillation which is called "flutter"
    b.   keep the control surface level
    c.   lighten the forces needed to control the surface
    d.   provide the pilot with "feel"

4.   On an aircraft fitted with an elevator incorporating an anti-balance tab, pulling back on the control column will cause the:

    a.   elevator to move up and the tab to move up
    b.   elevator to move down and the tab to move down
    c.   elevator to move down and the tab to move up
    d.   elevator to move up and the tab to move down

5.   The respective primary and secondary effects of the rudder control are:

    a.   yaw and pitch
    b.   pitch and yaw
    c.   roll and yaw
    d.   yaw and roll

6.   Fixed trim tabs on ailerons:

    a.   can be adjusted during flight
    b.   should never be adjusted
    c.   can be adjusted on the ground after a test flight to make wings-level flight easier
    d.   can be adjusted on the ground after a test flight to make turning easier

7.   The respective primary and secondary effects of the aileron control are:

        a.   roll and pitch
        b.   pitch and yaw
        c.   roll and yaw
        d.   yaw and roll

8.   On an aircraft with a simple trim tab incorporated into a control surface, when
        the control surface is moved, the tab remains in the same position relative to
        the:

        a.   relative airflow
        b.   control surface
        c.   boundary layer airflow
        d.   aircraft horizontal plane

9.   The primary and secondary effects of applying the left rudder alone are:

        a.   left yaw and left roll
        b.   left yaw and right roll
        c.   right yaw and left roll
        d.   right yaw and right roll

10.   Which flying control surface(s) give(s) longitudinal control?

        a.   The rudder
        b.   The ailerons
        c.   The elevator
        d.   The flaps

11.   Ailerons give:

        a.   lateral control about the lateral axis
        b.   longitudinal control about the lateral axis
        c.   directional control about the normal axis
        d.   lateral control about the longitudinal axis

12.   Yawing is a rotation about:

        a.   the normal axis controlled by the rudder
        b.   the lateral axis controlled by the rudder
        c.   the longitudinal axis controlled by the ailerons
        d.   the normal axis controlled by the elevator

13. If the control column is moved forward and to the left:

    a. the left aileron moves up, right aileron moves down, elevator moves up
    b. the left aileron moves down, right aileron moves up, elevator moves down
    c. the left aileron moves up, right aileron moves down, elevator moves down
    d. the left aileron moves down, right aileron moves up, elevator moves up

14. The purpose of differential-ailerons is to:

    a. increase the yawing moment which opposes a turn
    b. reduce the adverse yawing moment when making a turn
    c. induce a pitching moment to prevent the nose from dropping in the turn
    d. improve the rate of roll

15. When displacing the ailerons from the neutral position:

    a. the up-going aileron causes an increase in induced drag
    b. induced drag remains the same, the up-going aileron causes a smaller increase in profile drag than the down-going aileron
    c. both cause an increase in induced drag
    d. the down-going aileron causes an increase in induced drag

16. The purpose of aerodynamic balance on a flying control surface is:

    a. to bring the aircraft into balance
    b. to prevent flutter of the flying control surface
    c. to reduce the control load to zero
    d. to make it easier for the pilot to move the control surface in flight

17. An aileron could be balanced aerodynamically by:

    a. making the up aileron move through a larger angle than the down aileron
    b. attaching a weight to the control surface forward of the hinge
    c. having the hinge set back behind the leading edge of the aileron
    d. having springs in the control circuit to assist movement

18. A control surface may be mass balanced by:

    a. fitting a balance tab
    b. attaching a weight acting forward of the hinge line
    c. fitting an anti-balance tab
    d. attaching a weight acting aft of the hinge line

19.   If the control column is moved to the right, a balance tab on the left aileron should:

   a.   move up relative to the aileron
   b.   move down relative to the aileron
   c.   not move unless the aileron trim wheel is turned
   d.   move to the neutral position

20.   The purpose of an anti-balance tab is to:

   a.   trim the aircraft
   b.   reduce the load required to move the controls at all speeds
   c.   reduce the load required to move the controls at high speeds only
   d.   ensure that the pilot's physical control load increases with increase of control surface deflection

21.   When the control column is pushed forward, a balance tab on the elevator:

   a.   will move up relative to the control surface
   b.   will move down relative to the control surface
   c.   will only move if the trim wheel is operated
   d.   moves to the neutral position

22.   A fixed trim tab on an aileron should:

   a.   be adjusted on the ground after a test flight to achieve laterally level flight
   b.   not be adjusted once it has been set by the manufacturer
   c.   be adjusted on the ground after a test flight to achieve longitudinally level flight
   d.   be adjusted from the cockpit to achieve laterally level flight

23.   The purpose of a spring-bias trim system is:

   a.   to maintain a constant tension in the trim tab system
   b.   to increase the feel in the control system
   c.   to reduce to zero the effort required by the pilot to counter stick force, after making a control movement
   d.   to compensate for temperature changes in cable tension

24.   The purpose of a trim tab is:

   a.   to assist the pilot in initiating movement of the controls
   b.   to zero the load on the pilots controls in the flight attitude required
   c.   to provide feel to the controls at high speed
   d.   to increase the effectiveness of the controls

25. To trim an aircraft which tends to fly nose heavy with hands off, the top of the elevator trim wheel should be:

    a. moved forward to raise the nose and this would cause the elevator trim tab to move down, and the elevator to move up
    b. moved backwards to raise the nose, and this would cause the elevator trim tab to move down, and the elevator to move up
    c. moved backwards to raise the nose, and this would cause the elevator trim tab to move up, and the elevator to move up
    d. moved backwards to raise the nose, and this would cause the elevator trim tab to move up and cause the nose to rise

26. Following re-trimming for straight and level flight, in an aircraft with a C of G near its forward limit, and an elevator fitted with a conventional trim-tab:

    a. nose-up pitch authority will be reduced
    b. nose-down pitch authority will be reduced
    c. longitudinal stability will be reduced
    d. tailplane down-load will be reduced

27. An aircraft's rudder is fitted with a balance tab. Movement of the rudder bar to the right, to yaw the aircraft to the right, will:

    a. move the rudder to the left; the balance tab will move to the left
    b. move the rudder to the right; the balance tab will move to the right
    c. move the rudder to the left; the balance tab will move to the right
    d. move the rudder to the right; the balance tab will move to the left.

28. Adverse yaw is partially counteracted by:

    a. Fowler flaps
    b. a fixed aileron trim tab
    c. aileron anti-balance tabs
    d. differential ailerons

29. 'Differential Ailerons' are a design feature that helps to counteract:

    a. stability about the longitudinal axis
    b. adverse yaw
    c. positive aircraft stability
    d. adverse roll

30. Controls are mass balanced in order to:

    a. eliminate control flutter
    b. aerodynamically assist the pilot in moving the controls
    c. provide equal control forces on all three controls
    d. return the control surface to neutral when the controls are released

31. Where are mass balance weights located relative to a control surface hinge line?

   a. Always on the hinge line, irrespective of the type of aerodynamic balance
   b. On the hinge line if the control surface does not have an inset hinge
   c. On the hinge line if the control surface has an inset hinge
   d. In front of the hinge line

32. Roll is:

   a. a result of aileron deflection and is motion about the lateral axis
   b. rotation about the normal axis
   c. a pitching movement about the lateral axis
   d. rotation about the longitudinal axis

33. If mass balance is used to eliminate flutter, it should be attached to a control surface:

   a. on the hinge
   b. behind the hinge
   c. above the hinge
   d. in front of the hinge

34. If the pilot moves the cockpit trim lever or wheel such that the trim tab on the elevator moves up relative to the control surface, how has the aircraft's trim been altered?

   a. It has not been altered
   b. More nose up
   c. More nose down
   d. More nose left

Question	1	2	3	4	5	6	7	8	9	10	11	12
Answer												

Question	13	14	15	16	17	18	19	20	21	22	23	24
Answer												

Question	25	26	27	28	29	30	31	32	33	34
Answer										

The answers to these questions can be found at the end of this book.

CHAPTER 13
THE STALL AND SPIN

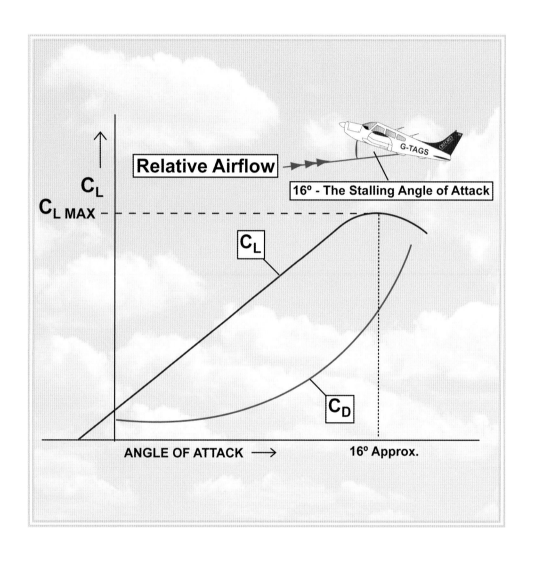

STALLING.

The Stalling Angle of Attack.

You learnt in the chapter on **Lift**, that the **coefficient of lift**, C_L, increases with increasing angle of attack, until C_L reaches a maximum, at about **16° angle of attack** for the type of wing used on most light aircraft. Above this angle, C_L decreases sharply. This situation is illustrated by the red C_L line in the graph at *Figure 13.1*.

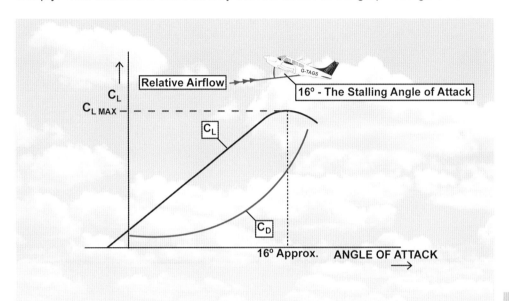

Figure 13.1 At the stalling angle of attack, C_L decreases sharply but C_D carries on increasing.

As the lift force developed by a wing is directly proportional to C_L, (**Lift = C_L ½ ρ v^2 S**), we can see from *Figure 13.1* that, whereas for small angles of attack any increases in angle of attack will produce an increase in lift force, when a certain angle is reached (16° in the diagram), any further increase in angle of attack will result in a reduction in the lift force. This angle is called the **stalling angle of attack**. (Note that *Figure 13.1* shows that the **coefficient of drag**, C_D, **continues to rise**, beyond the **stalling angle of attack**.)

It is important to realise that the speed at which a wing is moving through the air makes no difference to the angle of attack at which the wing stalls. An aerofoil stalls at a given angle of attack, not at a given speed.

Given that a wing stalls at a given angle of attack and not at a given airspeed, it is interesting to consider why the Pilot's Operating Handbook contains a **stalling speed** for an aircraft. We will return to that point in a moment. But first, let us look a little more closely at what happens at the point of stall.

The Coefficient of Lift is at a maximum value immediately prior to the stalling angle of attack being reached.

An aircraft will stall when the angle of attack reaches the critical angle, regardless of airspeed.

The Point of Stall.

As we have established, an aircraft's wing will always stall at the same **angle of attack**. As the **angle of attack (α)** increases, the pressure pattern around the wing changes and the **centre of pressure (CP)** moves forward, as depicted in *Figure 13.2*. The **CP** is at its most forward point just before the **stalling angle of attack** is reached. This situation is illustrated in *Figure 13.2* at α = 15°.

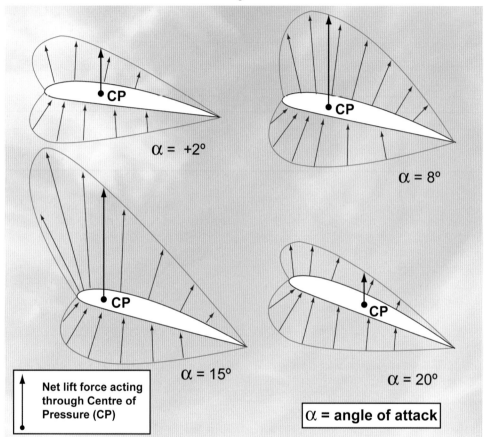

Figure 13.2 Changes in pressure pattern and lift force with an increasing angle of attack.

As detailed in *Figure 13.3*, as the **CP** moves forward, the pressure distribution around the wing is such that the airflow over the wing meets an increasingly rising pressure as it moves towards the wing's trailing edge. The **boundary layer**, consequently, begins to thicken, becomes more turbulent, and then separates from the upper surface of the wing. As the **angle of attack** continues to increase, the **separation point** moves forward.

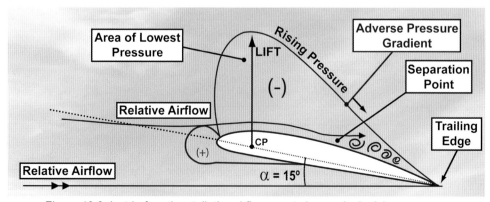

Figure 13.3 Just before the stall, the airflow meets increasingly rising pressure.

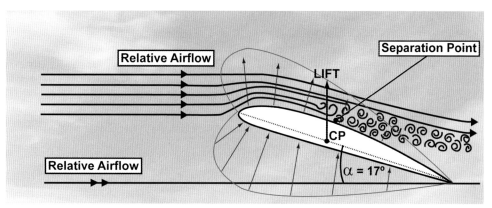

Figure 13.4 As the stalling angle of attack is reached and surpassed, most of the airflow separates from the wing. The CP moves rearwards and lift reduces abruptly.

At an **angle of attack**, above approximately 16°, most of the airflow separates from the wing upper surface. The **CP** moves sharply rearwards and the lift force decreases abruptly and is no longer sufficient to balance the weight of the aircraft. *(See Figure 13.4)*. The wing has **stalled**. At the **stall**, the controls lose a great deal of their effectiveness and the aircraft loses height rapidly, until the aircraft is recovered from the stall.

An aircraft can be stalled in any attitude regardless of speed.

The Straight Flight Stalling Speed.
In straight flight, the stall occurs at an indicated airspeed which is defined in the Pilot's Operating Handbook (POH) as the **stalling speed**. But we have just established that a wing stalls at a given angle of attack, not at a given airspeed. So what is meant by the stalling speed contained in the POH?

In order to answer this question, we will assume that an aircraft whose wing stalls at an **angle of attack** of 16° is flying straight and level at 90 knots, with the relative airflow meeting the wing at a typical cruising angle of attack of 4°. As the aircraft is in straight flight, the lift produced by the wings balances the aircraft's weight exactly. Now, you will recall from the **lift formula**, **Lift = $C_L \frac{1}{2} \rho v^2 S$**, that the factors contributing to the generation of this lift force, which just balances the aircraft's weight, are: the density of the air, ρ, the area of the lifting surfaces, **S**, the aircraft's airspeed, **v**, and the coefficient of lift, C_L, which represents wing camber and configuration, as well as angle of attack.

If the pilot now closes the throttle, which in level flight is providing the speed of the airflow, **v**, the value of **v** in the **lift equation** reduces, leading to a reduction in the lift force. Consequently, as lift just balanced weight before the pilot closed the throttle, unless the pilot takes some other action, weight will be greater than lift and the aircraft will begin to lose height.

If the pilot wishes to maintain height, he can choose to maintain the lift equal to weight by increasing the value of C_L. The only way the pilot can increase C_L without lowering the flaps is by moving the control column rearwards to increase the wing's **angle of attack**.

If he chooses to take this action, airspeed, **v**, will decrease further because an aircraft cannot continue to fly level at a constant speed unless the propeller produces sufficient thrust to counteract drag, **induced drag** having also risen with increasing **angle of attack**. With the throttle closed, of course, thrust is effectively zero. (There is a small residual thrust, because the engine is idling, but that is insufficient to balance drag and can be discounted.) As the airspeed decreases, the lift will necessarily also reduce (**Lift = C$_L$ ½ ρ v^2 S**) unless lift is maintained equal to weight by the pilot further increasing the **angle of attack** (and, thus, **C$_L$**) through a continued rearward movement of the control column. And, of course, because of the continuing increase in **angle of attack**, airspeed will further decrease and induced drag increases, and so forth and so on until the **angle of attack** reaches the **stalling angle of attack**, and the wing **stalls**, causing the aircraft to lose height rapidly until the pilot recovers from the stall.

When the stall occurs, in this straight flight scenario, the airspeed will have reduced to a certain value which, in the Pilot's Operating Handbook, is given as the <u>stalling speed</u> for this particular aircraft. This quoted stalling speed only applies to the speed at which the wing reaches the stalling angle when the pilot attempts to keep the aircraft flying straight and level without any thrust from the propeller; (that is, with the throttle closed).

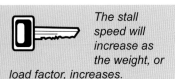

The stall speed will increase as the weight, or load factor, increases.

An aircraft's stalling speed quoted in the Pilot's Operating Handbook is, therefore, the speed at which the aircraft stalls in straight flight only, at a given all-up weight.

The very term **stalling speed** is misleading, because of the suggestion contained within the term that the stall is dependent on airspeed. This is not the case. **The aircraft will stall over a range of speeds** provided that the **stalling angle of attack** is reached at the given speed. Let us look into this statement more deeply.

FACTORS AFFECTING THE STALL.

The Effect of Weight on the Stall.
We have established that a given wing will always stall at the same **angle of attack**, which is approximately **16°** for a typical light aircraft aerofoil cross section. The **stalling angle of attack** can be defined as that **angle of attack** at which the **lift coefficient**, **C$_L$**, reaches a maximum, and beyond which **C$_L$** will decrease sharply. We may represent this maximum value of **C$_L$** at the point of the stall as **C$_{L\,MAX}$**.*(See Figure 13.1)*.

Therefore, the **lift equation**, which defines the **lift force at the point of stall** becomes:

Lift = C$_{L\,MAX}$ ½ ρ v^2 S

Also, at the point of the stall, from **straight and level flight**, immediately before the angle of attack is further increased causing the stall to occur, lift must equal weight. It follows, then, that, for the situation just before the stall occurs, in straight and level flight, we may re-write the above equation as:

Weight = Lift = C$_{L\,MAX}$ ½ ρ (v$_{stall}$)^{2}S

In this equation, (applied to the point of stall from straight and level flight, remember), **v** now represents the stalling speed quoted in the Pilot's Operating Handbook, so we have represented stalling speed as **v$_{stall}$**.

Now, as **C$_{L\,MAX}$** is constant, for a given wing (because a given wing will always stall at the same angle of attack) and taking wing area, **S**, to be also constant (i.e.

discounting use of flap), we can see that **any increase in aircraft weight will require an increase in v_{stall} to make the lift equation balance**. Conversely, a decrease in weight would require a decrease in v_{stall} to make the equation balance.

The stall speed increases as aircraft weight increases.

It follows, then, from the lift equation, that a heavier aircraft will stall at a higher airspeed than a more lightly loaded aircraft.

Manoeuvring with Varying Load Factors.

We have seen that the **lift equation** applied to the point of stall, from straight and level flight, can be written as:

Weight = Lift = $C_{L\,MAX}$ ½ ρ $(v_{stall})^2$ S where v_{stall} is the aircraft's straight and level stall speed.

But, as you learnt in the chapter on '**Flight Forces**', in manoeuvres such as turning flight, lift needs to be greater than the weight of the aircraft.

In a 60°-banked level turn, for instance, **the lift force** required to generate the necessary centripetal force for the turn, and, at the same time, continue to balance the aircraft's weight in order to maintain level flight in the turn, **is twice as great as the aircraft's weight**. During the turn, the **inertial reaction to this increase in lift is equal in magnitude to the increased lift**, and acts in the opposite direction to the line of action of the lift, as depicted in *Figure 13.5*.

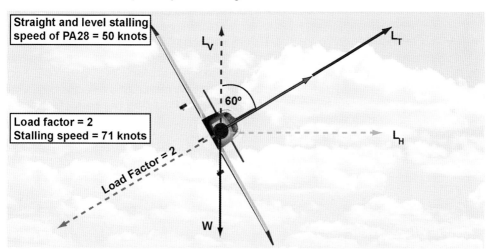

Figure 13.5 A 60° banked turn. The lift required for the turn is twice its straight flight value, Load Factor is 2, and the stalling speed is 71 knots.

The complete aircraft, including its occupants, will be subjected to this **inertial reaction** which is known as **load factor**. The **load factor** acting on the aircraft during a 60°-banked turn is **2**, because the lift force is twice its value for level flight, and the aircraft and its occupants sense this **load factor** as an **apparent increase in weight** by a factor of **2**. In popular parlance, the pilot will say that he is pulling **2g**.

We are now in a position to refer once more to the **lift equation** and to apply it to turning flight to see what it has to teach us in terms of **stalling speed in the turn**. As we have learnt, immediately before the stall occurs:

Lift = $C_{L\,MAX}$ ½ ρ $(v_{stall})^2$ S

Now, in the **60°- banked level turn** that we are considering, we have learnt that, because the **load factor = 2, lift** must be twice the value of that required for straight and level flight. So, from the **lift equation** we can deduce that as **lift** is increased by a factor of **2** in the **60° turn**, and as $C_{L\,MAX}$, ½, ρ, and **S** are all constants, $(v_{stall})^2$, which represents the aircraft's airspeed at which the aircraft stalls in straight and level flight, must also increase by a factor of **2**. We can see immediately, then, that an **aircraft's stalling speed increases in a turn**, because of the increase in **load factor**.

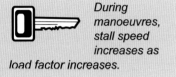

During manoeuvres, stall speed increases as load factor increases.

And, of course, the stalling speed is getting higher because, with the increased load factor, the relative airflow meets the wing at the stalling angle of attack (16° for a conventional aerofoil section) at a higher speed than if the aircraft were in level flight.

But by how much does the **stalling speed** increase in a turn?

Well, if $(v_{stall})^2$ has doubled in the **60°-banked level turn**, then, **for the 60°- banked turn:**

v_{stall} has increased by a factor of $\sqrt{2}$

In other words, v_{stall} has increased by a factor of 1.414

In a 60°-banked turn, then, stalling speed increases by a factor of 1.414 times the straight and level stalling speed.

Now, in the **lift equation**, v_{stall} is the **True Airspeed (TAS)** at the stall. But, as you learn elsewhere in this book, **TAS** is directly proportional to the **Indicated Airspeed (IAS)** that the pilot reads from the Airspeed Indicator. **Therefore, in the 60° - banked turn, if the stalling speed, expressed as TAS, has increased by a factor of 1.414, the stalling speed expressed as IAS has also increased by the same factor.**

So if we know an aircraft's **stalling speed** from straight flight, it is easy to calculate its **stalling speed** in a turn. For instance, if an aircraft's straight flight **stalling speed** is 50 knots, indicated, its stalling speed in a 60°-banked level turn will be (50 × 1.414) knots, which is approximately 70 knots, indicated.

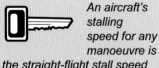

An aircraft's stalling speed for any manoeuvre is the straight-flight stall speed multiplied by the square root of the load factor.

Furthermore, if we know the **load factor** to which an aircraft is subjected during a turn, **or in the course of any other manoeuvre**, and if we also know the aircraft's straight-flight **stalling speed** (given in the **Pilot's Operating Handbook**), we can easily calculate the **stalling speed for the manoeuvre**, from the equation:

$$v_{stall(m)} = v_{stall(SF)} \times \sqrt{\text{Load Factor}}$$

where $v_{stall(m)}$ is the indicated stalling speed for the particular manoeuvre, and $v_{stall(SF)}$ is the stalling speed from straight and level flight.

We can also immediately deduce that any manoeuvre which increases the load factor on an aircraft will also increase its stalling speed during the manoeuvre. So an aircraft pulling out of a high speed dive will stall at a speed considerably higher than the straight flight stalling speed; in other words, its wing will reach the **stalling angle of attack** during the pull-out while the aircraft is still flying at high speed. This situation is depicted in *Figure 13.6*.

For example, if, during the pull-out manoeuvre depicted in *Figure 13.6*, the **load factor** were to reach **4** (that is, if the aircraft "pulled **4g**"), the equation in the blue box, above, tells us that aircraft would stall at a speed twice as high ($\sqrt{4}$) as that published in the **Pilot's Operating Handbook**. So, if the aircraft's published **stalling speed** were 50 knots IAS, it would stall at 100 knots IAS, while pulling out from the dive that we are considering.

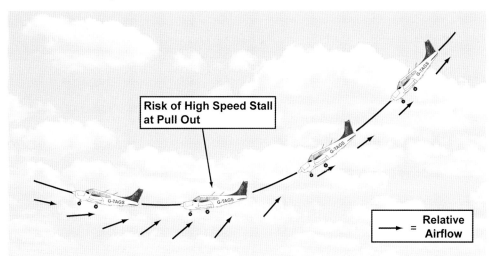

Figure 13.6 An aircraft will stall at any speed when its wing reaches the stalling angle of attack.

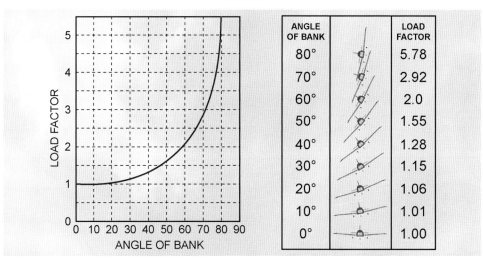

Figure 13.7 Load Factors in the turn for various angles of bank (applies to all aircraft).

Figure 13.7 shows the **load factor** to which an aircraft is subjected for turns at various **angles of bank**. Note that the **load factors** shown apply to **all aircraft**, at the **angles of bank** indicated. So, if you know the straight flight stalling speed $v_{stall(SF)}$ for a particular aircraft, you can easily calculate its stalling speed for any angle of bank, by noting the corresponding **load factor** for that angle of bank and applying the equation:

$$v_{stall(m)} = v_{stall(SF)} \times \sqrt{\text{Load Factor}}$$

Figure 13.8 overleaf gives **stalling speeds for turns of various angles of bank**. The speeds in the graph overleaf are based on a **stalling speed from straight and level flight** of **50 knots**, indicated.

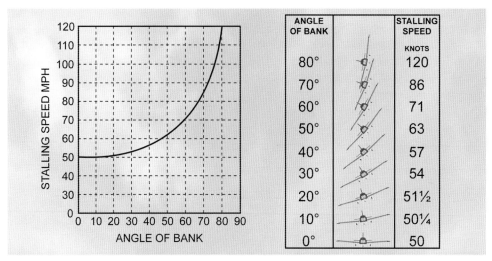

Figure 13.8 Stalling speeds for various angles of bank based on a straight-flight stalling speed of 50 knots.

You should note that only aircraft fitted with very powerful engines are able to fly level turns at angles of bank above 70°. The engine needs to be powerful in order to overcome the high levels of induced drag at the angles of attack necessary to fly very steep level turns. Such aircraft also need to have structures which can support the stress of the **high load factors** generated by very steep turns. Training aircraft rarely execute turns above 60° angle of bank. 45° angle of bank will most probably be the steepest turn that you will be required to fly in PPL training.

For your general interest, we include in the blue box the mathematics required to derive the formula for calculating **load factor** for a turn of any angle of bank, θ.

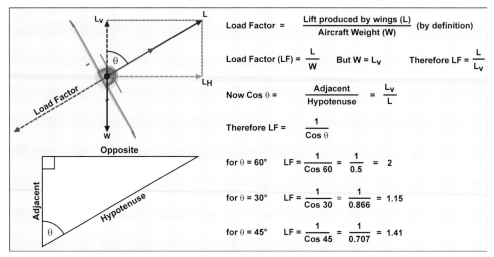

Figure 13.9 Calculating load factor from angle of bank.

The Effect of Altitude on Stall Speed.
In the lift equation, **Lift = $C_L \frac{1}{2} \rho v^2 S$**, **v** represents the aircraft's **True Airspeed (TAS)**.

So, immediately before the stall where **Lift = $C_{L\,MAX}\,\frac{1}{2}\,\rho(v_{stall})^2 S$**, v_{stall} is also a **TAS**.

TAS always represents the actual speed of the aircraft through the air.

On the other hand, as you learnt in Chapter 4, **Airspeed Indicators (ASI)** fitted to aircraft are calibrated to read **TAS** in ICAO Standard Atmosphere sea-level conditions only, where the air density, ρ, is **1.225 kg/m³**.

For any given **TAS**, if ρ decreases below **1.225 kg/m³**, the corresponding **Indicated Airspeed (IAS)**, the speed that a pilot reads from the **ASI**, will decease too.

Consequently, because ρ decreases with increasing altitude (mostly because pressure also decreases with altitude), we may deduce that, in general, for any given **TAS**, the corresponding **IAS** will decrease, the higher an aircraft climbs.

What we can state with absolute confidence is that **IAS** is equal to **TAS** only when ρ **= 1.225 kg/m³**; and it is a sound general assumption that, at altitude, **IAS** will always be less than **TAS**.

So, if the **Pilot's Operating Handbook** for a particular aircraft tells us that the aircraft stalls at an **IAS** of **60 knots**, what happens to the **indicated stall speed** that the pilot reads from the **ASI**, as the aircraft changes altitude?

The question is not difficult to answer. All you have to remember is that the **IAS** is read from the **ASI** and that the **ASI** is actually reading the dynamic pressure, **Q**, that the airflow is exerting on the aircraft as it advances through that air. If you need to refresh your memory on this topic, take another look at Chapter 4.

You may recall, though, that the expression for dynamic pressure, **Q**, is:

Q = ½ ρ v²

If we examine the **lift equation**, we see that the expression for dynamic pressure, **Q**, is part of that equation. We see that:

Lift = C_L½ ρv²S

and   **Q = ½ ρ v²**

So,   **Lift = C_LQS**

We can also see that, at the point of stall, the dynamic pressure, **Q_{stall}**, acting on the aircraft is given by the expression:

Q_{stall} = ½ ρ(v_{stall})²

It is, of course, **Q_{stall}** which determines the **IAS** at the stall.

So, at the point of stall,

Lift = $C_{L\,MAX}$ Q_{stall} S

And because, right up to the moment the aircraft stalls, **lift** must equal the aircraft's **weight**, we may write, for the stall:

Weight = Lift = $C_{L\,MAX}$ Q_{stall} S

Now, an aircraft's straight-flight stall speed is always quoted in the **Pilot's Operating Handbook** for a given **all-up weight**. We may deduce, then, that:

Weight is a constant, at the point of stall.

And, as **Weight = Lift**

Lift is also a constant, at the point of stall

Likewise, as **Weight = Lift = $C_{L\,MAX}$ Q_{stall} S**

The expression, **$C_{L\,MAX}$ Q_{stall} S** must be a constant, at the stall:

Finally, **$C_{L\,MAX}$** is, by definition, a constant, and, likewise, if the pilot does not alter his flap setting, wing area, **S**, is also a constant. It follows then that:

Q_{stall} is a constant

And **Q_{stall}** is the **Indicated Air Speed (IAS)** at the stall.

The stalling IAS for a given aircraft and a given weight or load factor will be the same at all altitudes.

We may conclude, then, that an aircraft always stalls at the same **IAS** from straight and level flight, whatever the altitude the aircraft is flying at, even though the stalling **IAS** will represent different values of **True Airspeed (TAS)**, depending on the prevailing value of air density, ρ.

By looking again at the original **lift equation** for the point of stall,

$$\text{Lift} = C_{L\,MAX}\ \tfrac{1}{2}\ \rho(v_{stall})^2\ S$$

Where **v_{stall}** is the **TAS** at the stall, we can see that as ρ decreases with increasing altitude, **v_{stall}** (the **TAS**) must increase to make the **lift equation** balance.

However, the **IAS** at the stall is an indication of the term $\tfrac{1}{2}\ \rho(v_{stall})^2$ (i.e. **Q_{stall}**) and the value of this term **remains constant at all altitudes**. Therefore the **indicated stalling speed remains constant at all altitudes**.

The Effect of Aerofoil Section on the Stall.
The **shape** of a wing's **aerofoil section** will affect the aircraft's behaviour at the stall.

Some **aerofoil sections** have benign stall characteristics. With these sections the approach to the stall is gradual and undramatic, leading to little height loss and rapid recovery. Aircraft used for elementary flying training generally have wings with benign stall characteristics. With other types of **aerofoil section**, however, the stall can be quite vicious. Aircraft fitted with this type of section may stall abruptly, lose significant height and require a very positive application of the stall recovery procedure.

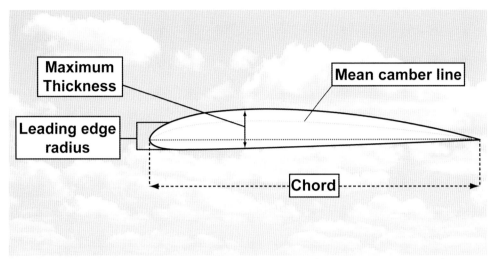

Figure 13.10 Some aerofoil characteristics which affect behaviour at the stall.

Among the **aerofoil features** which determine its behavioural characteristics at the stall, are: **leading-edge radius**, **degree of camber**, particularly near the leading-edge, **thickness-chord ratio**, **point of maximum thickness** and **maximum camber**. *(See Figure 13.10).*

A thick, highly cambered wing will stall more gently than a thin wing.

Generally speaking, the stall will be more abrupt the thinner the **aerofoil section**, and the further back the positions of **maximum camber** and **maximum thickness**. *Figure 13.11* depicts graphs of **C$_L$ against angle of attack** for two aerofoils, the graph on the left representing an aerofoil with more benign stall characteristics than the graph on the right.

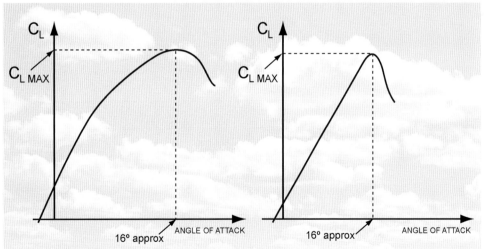

Figure 13.11 Graphs of C$_L$ against angle of attack. The graph on the left depicts an aerofoil of benign stall characteristics. The graph on the right depicts an aerofoil of less benign stall characteristics.

Variations of Aerofoil Section.

The aircraft designer may opt to use a **wing section**, at the root, which has a sharper leading edge and less pronounced camber than the section at the wing tip. The stall characteristics of such a wing would help ensure that the stall occurred at the root first *(See Figure 13.12 overleaf).*

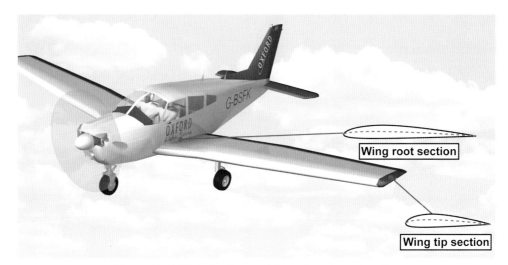

Figure 13.12 Variation in aerofoil section along the wing.

Stall Strips.

You have just learnt that an aerofoil with a sharper leading-edge radius will stall before one with a more rounded, leading-edge. Consequently, some aircraft have small triangular **stall strips** attached to the wing leading-edge in the region of the wing root. At high angles of attack, these **stall strips** promote separation of the airflow, helping to ensure that the wing root stalls before the wing tip. *(See Figure 13.13)*

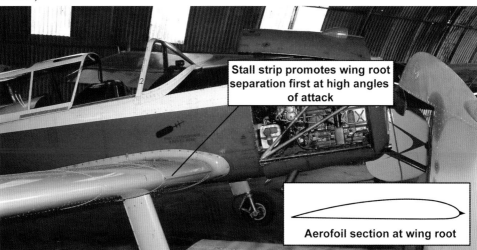

Figure 13.13 Stall strips help to ensure that the wing root stalls first.

Vortex Generators.

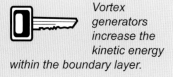

Vortex generators increase the kinetic energy within the boundary layer.

Vortex generators are small aerofoil-shaped blades, normally attached in rows as depicted in *Figure 13.14*, which project about 2.5cms (1 inch) vertically from the upper surface of the wing. These devices are designed to generate a small **vortex** within the boundary layer.

Vortex generators cause swirling motions in the boundary layer. This greater turbulence energises the boundary layer and delays separation, thus increasing control effectiveness, especially at the ailerons.

Figure 13.14 Vortex generators delay separation of the boundary layer.

Leading Edge Slots.

You have already learnt how **slots** energise the boundary layer, retard the onset of turbulent flow and delay separation *(See Figure 13.15)*. Generally, then, **slots** will cause the wing to stall at a higher angle of attack. Their use on the outboard leading-edge gives rise to a local increase in C_L which helps delay separation at the wing tip and retains aileron effectiveness.

Slots cause the stalling angle of attack to increase because they retard the onset of turbulence in the airflow and delay separation.

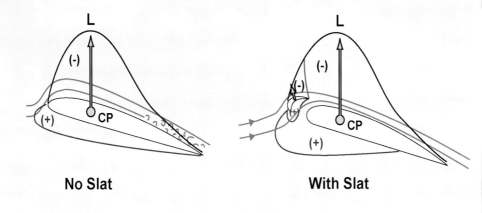

No Slat   **With Slat**

Figure 13.15 Slots/slats on the leading-edge of a wing energise the boundary layer and delay the onset of the stall.

The stall speed quoted in the Pilot's Operating Handbook refers to Maximum Take-Off Weight with the most forward C of G position.

The Effect of the Position of Centre of Gravity on the Stall.

You learnt in the **Mass and Balance** section of this series of text books that if the aircraft's **centre of gravity (C of G)** is at its most forward limit, the tailplane or stabilator has to produce a greater downforce in order to balance the lift-weight couple *(See Figure 13.16 overleaf)*. This greater tailplane force acting in the same direction as weight, effectively increases the weight of the aircraft. Consequently, for the reasons you have already learnt, the stalling speed increases. As the **C of G** moves aft, less tailplane downforce is required. This condition decreases the total weight of the aircraft and, consequently, decreases the stalling speed, too. *(See Figure 13.17 overleaf)*. During flight testing, the stalling speed is calculated for the worst case scenario, i.e. maximum weight, with the **C of G** at its most forward position.

The downforce produced by the tailplane influences the stall speed.

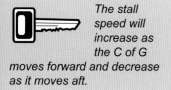

The stall speed will increase as the C of G moves forward and decrease as it moves aft.

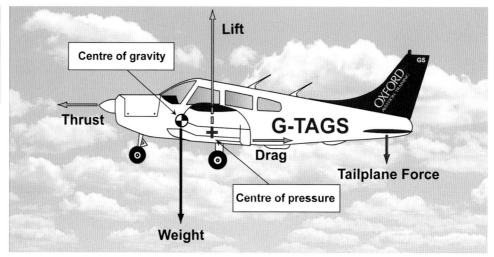

Figure 13.16 A forward C of G position requires an increased tailplane down-force, leading to an increase in stall speed.

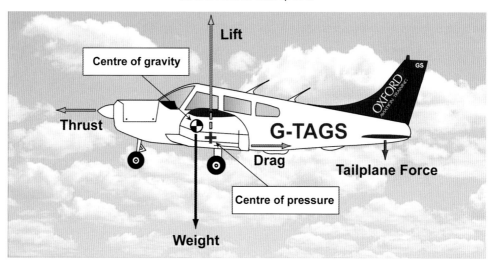

Figure 13.17 Stall speed decreases as the C of G moves aft, because the required tailplane down-force is less.

The Effect of Flaps on the Stall .

Chapter 10, **Lift Augmentation**, considers in detail the effect which the deployment of **flaps** has on the stall. As you have learnt from Chapter 10, deploying **flaps** alters the shape and camber of the wing's aerofoil section and increases $C_{L\,MAX}$. So, from the **lift equation** for the point of stall, we see that (v_{stall}) must decrease to keep the equation balanced.

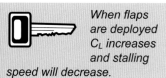

When flaps are deployed C_L increases and stalling speed will decrease.

Weight = Lift = $C_{L\,MAX}$ ½ ρ $(v_{stall})^2$ S

You have also learnt that lowering flaps, while increasing $C_{L\,MAX}$, reduces the angle of attack at which the aircraft stalls. **This means that if the aircraft stalls from straight and level flight, the nose attitude, with flaps deployed, will be lower than for an equivalent stall exercise with flaps raised.**

The fact that deploying **flaps** lowers the aircraft's stalling speed is, of course, one of the main advantages of **flaps,** allowing shorter take-off and landing distances to be achieved, as well as low-speed cruising flight, should a pilot become lost or find himself in deteriorating weather conditions such as a lowering cloudbase.

Note, however, that if the aircraft stalls when **flaps** are deployed, wing drop at the stall may be more marked than with **flaps** retracted, because the inward section of the wing will have a higher local C_L than the outer section.

Wing Contamination.

Stalling speed may be increased significantly if the wing is **contaminated** *(See Figure 13.18)*. Snow, frost, and ice deposits on the wing, and even heavy rain, can reduce the value of $C_{L\,MAX}$ by as much as 30% because of their modifying effect on wing profile. Deposits on the airframe will also increase aircraft weight, causing a further increase in stalling speed. Any **contamination** (ice, raindrops, squashed insects, etc.) must be removed from the wings before flight, especially from the leading edge.

Prior to flight, always ensure that the wing is free of all contaminants, especially at the leading edge.

Figure 13.18 Frost, snow and ice on the wings increase stall speed.

The Effect of Power, on the Stall.

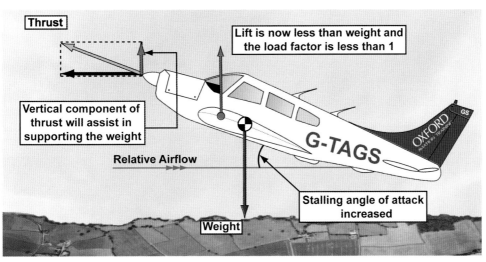

Figure 13.19 When stalling under power, thrust contributes to the Lift, and so the Load Factor is less than 1. Stall speed is, thus, reduced.

When the propeller is producing significant **thrust**, for instance, in cruising flight, the aircraft's stalling speed will be lower than with the engine throttled back. The reasons for this are twofold:

• The propeller **slipstream** energises the airflow over the inner region of the wings and, thereby delays separation. This action increases the value of $C_{L\,MAX}$ and, thus, decreases the stalling speed.

- The nose high attitude required to induce a stall under power means that the **thrust** force has a vertical component which helps to balance the aircraft's weight. Consequently, the lift force which must be generated by the wing to support the aircraft's weight is now less than the weight, and, so, **load factor** is less than **1**. As you learnt earlier in this chapter, reducing **load factor** reduces stall speed. *(See Figure 13.19 overleaf)*.

The Effect of Wing Plan Form on the Stall.

Rectangular Wings.

The separation of the airflow over a wing, which is the essential cause of the stall, does not necessarily occur simultaneously across the whole span of the wing. With a wing of rectangular **planform** (*see Figure 13.20*), separation tends to occur near the wing root and then progress outwards towards the wing tips.

The wing of rectangular **planform** can possess quite benign stall characteristics. The wing stalls first at its root, while the wing outer section is still effective. So, an aircraft with a rectangular wing is less prone to wing-drop at the stall.

With a wing of rectangular **planform**, the wing vortices cause high levels of induced drag near the stalling angle of attack. This increases downwash at the wing outer section, reducing the local angle of attack below that at the wing root. It is this situation which leads to the wing root stalling first. *(See Figure 13.20)*.

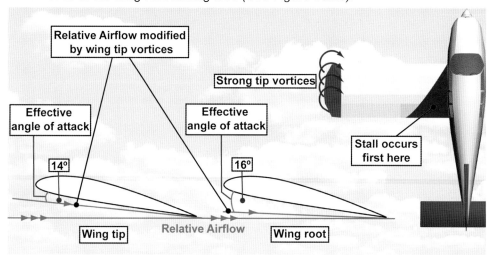

Figure 13.20 With rectangular wings, wing tip vortices reduce the angle of attack and ensure that the wing root stalls first.

Tapered Wings.

With wings of tapered **planform**, separation tends to occur first of all at the wing tips, and then spreads inboard. It follows, then, that if one wing stalls before the other, there will be pronounced wing drop at the stall.

The reason why the wing tips stall first with wings of tapered planform is, again, the nature of the wing-tip vortices. As you learnt in the chapter on drag, wing tip vortices for tapered wings are weak. Downwash at the tips is, therefore, less than at the root, resulting in a greater local angle of attack at the wing tip *(See Figure 13.21)*.

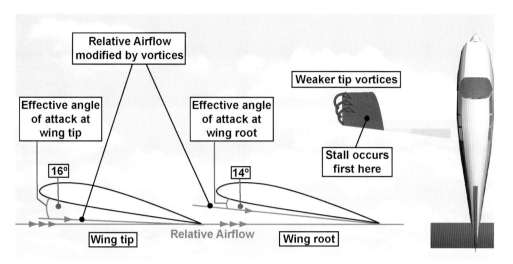

Figure 13.21 Wing tip vortices on tapered wings are weak, causing the wing tips to stall first.

WING CHARACTERISTICS WHICH DELAY WING TIP STALL.

The list below contains some of the most common wing design features which are used to delay the stall and to prevent the wing tips stalling first.

- **Stall strips**.
- **Variations of aerofoil section**.
- **Vortex generators**.
- **Leading edge slots**.
- **Washout**.

Washout.

We have already examined how most of these features help to delay wing-tip stall, but we have not yet, however, mentioned **washout**.

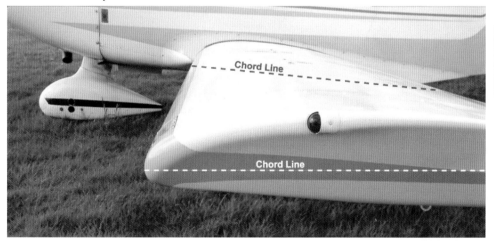

Figure 13.22 Washout is the name given to the reduction in a wing's angle of incidence towards the wing tip.

Washout ensures that the wing root stalls first.

Washout is the term used to describe the reduction in **angle of incidence** of the wing from root to tip. This feature helps ensure that the stall occurs at the wing root first *(See Figure 13.22)*. (NB. The angle of incidence is the angle between the wing chord line and the aircraft's longitudinal axis.)

SIGNS OF THE APPROACHING STALL.

During your PPL flying training, your instructor will demonstrate fully developed stalls to you, and teach you how to recover from the stall, using the **standard stall recovery procedure**. But while it is instructive to carry out stalls in the upper air under your instructor's supervision, and to practise stall recovery, **you must never allow your aircraft to stall unintentionally or inadvertently**. Several hundred feet can be lost while recovering from the stall, so, if your aircraft were to stall inadvertently at low height, on the approach, say, you may not have time to recover before the aircraft hits the ground.

It is, therefore, of vital importance for the pilot that he should be able to recognise the signs and symptoms of an approaching stall so that he can intervene early to prevent the stall from occurring. By learning the symptoms of the approaching stall, you are unlikely to allow your aircraft to stall inadvertently.

If you bear in mind all you have learnt about the stall in this chapter, you should have little difficulty in recognising the warning signs that the aircraft is in danger of stalling. Those warning signs are listed below. They may be present individually or in combination.

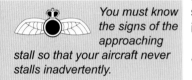

You must know the signs of the approaching stall so that your aircraft never stalls inadvertently.

- Possibly, **a high nose attitude, though this is not an essential sign** because, as you have learnt, a stall can occur at any attitude and at any speed. The stall occurs when the wing reaches the stalling angle of attack. **The stalling speed will vary**, among other things, **with the load factor** acting on the aircraft. If the stall occurs from straight and level flight, however, **nose attitude** will be high.

- **Decreasing airspeed**. When the stall is approached from level flight or the glide, the higher-than-normal nose attitude will be accompanied by decreasing airspeed.

- **Sloppiness and decreasing effectiveness of the controls**. Again, if the stall is approached from level flight, nose attitude will be high, speed will be decreasing and, consequently, the controls become noticeably less effective, feeling **sloppy** instead of firm.

- **Airframe buffeting**. As you have learnt, as the angle of attack increases in the approach to the stall, the airflow begins to separate and break away from the wing surface. Airflow in this condition is turbulent and gives rise to airframe **buffeting**. As the turbulence strikes the elevator, it is felt through the control column as vibration.

- **Stall warning device**. At the point of the stall (at $C_{L\,MAX}$) airframe buffeting becomes more severe. On some aircraft, such as the PA28 Warrior, **a stall warning horn operates at a preset angle of attack,** just before the onset of the stall.

Your flying instructor will teach you how to react to the signs of the approaching stall in order to prevent the stall from occurring. If you are operating normally in the climb, cruise or descent, in order to prevent the stall from occurring it will, generally, be sufficient for you to reselect the correct altitude for the phrase of flight that you are in, and to confirm that you have the appropriate power setting.

THE POINT OF STALL AND RECOVERY FROM THE STALL.

During normal flying operations, you should never stall the aircraft except, in the case of a tail-wheel aircraft, at the moment of touchdown, when the aircraft wheels are only a few inches above the ground, with the aircraft in the correct attitude for a three-point landing.

The most important lesson you learn from the stalling exercise, then, will most certainly be how to recognise the signs of the approaching stall, so that you can make sure that no stall occurs.

However, in your flying training, your instructor will demonstrate the **fully-developed stall** to you and teach you how to recover from it using the **standard stall recovery procedure**.

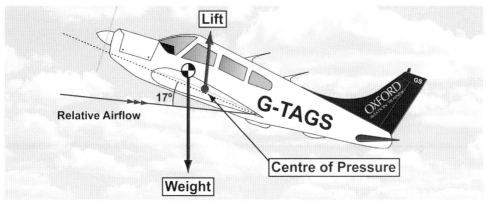

Figure 13.23 The point of stall. Lift has decreased below the value of weight, and the Centre of Pressure has moved rearwards.

First of all, let us remind ourselves that when a fully-developed stall occurs the wing has reached the angle of attack for maximum coefficient of lift, $C_{L\ MAX}$, around 16° for most wing aerofoil sections on training aircraft. Any further increase of angle of attack will cause the lift to decrease abruptly, while drag increases rapidly. *Figure 13.23* depicts the **lift-weight couple** as the aircraft is about to enter the stall. Lift has decreased below the value of weight, and the **centre of pressure** has moved rearwards. Notice that this sequence of events sets up a nose-down couple which

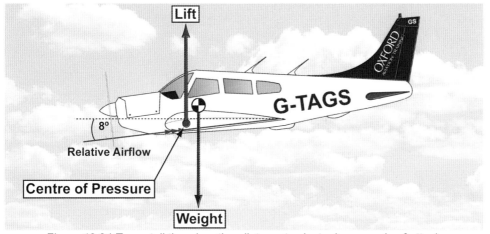

Figure 13.24 To unstall the wing, the pilot must select a lower angle of attack.

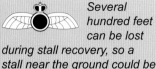

Several hundred feet can be lost during stall recovery, so a stall near the ground could be catastrophic.

will actually cause the nose to pitch downwards and so aid in the **recovery from the stall**. Many aircraft wings are designed with lift characteristics which aid in stall recovery in this way.

When the nose pitches down at the stall, the aircraft loses height, by several hundred feet generally speaking, and accelerates. The **angle of attack** is then reduced such that the wing becomes un-stalled. *(See Figure 13.24).*

However, unless the pilot carries out the **standard stall recovery procedure**, this "**design feature**" recovery will be unstable. The lift force would increase, the centre of pressure would move forward again, causing the nose to rise sufficiently for the aircraft to enter a second stall. The **standard stall recovery** should, therefore, always be carried out, with the controls being operated in a smooth and progressive manner. Power may or may not be used in stall recovery.

To recover from a fully-developed stall, always use the standard stall recovery procedure.

Your flying instructor will teach you all about the details of the **standard stall recovery procedure**; here, we consider only the **Principles of Flight** aspects of stall recovery.

These are fairly simple.

You have learnt that a **stall** occurs because the **angle of attack** between the relative airflow and the aircraft's wing has reached the stalling angle of attack. An approaching **stall** which is developing from an initial situation of level flight, or a glide, will be indicated to the pilot by a higher than normal nose attitude and decreasing speed. To recover from a **stall** from level flight or a glide, therefore, the pilot must select a lower **angle of attack** and allow the speed to increase to normal flying speed. The initial action, then, will be for the pilot to move the control column centrally forward, to select a suitable **stall recovery attitude**. It is vitally important that the control column is not displaced laterally as the pilot selects the **recovery attitude**. We discuss this issue in greater detail below. Your instructor will teach you the rest of the **stall recovery procedure**.

Always be aware that, with a load factor of greater than **1** acting on the airframe, for instance in a turn or when recovering from a high-speed dive, the aircraft can stall from any attitude. Nevertheless, you would still recover from the stall, or prevent the stall occurring, by decreasing the angle of attack, sometimes referred to, in these circumstances, as "unloading" the aircraft.

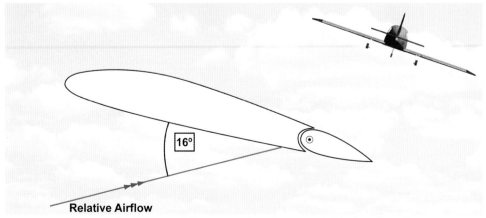

Relative Airflow

Figure 13.25 When a stall occurs, one wing may stall before the other.

Wing Drop at the Stall.

You have learnt that, for several reasons, for instance, wing design, wing contamination or even small differences in the manufacture of the wings, when a stall occurs, one wing may stall before the other.

If one wing stalls before the other, that wing will drop and the aircraft first rolls and then yaws towards the more stalled wing; if the pilot does not intervene, this situation may lead to **autorotation**. **Wing drop** at the stall is, therefore, an unstable and potentially hazardous situation. You will learn about **autorotation** and the **spin** in the next section of this chapter. Here, we will look at the **Principles of Flight** considerations of why **wing drop** at the stall is an unstable condition, and how it can be corrected.

If you experience a **wing drop** at the stall it must be dealt with immediately. On first consideration, the **wing drop** indicates a roll and your instinctive reaction may be to correct the roll by applying aileron in the opposite direction. **However this would be an incorrect and dangerous action.**

As we have already mentioned, the basic reason why the **wing-drop** may occur at the stall is because one wing stalls <u>before</u> the other. As the wing drops, its angle of attack increases still further, and so the dropping wing becomes even more stalled. Conversely, the angle of attack of the up-going wing decreases; this wing, therefore, is less stalled and may even have become unstalled. The increased drag of the stalled, down-going wing causes the aircraft to yaw towards it. This yaw, in turn, tends to speed up the up-going wing and, thus add to its lift. The rolling and yawing will continue until the pilot intervenes. If he does not intervene, the aircraft will enter a spin.

How, then, should a pilot react to **wing-drop** at the stall? Firstly and most importantly, he must not try to prevent the **wing-drop** with aileron. That action, by deflecting the aileron on the dropping wing downwards would increase the angle of attack of the dropping wing still further. As the dropping wing has already exceeded its stalling angle of attack, using aileron to try to raise the wing would make the wing even more stalled and so make the wing drop even more severe. *(See Figure 13.26).*

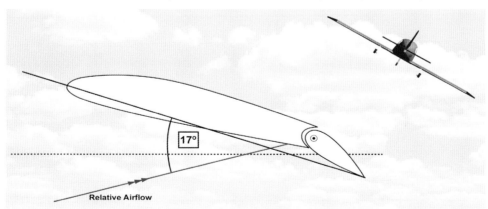

At the stall, never attempt to lift a dropping wing with aileron.

Figure 13.26 The dropping wing has already exceeded its stalling angle of attack. Using aileron to prevent wing-drop would aggravate the stall and so make the wing-drop even more severe.

Increasing the severity of the **wing-drop** would, of course, reinforce the roll. Increased roll would lead to yaw which would induce more roll, and so on, until **autorotation** set in, putting the aircraft into a **spin**. **Therefore, on no account should aileron be used to prevent wing drop at the stall.**

As you have learnt, the extra drag of the down-going wing causes **yaw** in the direction of the **wing drop** which, because it increases the speed and therefore the lift of the up-going wing, may give rise to aerodynamic conditions which may lead to further **roll** and further **yaw** and, then, to **autorotation** and the **spin**.

But, if the pilot prevents any further yaw, the above sequence of events will be broken.

Rudder is, therefore, the answer to **wing drop** at the stall. Rudder is used to stop the yaw and minimise the roll. The pilot should <u>not</u> try to <u>level</u> the wings with rudder; he should apply **sufficient rudder to prevent further yaw** while, at the same time, **unstalling the wings using the elevator**. As soon as the wings are unstalled, the pilot can centralise the rudder and roll the wings level using coordinated aileron and rudder.

The flying aspects of dealing with **wing drop** at the stall will be covered by your flying instructor.

Stall Warning.
Warning of the approaching stall may be aerodynamic in nature, as in the case of the **pre-stall buffet**, **decreasing speed**, **ineffective controls** or **high load factor**. Or, the **stall warning** may be electro-mechanical as in the case with audio warning devices.

THE SPIN.

When an aircraft **spins**, it is in **a state of stalled flight**, and is losing height rapidly in a steep helical descent, **yawing, rolling and pitching, at the same time**. Both wings are stalled, and the aircraft is **auto-rotating** under the influence of yawing and rolling moments.

Figure 13.27 The spin is a state of stalled flight with the aircraft in a steep descent, yawing, rolling and pitching at the same time.

Unless an aircraft is being spun intentionally, the **spin** will almost certainly have arisen because its controls were mishandled during a stall. We examined above how a wing drop at the stall can lead to a **spin** if the pilot does not react correctly. (*See Figure 13.28*).

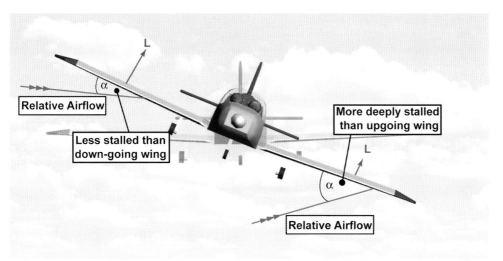

Figure 13.28 Wing drop at the stall may lead to a spin.

Now we can make a further fundamental statement about the **spin. For a spin to develop, yaw must be present at the point of the stall**. This **yaw** is very often caused by one wing stalling first and dropping.

In order better to understand how yaw may be present at the stall, we need to look at the drag situation if wing drop does occur at the stall.

At **low speeds** and **high angles of attack**, **total drag** consists almost exclusively of **induced drag**. When both wings are stalled, both wings experience high levels of **induced drag**. But if a wing drops at the stall, the up-going wing is less stalled than the down-going wing *(See Figure 13.28)*. The drag on the up-going wing is, therefore, less than that on the down-going wing, while its lift is greater. This state of affairs is depicted in *Figure 13.29* where C_L and C_D curves are plotted against **angle of attack**.

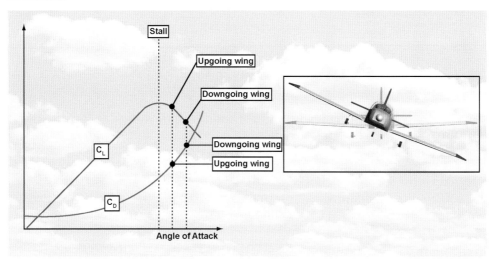

Figure 13.29 Wing-drop at the stall - C_L and C_D curves for the up-going and down-going wings.

In this situation, then, the aircraft first rolls and then yaws towards the more stalled wing. The angle of attack on the up-going wing is then reduced, increasing lift and reducing drag on that wing. The dropping wing, consequently, drops even more sharply, increasing angle of attack, aggravating the stall, decreasing its lift, and increasing induced drag, and so on. If the pilot were now to attempt to lift the dropping wing with aileron he would merely aggravate the stall on that wing and the unstable rolling and yawing movements towards the lower wing would reinforce each other, leading to **autorotation**. The aircraft would then begin to **spin**, losing height rapidly in a steep, helical, auto-rotating descent, yawing, rolling and pitching, at the same time.

The aircraft eventually settles down at a steady rate of **autorotation**. In the **spin**, although the rate of descent is high, airspeed is not excessive because total drag also remains very high. Because of the relatively low airspeed, load factors are low posing little danger of structural damage to the aircraft.

The situation of the **spin**, then, is entirely different to that of the **spiral dive** where speed increases rapidly and structural loads are high.

Determining Direction of the Spin.
There are basically two ways to determine the **direction of spin**. In good visual flight conditions the **direction of spin** can be established by looking along the nose of the aircraft to the ground.

Figure 13.30 The turn needle will always indicate the direction of spin.

Alternatively, the Pilot may refer to the **Turn and Slip Indicator**. The **turn needle** of the **Turn and Slip Indicator** will be fully deflected in the direction of the spin. The **Turn and Slip Indicator** in *Figure 13.30* is indicating a spin to the right.

Spinning is not taught in the Private Pilot's Licence flying syllabus. But it is essential that you understand what makes an aircraft **spin** so that you can avoid any mishandling of the controls that may lead to a **spin**. If you undertake the necessary training in an aircraft approved for **spinning,** you may have an opportunity to try **spinning** for yourself. However, in your PPL training emphasis will be on **spin avoidance**, so that you never enter a **spin** unintentionally.

Spin Recovery.
As a PPL student you will not be required to practise **spins**; neither is this book a manual of flying instruction. But the general **Principles of Flight** considerations for **spin recovery** may be of interest to you. Note that, because both wings are stalled

in a **spin**, the ailerons are ineffective and cannot be used to recover from a **spin**. Use of the ailerons will merely deepen the stall on the respective wing.

Spin recovery is effected in the following manner:

•   Rudder is applied against the direction of spin. This action has the effect of reducing the yaw and slowing down rotation.

•   The control column (held central so that there is no aileron deflection) is moved progressively forward to reduce angle of attack and unstall the wings. The forward movement of the control column is continued until the spin stops.

•   The rudder is centralised as soon as the spin stops.

•   There should then be no delay in levelling out from the dive, or else the aircraft will accelerate rapidly and could exceed V_{NE}. Unnecessary loss of height must also be avoided. The recovery from the dive should be smooth in order to avoid subjecting the aircraft to high load factors which might lead to a further stall.

Spin Avoidance.
Your PPL training, in terms of the spin will most probably be confined to **spin avoidance** training.

You have learnt that the spin can only occur when the aircraft is stalled, and when the aircraft is moving in the yawing plane at the moment of the stall, either because the pilot is misusing the rudder or because a wing drops at the stall, inducing a yaw in the direction of wing drop.

Consequently, the first lesson to learn about **spin avoidance**, is that you should **avoid the stall. If you never allow your aircraft to stall, it cannot spin**.

A second very important aspect of **spin avoidance** is that you should <u>understand</u> how a spin <u>may</u> develop from a stall through mishandling of the controls. With this understanding, you are unlikely ever to spin inadvertently.

The spin is a condition of stalled flight. Never allow your aircraft to stall, and it will not spin.

Three very important considerations about correct use of the controls at the stall are:

•   If you are practising stalling and stall recovery, make sure that you are applying no yaw at the moment of stall; otherwise the stall may lead to a spin.

•   If you experience wing drop at the stall, respond to this in the correct manner. Never attempt to use aileron to lift a dropping wing at the stall. Apply rudder in the opposite direction to the wing drop to stop further yaw and minimise the roll. Do not try to level the wings with rudder. At the same time, move the control column centrally forward to unstall the wings. As soon as the wings are unstalled and normal flying speed in indicated on the ASI, centralise the rudder and roll the wings level using coordinated aileron and rudder.

•   Ease out of the dive, smoothly.

Distractions when you are flying at high angles of attack may lead to mishandling of the controls. System malfunctions, preoccupation with equipment, navigation, radio calls and avoidance of other aircraft are just some of the everyday distractions that you might encounter and which might lead to uncoordinated control movements at a critical stage of flight.

Conclusion.

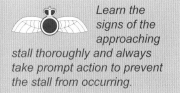

Learn the signs of the approaching stall thoroughly and always take prompt action to prevent the stall from occurring.

Finally, to end this chapter, the importance of **stall recognition** and **prompt application of correct recovery action** cannot be over-emphasised. Remember, too, that on take-off and landing, when the aircraft is close to the ground, the airspeed is low and the controls sluggish, with the possible presence of turbulence, and all the other distractions that take your attention at these critical stages of flight, there may be insufficient height to complete a recovery if the aircraft should stall and spin.

Always remain vigilant, therefore, and never get into a situation where your aircraft can stall without your having intended it.

Representative PPL - type questions to test your theoretical knowledge of Stalling and Spinning.

1.   An aeroplane will stall at the same:

      a.   angle of attack and attitude with relation to the horizon
      b.   airspeed regardless of the attitude with relation to the horizon
      c.   angle of attack regardless of the attitude with relation to the horizon
      d.   indicated airspeed regardless of altitude, bank angle and load factor

2.   A typical stalling angle of attack for a wing without sweepback is:

      a.   4°
      b.   16°
      c.   30°
      d.   45°

3.   If the aircraft weight is increased, the stalling angle of attack will:

      a.   remain the same
      b.   decrease
      c.   increase
      d.   the position of the C of G does not affect the stall speed

4.   If the angle of attack is increased above the stalling angle:

      a.   lift and drag will both decrease
      b.   lift will decrease and drag will increase
      c.   lift will increase and drag will decrease
      d.   lift and drag will both increase

5.   The angle of attack at which an aeroplane stalls:

      a.   will occur at smaller angles of attack flying downwind than when flying upwind
      b.   is dependent upon the speed of the airflow over the wing
      c.   is a function of speed and density altitude
      d.   will remain constant regardless of gross weight

6.   In a steady, level turn, at 60° angle of bank, the stalling speed of an aircraft which has a straight flight stalling speed of 60 knots IAS, would be:

      a.   43 kt
      b.   60 kt
      c.   84 kt
      d.   120 kt

7.   The stalling speed of an aircraft in a steady turn would be:

    a.   the same as in level flight
    b.   lower than in level flight
    c.   higher than in level flight, and a lower angle of attack
    d.   higher than in level flight and at the same angle of attack

8.   A wing with washout would have:

    a.   the tip chord less than the root chord
    b.   the tip angle of incidence less than the root angle of incidence
    c.   the tip angle of incidence greater than the root angle of incidence
    d.   the tip camber less than the root camber

9.   If aircraft weight is increased, stalling speed will:

    a.   remain the same
    b.   decrease
    c.   increase
    d.   weight does not affect the stalling speed

10.   Stalling may be delayed until a higher angle of attack is reached by:

    a.   increasing the adverse pressure gradient
    b.   increasing the surface roughness of the wing top surface
    c.   distortion of the leading edge by ice build-up
    d.   increasing the kinetic energy of the boundary layer

11.   Slots increase the stalling angle of attack by:

    a.   Increasing leading edge camber
    b.   Retarding the onset of turbulence and delaying separation of the boundary layer
    c.   Reducing the effective angle of attack
    d.   Reducing span-wise flow

12.   An aeroplane wing stalls when:

    a.   The indicated airspeed is too low
    b.   The critical angle of attack is exceeded
    c.   The laminar airflow becomes turbulent
    d.   It is subjected to unusually high 'G' forces

13.   The stalling speed of an aircraft is a function of the:

    a.   Inverse of the Load Factor
    b.   Indicated airspeed
    c.   Square of the weight
    d.   Square root of the Load Factor

14.   If the Angle of Attack is increased beyond the Critical Angle of Attack, the wing will no longer produce sufficient lift to support the weight of the aircraft:

    a.   Unless the airspeed is greater than the normal stall speed
    b.   Regardless of airspeed or pitch attitude
    c.   Unless the pitch attitude is on or below the natural horizon
    d.   In which case, the control column should be pulled-back immediately

15.   With the flaps lowered, the stalling speed will:

    a.   Increase
    b.   Decrease
    c.   Increase, but occur at a higher angle of attack
    d.   Remain the same

16.   The reason for washout being designed into an aircraft wing is to:-

    a.   Increase the effectiveness of the flaps
    b.   Cause the outboard section of the wing to stall first
    c.   Decrease the effectiveness of the ailerons
    d.   Cause the inboard section of the wing to stall first

17.   When the aircraft is in a spin, the direction of spin is most reliably found by reference to which of the following indications?

    a.   Artificial horizon
    b.   Slip indicator
    c.   Direction indicator
    d.   Turn needle

18.   At the stall, the Centre of Pressure moving backwards will cause the nose to _____ , and the decreased lift will cause the aircraft to _____.

    a.   Yaw, reduce speed
    b.   Drop, lose height
    c.   Rise, sink
    d.   Drop, reduce speed

19.   When flaps are lowered the stalling angle of attack of the wing:

    a.   Remains the same, but C_{LMAX} increases
    b.   Increases and C_{LMAX} increases
    c.   Decreases, but C_{LMAX} increases
    d.   Decreases, but C_{LMAX} remains the same

20.   On a given type of aircraft, the C of G moves forward as fuel is used; therefore:

    a.   The stalling speed will increase
    b.   The stalling speed will decrease
    c.   The stalling speed will remain exactly the same
    d.   Any of the above could be true

21.   If a wing drops at the stall:

      a.   The downgoing wing becomes more stalled while the upgoing wing becomes less stalled
      b.   The wings should be immediately levelled by use of aileron
      c.   The secondary effect of yaw should be utilised
      d.   The upgoing wing becomes more stalled than the downgoing wing

22.   Following a stall from straight flight, which of the symptoms below best describes the fully developed stall?

      a.   The airspeed begins to decrease
      b.   The nose pitches down and the aircraft loses height
      c.   The nose pitches up and the aircraft controls become sloppy
      d.   A wing tends to drop

23.   When is the coefficient of lift at a maximum?

      a.   At or just before the stall
      b.   With the elevator fully deflected upwards
      c.   When the lift/drag ratio is at its most favourable
      d.   At about 4° angle of attack

Question	1	2	3	4	5	6	7	8	9	10	11	12
Answer												

Question	13	14	15	16	17	18	19	20	21	22	23
Answer											

The answers to these questions can be found at the end of this book.

CHAPTER 14
FLIGHT AND GROUND LIMITATIONS

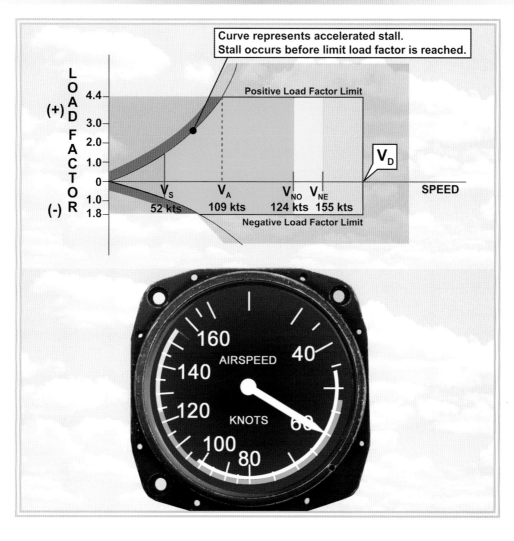

AIRCRAFT STRUCTURAL INTEGRITY.

An aircraft's structure must be able to withstand the loads to which it is subjected during normal operations, in flight and on the ground.

In order to obtain type approval, the design of a light aircraft must conform to certain standards, among which is the requirement that the aircraft structure should have adequate strength and stiffness to withstand, without suffering structural damage, in-flight manoeuvring loads, plus induced, transient loads caused by turbulence, so that the aircraft may operate within its prescribed category; for instance, normal, utility, or aerobatic. Aircraft categories are defined in the **'Aeroplanes'** volume of this series.

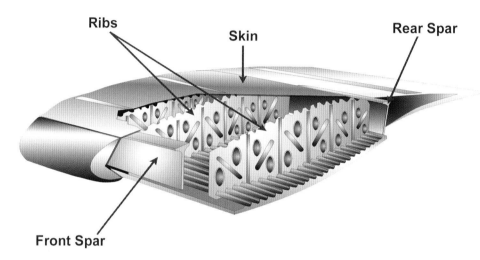

Figure 14.1 An aircraft's structure must be able to withstand the flight loads it will encounter in its operational role.

The safety and integrity of the aircraft also demand that the aircraft's structure be able to withstand loads which exceed the **design loads** by a prescribed safety margin. The factor which is allowed by the aircraft designer, in terms of the strength of the aircraft's structure, for flight beyond normal operating limits is called the **safety factor**. The designer cannot afford, however, to make the **safety factor** too great, or else the aircraft would become too heavy and could not operate efficiently. For a light aircraft, the **safety factor** is normally in the order of **1.5**. That means that the aircraft's structure will support, without catastrophic damage, a load 1.5 times the greatest load envisaged by the designer. Loads greater than those allowed for by the **safety factor** will almost certainly cause serious structural damage to the airframe.

In order that an aircraft is not flown in a manner or configuration which would impose loads on the aircraft's structure that it is not designed to withstand, the aircraft manufacturer specifies certain **limitations** on the operation of the aircraft. These **limitations** are generally expressed in terms of **mass (or weight), airspeed, load factor, position of centre of gravity** and **wind speed**.

General limitations are published in the **Pilot's Operating Handbook** for the aircraft, and in the aircraft's **Check List**, so that the pilot may know that he is to operate within these limitations, in order to ensure the safety of his aircraft. A number of limitations, expressed in terms of selected **limiting speed ranges**, are also displayed to the pilot on the Airspeed Indicator (ASI), in the form of coloured arcs.

Figure 14.2 The Pilot's Operating Handbook.

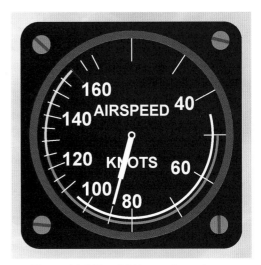

Figure 14.3 The ASI has coloured arcs showing certain limiting speed-ranges.

LIMITATIONS.

The designed structural strength of an aircraft is determined by the magnitude and direction of the **loads** that the designer expects to be imposed on the aircraft, in flight and on the ground. The word **load** is just another name for **force**. You have already learnt a considerable amount about the main **loads** acting on an aircraft: **lift**, **weight**, **thrust** and **drag**.

Stress and Strain.
All loads induce **stresses** in an aircraft's structure which must be limited to ensure the aircraft's continuing structural integrity. **Stress** is defined simply as **load per unit area of the structure supporting the load**.

$$\text{Stress} = \frac{\text{Load}}{\text{Area}}$$

The greater the **load**, the greater the **stress**. The greater the surface area, the lower the **stress**.

Any amount of **stress** produces a **deflection** or **deformation** in the component under **stress**. Such deflection and deformation is called **strain**. Normal operating **stress** is not a problem for an aircraft. All airframe components will experience acceptable levels of **strain** under normal flight **loads and stresses**, (for instance, the wings may deflect markedly under certain **load factors**, as they are designed to do) but will return to normal dimensions and positions when the **loads** are removed. If, however, **stresses** on the airframe become excessive, due to the application of excessive flight **loads**, **strain** in a component may become permanent. Any permanent deformation must be regarded as damage to the airframe. If an airframe is loaded beyond its **design limit**, the associated **stresses** will result in such excessive **strain** that one or more components may break. The **stress** imposed on an aircraft by thrust **forces** are low, in a light aircraft.

Stresses arising from lift and weight **loads** can be very high, however; so it is lift and weight which are the **principal loads** which must be limited in flight and on the ground. The lift **forces** acting on an airframe are dependent, practically, on speed, load factor (manoeuvres) and angle of attack (**Lift = C$_L$ ½ ρV^2 S**). Consequently, **limit load** considerations are closely related to **speed limitations**. Drag **forces** are also dependent on speed.

In this Chapter we shall be looking, primarily, at how aircraft manoeuvres and speeds need to be subject to **limitations** in order to ensure the aircraft's safety. But first let us look, briefly, again at some of the **Principles of Flight concepts** that we have already met; this time from the point of view of their importance in setting **ground and flight limitations**, designed to ensure the safety of an aircraft. We will reconsider briefly the concepts of **lift**, **weight**, **Centre of Gravity position**, **airspeed**, **load factor**, and **windspeed**.

Lift.

We have considered **lift** as acting through the **Centre of Pressure** on the wing. This is a sound assumption for predicting and measuring the resultant effect of **lift on the aircraft**. But, in reality, **lift** is actually developed over the whole surface area of the aircraft, and is a **spread load**, though not equally spread.

In flight, the various degrees of magnitude of the **lift** force, necessary to support the **load factors** of different manoeuvres, cause bending moments to be applied to the wing spars. The bending-moments, themselves, vary in magnitude along the wing. The stress caused by bending is greatest at the point at which the wings are attached to the fuselage; that is, at the wing root. The bending-moment will be zero at the wing-tip and maximum at the root. If a limit is not set for the **lift force** that an aircraft generates, bending moments in the wing may become dangerously large, causing stresses and strains that the wing structure has not been designed to deal with.

Weight.

Even though the **weight** of an aircraft may be considered as acting as a point load through the aircraft's **Centre of Gravity**, **weight**, like lift, may be viewed as a **spread load**. Each individual component part of an aircraft possesses its own **weight**. Where the phenomenon of **flutter** on a control surface is concerned, for instance, it is the **weight** and **Centre of Gravity** of the control surface, alone, which must be considered.

The aircraft's **all-up weight** is of considerable importance, and must have prescribed limits because of the effect on the aircraft's structural integrity, both in flight and on the ground. **All-up weight** will also affect the various limiting speeds, including stalling speed, both straight and level and under different load factors. The combined **weight** of individual components, and their position in the aircraft will determine the position of the aircraft's **Centre of Gravity.** In this respect, certain **weights**, such as **crew weight**, will have minimum as well as maximum limits, or else there is a danger that the position of the aircraft's **Centre of Gravity** could lie outside its prescribed limits.

During flight, the aircraft consumes fuel, so the **weight** of the aircraft constantly changes. As fuel tanks empty, the distribution of the **weight** throughout the aircraft changes; consequently, the position of the aircraft's **Centre of Gravity** changes, too. For reasons that you learnt earlier in this volume, it is important that the aircraft's **Centre of Gravity** should remain within limits for the duration of the flight.

All aircraft have published maximum **weights** designed to protect their structure, and which the pilot must ensure are not exceeded. Among these are: **maximum gross weight**, **maximum take-off weight** and **maximum landing weight**. If **weight** is increased, lift will have to increase; so, as the lift formula teaches us, in any given phase of flight, a heavy aircraft will either have to fly at a greater angle of attack (i.e. higher C_L) than a lighter aircraft, or with the same C_L and at greater speed.

You will often find the word **mass** substituted for **weight**, and, when manoeuvring, it is, scientifically speaking, **mass** which is the true consideration. In your practical flying, though, do not worry about the difference between **mass** and **weight**. As you have learnt, the Earth's gravitational acceleration is as good as constant in the realms in which aircraft fly, so **weight** and **mass** can be considered as giving us the same type of information. However, as a student of **Principles of Flight**, you now know that 1 kg **mass** is equal to 9.81 Newtons **weight**. This issue has been dealt with fully in the chapter on **Weight & Mass**.

Performance considerations, as well as **structural considerations**, lead to the imposition of **maximum weights**. Performance considerations are related to **temperature**, **density**, **runway conditions**, etc, and are dealt with later in this book, in the section on **Aircraft Performance**.

You will learn more about **maximum weights** and **masses** in Volume 5 of this series which contains the topic **Mass and Balance**.

The Line of Action of a Force or Load.

The four **principal** flight forces also give rise to **secondary** forces which impose different types of load and stresses on the aircraft. We have already seen that **lift** can cause considerable **deflections** and **oscillations** of the control surfaces (**flutter**) at high speeds. If the aircraft, when flying fast, is also subjected to turbulence, the **transient loads** caused by the turbulence can be very high. If the pilot manoeuvres his aircraft in this situation, displacement of the control surfaces will impose even higher, **twisting loads** on the wings, tailplane and fuselage. The lowering of flaps and undercarriage would exacerbate the situation when **transient loads** are high.

This latter point is important. It is not only the **magnitude of a load** acting on the aircraft's structure which determines whether the load remains within limits, but also the **line of action of the applied load**. The flight forces developed by the ailerons when they are deflected, for instance, apply a **twisting moment** to the control surface and wing. It is only the degree of **stiffness** of the aileron (that is, its resistance to strain) which allows the aerodynamic force generated by the aileron to cause the aircraft to roll. The wing is subject to **twisting forces** whose line of action changes because the centre of pressure of the wing moves fore and aft with changing angle of attack. The same phenomenon occurs at the tailplane, which in turn can apply a **twisting moment** to the fuselage.

All these considerations have to borne in mind by the aircraft designer when he is deciding on how strong an aircraft structure needs to be, and when establishing **flight limitations**.

Airspeed.

As the lift and drag equations (**Lift = C_L ½ ρ v^2 S** and **Drag = C_D ½ ρ v^2 S**) tell us, the **aerodynamically generated lift and drag loads applied to an aircraft's structure are directly proportional to the square of the airspeed**. Of these two loads, it is

lift which is the greater, and which gives rise to the loads which can cause structural damage to the aircraft.

In the lift equation, **v** is the **true airspeed**. You have already learnt, though, that **indicated airspeed** (the speed given by the **airspeed indicator** (ASI)) is a measure of that part of the lift equation designated by the term ½ ρ **v²**, otherwise known as **dynamic pressure**. Therefore, as **dynamic pressure** is, at the same time, a factor in the lift equation which determines the magnitude of the **lift**, <u>and</u> also a factor which can be read directly by the pilot from the ASI as indicated airspeed, <u>**all speed limitations published by the manufacturer are indicated airspeeds**</u>.

You may remember from Chapter 4 that indicated airspeed, v_i, is related to true airspeed, **v**, by a factor, known as **relative density**, which represents the ratio between the actual density of the airflow being measured, ρ, and the density at sea-level in the ICAO Standard Atmosphere (ISA), ρ_{isa}, which is **1.225 kg/m³**. The formula relating v_i to **v** is as follows:

$$v_i = v\sqrt{\frac{\rho}{\rho_{isa}}}$$

So, as **lift** is directly proportional to **v²**, and as v_i is directly proportional to **v**, **lift** is also directly proportional to v_i^2. This **square relationship** between **lift** and **airspeed** means that if a **limiting airspeed** is exceeded by even a small amount, the effect on **lift** can be great. For instance, doubling the **airspeed** will increase the **lift** force by 4. Great attention must, therefore, be paid to your **airspeed** if you are flying near the **upper airspeed limitations**.

The airspeed that should never be exceeded is designated as V_{NE}. V_{NE} is indicated on airspeed indicators by a red line. This airspeed is calculated by the designer for each aircraft model. If an aircraft exceeds V_{NE}, deformation of or structural damage to one or more airframe components may occur. An aircraft may be safely flown at V_{NE} in smooth, calm conditions, but it is not safe to fly at or near V_{NE} in turbulence.

Of course, flying at too low an **airspeed** can cause lift to reduce below the value necessary to support the weight of the aircraft, and lead to a stall. Consequently, there are lower **airspeed limits**, too. The principal **airspeed limitations** are: the **stall speed from straight and level flight** (i.e. where the **load factor =1**), V_S, the **never- exceed speed**, V_{NE}, the **maximum normal operating airspeed**, V_{NO}, the **maximum manoeuvring speed**, V_A, the **maximum speed with flaps extended**, V_{FE}, and **maximum speeds related to the extension and retraction of retractable undercarriages**, V_{LO} and V_{LE}.

The importance of **airspeed** as a measure of an aircraft's **structural limitations** is dealt with in more detail later in this chapter, in the section on the **Manoeuvring Envelope**.

Load Factor.

The designed strength of the aircraft structure is not only determined by the basic aerodynamic loads imposed on it, in flight, or by its weight alone when it is stationary on the ground. **In flight, loads are increased whenever the aircraft manoeuvres.**

The **"inertial multiplication" of the lift and weight forces during manoeuvring** subjects the aircraft to stresses which the designer must take into account when he is calculating the required strength of the aircraft's structure. Two very similar aircraft may need to have different structural strengths depending on the role for which they are designed; for instance, whether they are aerobatic aircraft or touring aircraft. An aircraft whose structure is designed to be strong enough for touring flight and basic manoeuvres only (plus a safety factor), could suffer catastrophic damage if it were to carry out certain aerobatic manoeuvres for which it was not "stressed". An aircraft must be cleared for any aerobatic manoeuvres that a pilot may wish to carry out. In a touring aircraft, manoeuvres which could cause damage to the airframe will be explicitly forbidden in the aircraft's Type Certificate, and in the Flight Manual or Pilot's Operating Handbook. These documents will also contain details of **limiting speeds** and **load factors** which may be different for two seemingly identical aircraft.

An aircraft manufacturer will specify a limit to the **load factor** both **positive and negative**, to which the aircraft may be subjected. Exceeding those limits can lead to structural damage or failure.

You have learnt that whereas lift is always equal to weight, in steady, straight flight, lift must be greater than weight during turns. When lift is greater than weight, the loads acting on an aircraft increase by a factor called the **load factor**. **Load factor** is expressed by the ratio of lift to weight, such that:

$$\text{Load Factor} = \frac{\text{Lift}}{\text{Weight}}$$

In steady straight flight, then, with lift equal to weight, **load factor** is 1, but in any form of accelerated flight, when the velocity of the aircraft is changing, the **load factor** will be greater or less than one 1. In <u>positive</u> accelerations, such as turns, the load factor will be <u>greater</u> than 1. An inverted loop would bring the **load factor** below one, and could even cause it to be a negative factor. Remember that an aircraft is accelerating when either its speed or direction is changing.

A light aircraft's linear acceleration, along its line of flight, is usually small enough to be neglected. Linear acceleration is greatest at take-off, or when bringing the aircraft to a rapid stop after landing (negative acceleration or deceleration), but, in neither case is the acceleration likely to be as great as that of a car. However, aircraft accelerations necessary for **turning flight**, **pulling out of dives**, or for **other manoeuvres**, are significant. Consequently, the **load factors** produced by those accelerations will be high, (or, less frequently, low, in negative g manoeuvres). For instance, a 60° banked level turn requires lift to be twice the magnitude of weight, generating a **load factor of 2**. Pulling out of a dive or flying a loop, may require the aircraft to be subjected to higher **load factors**.

We will return to **load factor**, later in this chapter.

Position of Centre of Gravity.
The effect of the position of the aircraft's **Centre of Gravity** (**C of G**) on aircraft stability and control has been covered earlier in this book. The topic is also dealt with in some detail in the subject **'Mass & Balance'**, elsewhere in this series of text books. We will just emphasise, here, that the aircraft's **C of G** must lie within the specified forward and aft limits *(see Figure 14.4)*, calculated by the aircraft designer, and must remain within those limits, throughout the flight. If the **C of G** is too far

forward, considerable force will be required to move the control column fore and aft, and elevator authority will be poor. An aircraft which has its **C of G** outside the aft limit may be dangerously unstable and display unfavourable stall and spin characteristics.

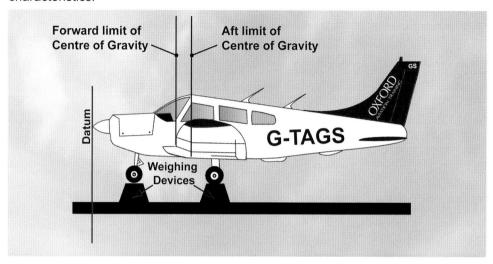

Figure 14.4 Representative fore and aft limits of the centre of gravity for a PA28.

Wind.

Wind will also affect aircraft operations. The **wind speed** (i.e. strength), **direction**, **degree of gustiness**, **turbulence** and the **possibility of wind shear** are all important considerations when deciding whether or not a light aircraft should be flown.

The aircraft that you normally fly will almost certainly have a maximum **crosswind limitation** placed on it by the manufacturer, established during a series of test flights. In **crosswinds** above a certain strength, an aircraft may not possess the **rudder authority** to keep straight on the runway, during a take-off run, touch-down or landing run. And, of course, even if a strong **wind** is blowing straight down the runway centre-line, an aircraft still may have to taxy **across wind**.

Certain light aircraft may also have an **overall windspeed limitation** because, again, even with a strong wind down the runway centre-line, the approach to land may have to be flown at an airspeed which, in order for the pilot to hold a suitable approach path, and to guard against the effects of **wind sheer**, would cause the aircraft to reach, or exceed, the **maximum manoeuvring speed, V_A**.

If an aircraft is cruising at its maximum normal operating speed, V_{NO}, and flies through an area of powerful gusts, V_{NO} can be exceeded. That is why, in gusty conditions, it is wise to leave a safety margin between your cruising speed and V_{NO}. Gust loads are dealt with in further detail, below.

Flight and Ground Limitations.

The **flight and ground limitations** in respect of a particular aircraft can be found in the **Pilot's Operating Manual** and Flight Reference Cards, or **Check List**, for the aircraft.

Representative limitations for a light training aircraft are contained in the table below, at *Figure 14.5*. These **limitations** are included here for illustrative purposes only, and must not be taken as authoritative, for any given aircraft. All airspeeds are **indicated airspeeds**.

REPRESENTATIVE LIMITATIONS FOR A LIGHT TRAINING AIRCRAFT	
Velocity Never to Exceed (V_{NE})	155 knots
Normal Operating Speed (V_{NO})	124 knots
Normal Manoeuvring Speed (V_A)	109 knots
Maximum Velocity Flaps Extended (V_{FE})	101 knots
Take-Off Safety Speed	65 knots
Stall Speed (flaps extended)	46 knots
Stall Speed (clean)	52 knots
Maximum Take-Off Weight (or Mass) (MTOW)/ (MTOM) - Normal Category	2150 lbs 975 kg
MTOW/MTOM – Utility Category	1950 lbs 884 kg
Maximum Demonstrated Crosswind	17 knots
Maximum Load Factor (Normal Category)	+3.8
Maximum Load Factor (Utility Category)	+4.4
No Negative Load Factors Approved	-

Figure 14.5 Table of representative general limitations for a typical, general aviation training aircraft.

MORE ABOUT LOAD FACTOR.

You were introduced to **load factor** in the chapters on **Forces in Flight** and **The Stall and Spin**. **Load Factor** was also considered above, from the general point of view of flight limitations. Here we will look a little more deeply into the **load factor** implications of various manoeuvres, but, before continuing, re-read the previous sections on **load factor**, especially the section in Chapter 13.

As you have learnt, in steady straight flight, **with lift equal to weight, load factor is 1**, but in any form of manoeuvring, when the direction of the aircraft is changing, with or without an increase in speed, the **load factor** will be greater or less than **1**. **Turning flight** and **pulling out of dives** require positive accelerations which generate **load factors** greater than 1. It is also possible to apply negative accelerations to the aircraft, such as in an inverted loop, which would produce **load factors** of less than 1, or even **negative load factors**. (See below.)

You discovered earlier that a 60°- banked level turn requires lift to be twice the magnitude of weight, in order both to support the aircraft's weight and to give the aircraft the necessary centripetal acceleration for the turn. The **inertial reaction** to the doubling of the lift imposes a **load factor** of **2** on the aircraft structure and occupants. This **load factor** causes the pilot to sense an apparent increase in weight because the **inertial reaction** to the **increased lift force** acts in the opposite direction to the lift force, through the vertical axis of the pilot's body (if the turn is properly balanced), pressing him into his seat *(see Figure 14.6)*.

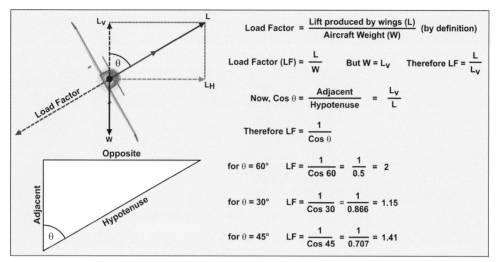

Figure 14.6 Calculating load factor from angle of bank.

Pulling out of a dive or flying a loop will, generally, subject the aircraft to higher **load factors** than 2. The derivation of the formula relating **load factor** to **angle of bank**, is at *Figure 14.6*. You are now familiar with the idea that an aircraft's structure must be able to support the loads to which it is subjected without permanent deformation or failure occurring. As we mentioned above, the **"inertial multiplication" of lift and weight during manoeuvring** subjects the aircraft to **stresses** which the designer must take into account when he is calculating the required strength of the aircraft structure. Aircraft must be cleared for any aerobatic manoeuvres that a pilot may wish to carry out. Details of permitted manoeuvres are given in an aircraft's Type Certificate, and in the Flight Manual or Pilot's Operating Handbook. As you can see, the representative training aircraft referred to in *Figure 14.5*, is cleared for manoeuvres which will impose a maximum positive **load factor** of **3.8** on the airframe, when the aircraft is being operated in the **Normal Category,** and **4.4** when it is flown in the **Utility Category**. Aircraft Categories are covered in the section on **Mass and Balance**, in the **'Aeroplane (General)'** volume of this series.

Load factor limits are technically expressed as numbers only, that is, without units, because they are factors expressing how many times the normal aircraft weight the aircraft's structure is able to support when manoeuvring, without risk of damage. **Load factor** can also be expressed in terms of the symbol, **g**. You have already seen that for a 60°-banked level turn the **load factor** to which the aircraft is subjected is **2**. The reaction of the pilot's body mass to the load factor will cause him to feel that his weight has doubled, and he may think of the turn as a **2g turn**. Though he may not know it, in using the expression, **2g**, he is making reference to the fact that what he senses as his **normal weight** is in fact a **1g acceleration** (the acceleration due to gravity) towards the centre of the Earth. When the pilot is standing on the ground, of course, the Earth's surface prevents him from actually moving towards the centre of the planet. What the pilot feels as his weight is, in fact, the reaction of the ground stopping that motion.

When the pilot is airborne and flies a properly balanced 60°-banked level turn *(see Figure 14.7)*, the **extra lift force** required to execute the turn will give rise to an **inertial acceleration**, acting on the aircraft and the pilot, of twice the acceleration due to the Earth's force of gravity. This, then, is the **2g acceleration**, or the **load factor of 2** which makes the pilot feel that his weight has doubled, and which subjects the aircraft's structure to the extra stress.

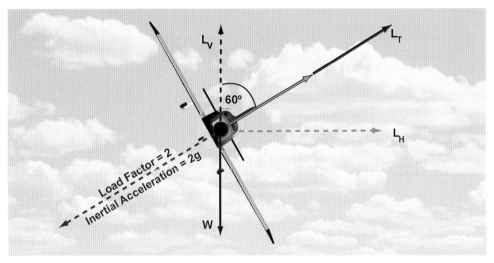

Figure 14.7 In a 60°-banked level turn, the aircraft is subjected to a load factor of 2.

Looked at another way, in a 60°-banked, **2g**, level turn the aircraft flies as if it were twice its actual weight, and the air is imposing an increased force (i.e. lift) on the aircraft's structure in the same proportion: with a **load factor** of **2**.

You may remember, too, from Chapter 13 that, if the aircraft's straight-flight stall speed occurs at an indicated airspeed of 60 knots, its stall speed with a load factor of 2 in the 60°-banked turn is 85 knots, indicated.

Stall speed in turn = Straight flight stall speed × $\sqrt{\text{Load Factor}}$

An aircraft will not be able to support **load factors** that increase indefinitely. For instance, the structure of the representative training aircraft, whose limitations we looked at above, is not designed to support a **load factor** of greater than 3.8, when flown as a Normal Category aircraft, or above 4.4, when flown in the Utility Category. Such an aircraft, then, could not safely fly an 80°-banked level turn, even if the aircraft's engine were powerful enough to enable the turn to be attempted, because the **load factor** in an 80°-banked level turn is almost 6, (1/Cos 80°).

The symbol **g**, then, is used to indicate an acceleration of, **9.81 metres/sec² or 32 feet/sec²**, the **acceleration due to gravity**. In straight, steady flight, the acceleration acting on the aircraft in the direction of weight force is termed **1g**. Therefore as **the apparent weight force** (equal and opposite to the lift force), in a given turn, increases by a factor which is numerically equal to the increase in **g**, known as the **load factor**, identifying the turn in terms of a certain number of **g** is acceptable, provided we understand clearly the context in which we use the term, **g**.

In fact, the **greatest load factor** that an aircraft has been subjected to, during a given flight, is measured on an instrument called an **accelerometer**, which is calibrated in units of g. This calibration, of course, is possible only because **g** and **load factor** are numerically equal.

Figure 14.8 An accelerometer, or g-meter, which records load factor.

Accelerometer needles do not return to zero of their own accord; they continue to indicate the maximum positive and negative **load factors** experienced in flight, until zeroed by the pilot. If a pilot sees that he has exceeded the maximum permissible **load factor**, he must report that fact to a responsible authority. To zero the **accelerometer** and say nothing, after having noted that a **load factor limit** had been exceeded, would be an irresponsible act, and may endanger the life of the next pilot to fly the aircraft. In *Figure 14.8*, the right-hand needle of the accelerometer shows that the maximum positive acceleration **(load factor),** to which the aircraft has been subjected is 2. The left-hand needle indicates that the aircraft has also been subjected to a maximum negative acceleration **(load factor)** of -0.6. The middle needle shows the current, instantaneous, acceleration.

Negative Load Factors - Negative g.

As we have mentioned above, in certain conditions of flight, load factors may also be less than 1 or even negative. You have doubtless heard mention of the expression **"negative g"**. So far in this book, we have discussed positive load factors only. But the direction of a positive load may act in reverse; if it does, the load factor is then described as negative, known popularly as **"negative g"**.

Even in straight and level flight, values of **negative g** can be experienced momentarily in severe turbulence. And an aircraft flying straight at a steady speed, that is, in equilibrium but inverted, will experience a **negative load factor** of **-1**, or **-1 g**.

Some aerobatic aircraft are capable of flying outside loops which will generate various degrees of **negative g**. **Negative g** can be a most uncomfortable experience for pilot and crew.

Inertial Loads.

Load factors imposed on an aircraft's structure are **inertial loads (inertial forces)** which arise because the aircraft is subject to an out-of-balance resultant force which imparts an acceleration to the aircraft. An **inertial load** is equal in magnitude to the force causing the acceleration and acts in the opposite direction to the accelerating force. Accelerations may be either positive or negative; (**negative accelerations** may be called **decelerations**).

Linear accelerations, along the line of flight (involving increases or decreases in speed), are small enough to be regarded as negligible, but accelerations which change an aircraft's direction, such as when the aircraft turns, flies a loop, or recovers from a dive, can be considerable. It follows, then, that the **inertial forces**, and the **associated load factors**, acting on an aircraft carrying out such manoeuvres can also be of a significant magnitude. An aircraft's structure must possess adequate strength and stiffness to withstand, without suffering structural damage, the **inertial**

forces arising from the manoeuvres for which the aircraft is approved.

The detailed study of the nature of the **inertial loads** which give rise to load factors is beyond the scope of this book, but a <u>basic</u> understanding of **inertial loads** is relatively easy to acquire.

PULLING OUT OF A DIVE.

Expressed in the most basic terms, a**n inertial load is a reaction to an out-of-balance force which causes an acceleration.** The magnitude of any accelerating force can be expressed by the equation:

Force = mass × acceleration, which is an expression of **Newton's 2ⁿᵈ Law**.

Therefore, the greater the acceleration to which an aircraft of a given mass is subjected, the greater must be the force acting on the aircraft to cause that acceleration.

In order to consider the phenomenon of **inertial loading** a little more deeply, let us consider the case of an aircraft pulling out of a dive requiring a maximum centripetal acceleration of **3.5g** (measured on the accelerometer) towards the centre of an imaginary circle *(see Figure 14.9)*. (**Always remember to check the load factor (g) limitations for your aircraft before flying any manoeuvres.**)

The actual value of a 3.5g acceleration is **3.5 × 9.81 metres/sec²**, which is approximately **34 metres/sec²**. This acceleration is necessary to change the direction of the aircraft as it recovers from the dive. The lift force required to produce this acceleration must be a force of a magnitude over and above the lift force required to support the aircraft's weight in straight flight. This accelerating lift force, then, is the out-of-balance force that we have learnt must be present to cause any acceleration. The equal and opposite reaction to this accelerating force will be the **inertial load** acting on the aircraft as it pulls out of the dive. That load will be a certain number of times the aircraft's weight; in other words, it will be greater than the aircraft's weight by a factor that we have already defined as the **load factor**.

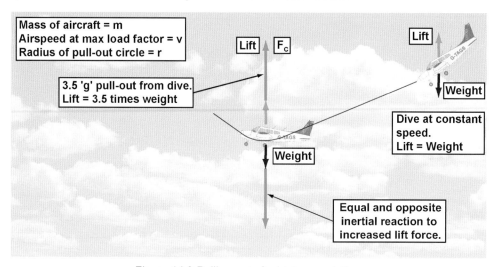

Figure 14.9 Pulling out of a high-speed dive.

Now, if the aircraft's **mass is 975 kg**, its **weight is 975 × 9.81 Newtons**, which is equal to, approximately, **9565 Newtons**. That means that, in straight, un-accelerated flight, the lift force acting on the aircraft' structure, in order to counterbalance its weight, is likewise **9565 Newtons**.

But during the **3.5g** recovery from the dive depicted in *Figure 14.9* the lift force acting on the aircraft would be:

Lift force = mass × acceleration = 975 kg × 34 metres/sec² = 33 159 Newtons

This force is, as we would expect with the pilot having pulled **3.5g**, 3.5 times the normal weight of the aircraft. This **load factor of 3.5** would be just within the permissible limit of 3.8 for the aircraft whose general limitations are shown in the table at *Figure 14.5*, when it is operating in the normal category

$$\textbf{Load Factor} = \frac{\textbf{Lift}}{\textbf{Weight}} = \frac{\textbf{33 159 Newtons}}{\textbf{9565 Newtons}} = 3.5$$

But, considering the lift equation, **Lift = C_L ½ ρ v² S**, it is not too difficult to imagine that a careless pilot might fly the recovery too abruptly, pulling back too hard on the control column and increasing **C_L**, and, consequently, the lift force, by too great a value, causing the **maximum permissible load factor of 3.8** (the **design limit load factor**) for our Normal Category aircraft to be exceeded, risking structural damage to the airframe.

Now, if the aircraft is fitted with an accelerometer, the pilot would be able to obtain early information from that instrument if he were about to exceed the maximum permissible load factor. (He may also get a clue from his rapidly increasing apparent weight.)

However, the speed that the pilot reads from his ASI would give him no clue at all.

But, if we knew the radius of the imaginary circle that the aircraft is describing as it pulls out of its dive in *Figure 14.9*, the aircraft's speed would give us a clue to the lift force, and, hence, load factor, generated by the wings. We can, of course, never know the radius of a recovery from a dive; indeed, the recovery path is unlikely to follow an arc of a single circle. But, at any given moment, including the moment of maximum load factor, the path being followed by the aircraft is an arc of some circle; so let us, for the sake of argument, imagine that we know the radius of that circle. With this information, we may illustrate a very important point about the **inertial forces** which give rise to **load factors** or **g**.

Monitoring Airspeed in a Dive.

From Newton's 2nd Law equation, **force = mass × acceleration**, we can derive an expression for centripetal force, **F_c**; in other words, the force that the wings would have to generate to pull the aircraft out of the dive in *Figure 14.9*.

This expression is:

$$F_c = m \times \frac{v^2}{r}$$

where **m** is the **mass** of the aircraft, **r** is the radius of the imaginary, **circular, recovery path**, and **v** is the **highest true airspeed** of the aircraft during the recovery manoeuvre. The expression, **v²/r** , is, in fact, the **centripetal acceleration** that the aircraft would have towards the centre of an imaginary circle during the pull out.

In *Figure 14.9*, then, $\mathbf{F_c}$ is the total lift required to be generated by the wings to recover the aircraft from the dive. The green section of the lift arrow is the <u>extra</u> lift required to recover from the dive, over and above the lift necessary to support the weight of the aircraft. The green section of the arrow acting in the direction of weight is the **inertial reaction** to the extra lift force generated by the wings in order to recover the aircraft from the dive. The <u>sum</u> of the green and red arrows acting in the direction of weight gives us the **load factor** acting on the aircraft.

You do not need, at this level of study, to know how the equation $\mathbf{F_c} = \mathbf{m} \times \dfrac{\mathbf{v^2}}{\mathbf{r}}$

is derived. You can learn that easily enough from any book on A-level Maths or Physics.

Let us, therefore, calculate first of all the **minimum radius** of the circular path that the aircraft could follow without exceeding its **maximum permissible load factor**, if its **maximum speed** during the recovery were to be **124 knots**, the maximum normal operating speed, $\mathbf{V_{NO}}$, of the training aircraft whose limitations are listed in *Figure 14.5*, when it is operating in the Normal Category.

As we mention above, the **v** in the equation $\mathbf{F_c} = \mathbf{m} \times \mathbf{v^2/r}$ is the aircraft's **true airspeed**. For the moment, though, we will make the assumption that **true airspeed** and **indicated airspeed** are the same. **This will rarely, if ever, be the case in real life**, but it simplifies our examination of basic principles. We will look at the implications of **v** being the true airspeed at the end of this section.

We have the following information about the aircraft:

- The positive limit load factor is **3.8,** in the **Normal Category**

- The mass of the aircraft is **975 kilograms**

- The weight of the aircraft is **9565 Newtons**

- Therefore, the maximum permissible lift force that the wings may safely generate is **3.8 × 9565 Newtons**, which is **36 347 Newtons**

- The aircraft's speed **124 knots**($\mathbf{V_{NO}}$) which is about **64 metres/second**

The minimum "radius of pull-out" from the dive can be calculated from rearranging

$\mathbf{F_c} = \mathbf{m} \times \dfrac{\mathbf{v^2}}{\mathbf{r}}$ to give us **r** as the subject of the equation:

$r = \dfrac{mv^2}{F_c}$

So, $r = \dfrac{mv^2}{F_c} = \dfrac{975 \times 64 \times 64}{36\ 347} = $ **110 metres (approximately).**

So, the minimum radius of pull-out that the pilot may fly without exceeding the **positive limit load factor** for his aircraft of **3.8**, is just a little more that the length of a football pitch. During the recovery, the pilot will have monitored the accelerometer attentively to make sure that he did not exceed the **load factor** (or **g**) **limitation**.

We can see from the above equation for the radius **r**, that if **r** were to be reduced, and the pull-out made more abruptly, $\mathbf{F_c}$, the lift force, would have to increase to keep the equation balanced. As a consequence, the maximum permitted limit load factor of **3.8** would be exceeded. (**Load Factor = Lift/Weight**)

But what if the pilot were flying an identical manoeuvre in an identical aircraft, but which was not fitted with an accelerometer? If he were to attempt to do this, he would need to think carefully both about his speed in the dive and about the manner in which he recovers from the dive. For instance, if the recovery from the dive were to follow an identical recovery path to the case we have just considered (radius of pull-out = 110 metres), but the pilot had allowed the aircraft to reach a speed in the dive of **145 knots** (**75 metres/second**), still well below the aircraft's $\mathbf{V_{NE}}$ of **155 knots**, the lift force generated by the wings would be:

$$F_c = m \times \frac{v^2}{r} = \frac{975 \times 75 \times 75}{110} = 49\ 858\ \textbf{Newtons}$$

The weight of the aircraft is still, of course, 9565 Newtons, so, in this case, the aircraft will have been subjected to a load factor of:

$$\textbf{Load Factor} = \frac{\textbf{Lift}}{\textbf{Weight}} = \frac{49\ 858}{9565} = 5.2$$

A **load factor** of **5.2** is significantly higher than the **maximum permissible load factor** of **3.8** for which the aircraft is cleared while operating in the Normal Category.

Consequently, it is of crucial importance for a pilot to understand that excessive speed can cause an aircraft to be subjected to load factors greater than that which the aircraft has been designed to withstand safely.

The **limiting speeds** which are published in the **Pilot's Operating Handbook** and in the **Check List**, for most light aircraft, are speeds (indicated airspeeds) in respect of straight, steady flight. **Positive g manoeuvres, at speeds above maximum manoeuvring speed, V_A, require lower limiting speeds to be observed in order to avoid over-stressing the airframe.**

True Airspeed and Indicated Airspeed.

Remember, too, that we pointed out that the **v**, in the equation $\mathbf{F_c} = m \times v^2/r$, is the aircraft's **true airspeed.** So, the greater the altitude at which the pull-out manoeuvre that we have been considering is flown, the greater the amount by which **true airspeed** will exceed **indicated airspeed.** Consequently, if the pilot pulls out of a dive at higher altitude, flown at the same **indicated airspeed** and following the same curved path as a similar manoeuvre flown at lower altitude, the higher **true airspeed** will mean that the force generated by the wings must be greater, leading to a greater **load factor** being imposed on the airframe during the manoeuvre. It is true that, during the dive, having the same **indicated airspeed** as at the lower altitude will mean that the aerodynamic forces acting on the aircraft in the dive will also be the same. However, as soon as the pilot begins to recover from the dive, that situation changes. For the pull-out, **it is the true airspeed which determines the force required to produce the positive acceleration necessary to recover the aircraft from the dive**. If the pilot pulls out from the dive following the same curved path as at the lower altitude, he will have to pull back on the control column more in order

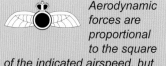

Aerodynamic forces are proportional to the square of the indicated airspeed, but inertial forces are proportional to true airspeed.

to generate the greater amount of lift required for the recovery. It is at the point of pull out, then, that the situation changes. **Aerodynamic forces are dependent on indicated airspeed, but inertial forces are proportional to the square of the true airspeed.**

The accelerometer measures inertial accelerations and, thus, is an indication of **load factor**.

The Consequences of Exceeding the Maximum Permissible Load Factor.

Exceeding the **maximum design limit load** to the extent in the example that we have just considered would be extremely hazardous, and would almost certainly cause permanent deformation of the wing structure.

If the maximum permissable load factor is exceeded, an aircraft must not fly again until it has been examined by a qualified aircraft technician.

During an abrupt pull-out from a dive, bending moments are high, and are at a maximum at the wing root. (The **centre of pressure** on both wings lies at about mid-span, whereas the greater part of the aircraft's total weight will most likely be concentrated in the fuselage. The wings deflect under any loading, and, under a **load factor** of **5.2**, the defection in the wings of an aircraft whose **positive design load limit** is **3.8** may be such as to cause permanent strain in the wing. The upper surfaces of the wing spar, wing skin and fuselage are subject to compression loads under positive load factors, while their lower surfaces experience loads in tension. Many other components of the airframe structure experience bending moments, too. All airframe components must be thoroughly examined by a qualified aircraft technician after the aircraft has exceeded its **maximum permissible load factor,** before the aircraft is allowed to fly again.

If the **maximum permissible load factor** were exceeded by too great a degree, airframe components would fail, resulting in loss of the aircraft. Current regulations, world-wide, require a minimum **safety factor** of **1.5** to be applied to a light aircraft's **designed load limits**. Consequently, airframe components should not break on an aircraft **with a maximum permissible load factor** of 3.8, until a load factor of 5.7 has been surpassed. However, it would be a very foolish pilot who relied on safety factors to preserve him and his aircraft.

Stall Speed During Recovery from a Dive.

While an aircraft is in the straight and steady descent part of its dive, the forces acting on the aircraft are in equilibrium, as shown in *Figure 14.10*.

In the descent, the lift is a fraction less than the weight because weight is counterbalanced by the resultant of the lift and drag forces, acting together. **In the descent, therefore, load factor will be a little less than 1;** (Load Factor = Lift/ Weight) But to recover from a dive by "pulling", say, **3.5g**, the lift force obviously has to increase to 3.5 times the aircraft's weight.

If you consider the lift force equation, **Lift = C_L ½ ρ v^2 S** , you see that the factors in the equation which the pilot would be able, practically, to control, in order to increase the lift force to recover from the dive are airspeed, **v**, and angle of attack, **C_L**. We will assume, that the pilot eases back on the control column. At a constant throttle setting, this action will increase angle of attack (and so **C_L**) and decrease speed.

In the dive, the angle of attack will have been very small: about 1°.

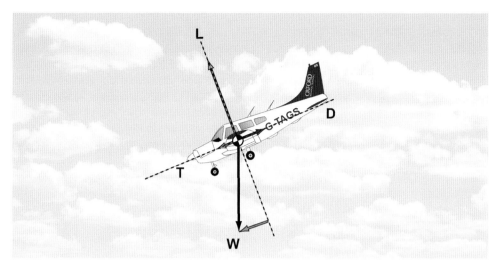

Figure 14.10 In the descent, the flight forces are in equilibrium.

We also know that the relationship between angle of attack and C_L is linear, until just below the stalling angle of attack *(See Figure 14.11)*.

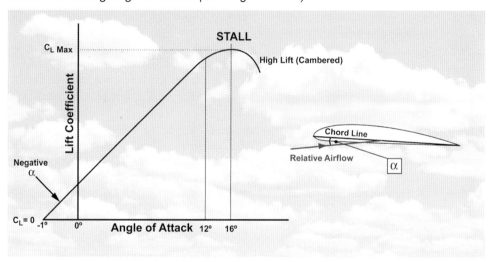

Figure 14.11 The relationship between angle of attack and C_L is linear until just before the stall.

As lift is a little less than weight in the dive, C_L will have to be increased by a factor of just under 4 in order to pull out of the dive by applying a load factor of 3.5, (3.5g) The pilot will, thus, ease the control column rearwards, increasing his angle of attack from 1° to just under 4°.

This is not a very great increase.

It is easy to see, therefore, that unless the pilot is very careful in his application of backward pressure on the control column, C_L may easily rise to a level where the lift force exceeds that which gives the maximum permissible load factor. Even if the maximum permissible load factor for the aircraft were 4.4 (typical of a Utility Category aircraft certified for "limited" aerobatics) an increase in angle of attack from 1° to 5°, still only a very small change, would overstress the aircraft.

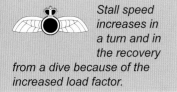

Stall speed increases in a turn and in the recovery from a dive because of the increased load factor.

However, the risk of damaging his aircraft by pulling the control column back too far and exceeding the load factor is not the only risk to which the pilot is exposed. As you have already learned, with increasing load factor, the stalling speed increases, too; (**Stall Speed = straight flight stall speed × $\sqrt{\text{Load Factor}}$**). At a load factor of 3.5, the stall speed will already be almost twice as high as in straight and level flight. So if the aircraft's stall speed from straight and level flight were 52 knots, the aircraft would stall at around 100 knots during a 3.5g manoeuvre. Stalling at such a high speed is a very real danger, especially if the aircraft is near to the ground. So, always allow plenty of time and height to pull out of a dive, and recover gently.

THE MANOEUVRE ENVELOPE (THE V-n DIAGRAM).

The **limiting load factor** and **limiting speeds** which must be allowed for during straight flight and manoeuvres are represented graphically by what is called the **manoeuvre envelope**, or **V-n diagram** (where **V** stands for **velocity** and **n** stands for **load factor**).

Separate manoeuvring envelopes can be produced for each **configuration** of an aircraft. (The word **configuration** refers to whether the aircraft is **clean**, or has **flaps** or **undercarriage extended** etc.) A typical clean **manoeuvring envelope** for a light aircraft, an example of which is represented at *Figure 14.12*, usually contains the following **critical airspeeds**:

- the **stall speed from straight and level flight** (where load factor = 1), V_S

- the **maximum manoeuvring speed**, V_A

- the **maximum normal operating speed**, V_{NO}

- the **never-to-exceed speed**, V_{NE}

- Sometimes, the **design dive speed**, V_D, may be shown, too.

Limiting Speeds and Loads.
The **horizontal axis of the graph** in *Figure 14.12* shows **indicated airspeed**, while the **vertical axis** indicates **load factor**. The **load factors** above the horizontal axis are positive, and those below the horizontal axis are negative. *Figure 14.12* represents an aircraft of the **utility category** certified for a **limiting positive load factor** of **+ 4.4** and a limiting negative load **factor** of **-1.8**. (The categorisation of aircraft is covered in some detail in the **'Aeroplanes (General)'** volume of this series.)

Flight outside the manoeuvre envelope, in the regions to the left of the accelerated stall curve is not possible because the wings will be stalled. The curve above the horizontal axis represents the accelerated stall speeds under various load factors; (that is: of $V_S \times \sqrt{\text{load factor}}$). For instance, the stall speed from straight and level flight, where the load factor is 1, is given as 52 knots, whereas under a load factor of 4.4, the aircraft will stall at 109 knots. 109 knots is also shown in the manoeuvring envelope as the **maximum manoeuvring speed**, V_A.

At low speeds, the stall is normally induced by full backward movement on the control column which produces a full upwards deflection of the elevator. As you see from *Figure 14.12*, at low speeds the aircraft will stall before the **positive limit load factor** is reached. This is the case for speeds up to V_A, the **maximum design manoeuvring speed**.

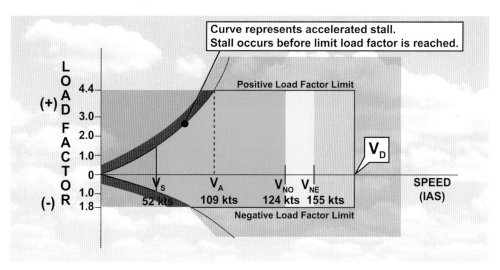

Figure 14.12 Representative manoeuvre envelope for a light aircraft showing limiting speeds and load factor.

But beyond **V$_A$**, the **positive limit load factor** may be reached <u>before</u> the aircraft stalls. The **manoeuvre envelope**, then, illustrates graphically that full backwards movements of the control column must not be made above **V$_A$**. In fact, no maximum deflections of the control surfaces or abrupt movements of the control column should be made when the aircraft is flying at speeds above **V$_A$**. However, bearing that precaution in mind, the aircraft may be operated safely above this speed.

V$_{NO}$, the **maximum normal operating speed**, marks the upper speed limit in turbulent air. **V$_{NO}$** must not be exceeded unless conditions are smooth. **V$_{NE}$** marks **the airspeed which should never be exceeded**, or structural distortion of the airframe is likely to occur.

Above V$_A$, the positive limit load factor may be reached before the aircraft stalls.

Structural failure is almost certain if the **design dive limit**, **V$_D$**, is exceeded. **V$_D$** is the maximum speed considered when assessing the structural strength of an aircraft. In general, **V$_{NE}$** is set about 10% lower than **V$_D$**.

V$_{NO}$ marks the upper limit of the normal operating speed range and should not be exceeded in turbulent air.

If you find yourself flying in atmospheric conditions which are very turbulent, you should consider maintaining your airspeed at or below **V$_A$**, and avoid any abrupt control movements, in order to prevent excessive flight loads damaging the structure of your aircraft.

The Gust Envelope.

Strong vertical gusts may impose severe loads on the wing structure by inducing rapid changes in angle of attack (and, thus, **C$_L$**), which generate associated changes in the magnitude of the lift force. The greater the aircraft's speed, the greater will be the loads on the airframe induced by the gusts.

Aircraft designers must, therefore, include a safety factor in the design of aircraft structures to allow for unexpected gust loads. The **manoeuvring envelope** for an aircraft which takes into account gust loading is sometimes referred to as a **gust envelope**. The **gust envelope** often takes the form of an overlay to the normal **manoeuvring envelope** diagram, having the effect of reducing the lateral and vertical extents of the normal envelope.

Many aircraft designers establish a **maximum turbulence penetration speed**, **V$_B$**, which assumes that a light aircraft at cruise speed will meet varying vertical gust components of up to 50 feet/second. For most light aircraft, there will probably not be a great difference between **maximum turbulence penetration speed**, **V$_B$**, and **maximum manoeuvring speed**, **V$_A$**. So, if no **V$_B$** is specified for the aircraft that you fly regularly, do not fly above **V$_A$** in severe turbulence.

Flap Limiting Speed.

Flaps are designed, amongst other things, to reduce take-off and landing distances. Lowering flap increases a wing's **C$_L$**, generating equivalent lift at lower speeds, thus enabling the aircraft to approach to land at the lowest speed possible. Flaps also, of course, increase drag and permit suitably steep approach paths on landing. The flap surfaces, their operating mechanism and attachment points to the structure are not designed to withstand the aerodynamic loads which occur at cruising airspeeds and above.

Figure 14.13 The flaps and their operating mechanism are not designed to withstand the aerodynamic loads which occur at high cruising speed.

A manoeuvre envelope can be drawn for an aircraft with flaps extended. *Figure 14.14* shows how a **"flaps extended" manoeuvring envelope** might look. You will see that the bounds of the **flaps extended** envelope are markedly reduced in comparison to the clean configuration envelope. The load factor limits are lower and maximum permissible speed also much reduced. The critical speed which must never be exceeded with flaps extended is termed **V$_{FE}$, (Velocity Flaps Extended)**.

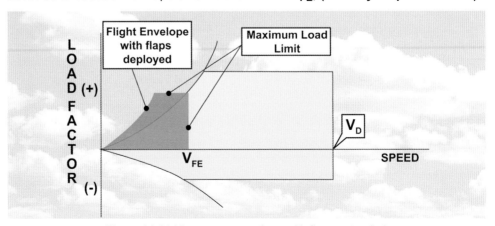

Figure 14.14 Manoeuvre envelope with flaps extended.

Landing Gear Limiting Speeds.

The **landing gear** (or undercarriage) will normally be retracted as soon as safely possible after take-off, in order to reduce drag and increase the climb gradient.

There is normally no requirement for the **landing gear** to be operated or extended during normal cruising flight. Therefore the size and strength of the gear mechanism is designed solely to meet landing and take-off requirements. Consequently, there are normally two speed limitations for the landing gear, depending on system design.

Figure 14.15 Gear is retracted when safely airborne.

V_{LO} is the **landing gear operating speed**. At or below V_{LO}, it is both safe to retract and extend the **landing gear**. On certain types of aircraft, it is permissible to fly with the gear remaining extended at a higher airspeed than that at which it may be retracted. If this is the case, a **maximum operating speed** with the gear extended is specified V_{LE}. But before the landing gear is retracted, speed must be reduced to V_{LO}.

Figure 14.16 Gear doors are not able to withstand large aerodynamic loads.

When the landing gear is operated, the gear doors must open first to allow the gear to move up or down before closing again. The purpose of the doors is merely to streamline the area of the undercarriage bay. Doors are not designed to withstand the aerodynamic loads to which they would be subjected at high indicated airspeeds; consequently V_{LO} is usually lower than V_{LE}.

LIMITING SPEEDS ON THE AIRSPEED INDICATOR.

In order to assist the pilot to take into account the **various speed limits** imposed on his aircraft's structure, the more **common limiting speeds** are marked on an aircraft's **airspeed indicator** by coloured arcs, as depicted in *Figure 14.17*.

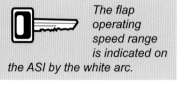

The flap operating speed range is indicated on the ASI by the white arc.

Figure 14.17 ASI.

- The **white arc** extends from the **stall speed with flaps extended,** in the landing configuration (full-flap, maximum all-up weight, gear down, power-off, wings level), to the **flap limiting speed**, V_{FE}.

- The **green arc** extends from the **clean, straight flight**, **1g stall speed**, V_s (maximum all up weight, flaps-up), to the **maxImum normal operating speed**, V_{NO}. The **green arc** represents the **normal operating speed range** for the aircraft. Flight at speeds within the **green arc** should be safe in all conditions.

- The **yellow arc** begins at V_{NO} and stretches to the **velocity never-to-exceed**, V_{NE}. The **yellow arc** marks the **caution range**. The aircraft should be operated in this speed range in smooth conditions only.

- V_{NE} is marked by a **short, red, radial-line** at the top end of the **yellow arc**.

GROUND LOADS.

After landing, the loads acting on the aircraft's structure are distributed differently from the way they are distributed in flight.

Consider, for instance, the case of the wing surface material, or skin, which is strong in tension but weak in compression. In flight, the wing bears the weight of the whole aircraft. When in the air, the skin on the under-surface of the wing is heavily loaded in tension and the skin of the upper surface is under compression, and may appear wrinkled. On the ground, the situation is reversed: the wing carries its own weight; its lower skin is under compression and its upper skin under tension

At the moment of touch-down, the wings are still developing lift equal, or almost equal, to weight; but additional shock-loads are imposed on the aircraft by the impulse of the first contact with the ground which causes the aircraft to decelerate abruptly in the vertical plane. A heavy landing imposes shock loads on the wings as well as the undercarriage. This type of shock load which may exceed 3g and which will be both positive and negative. A shock load, or impulse, of 3g transmitted to point locations may cause structural damage, whereas a gradually applied load of 3g over the whole aircraft structure will not. Following a suspected heavy landing, an engineer may find evidence of damage by examining the upper surface of the wing, near centre span where the bending moments will have been at their most powerful.

On the ground, then, without any significant forward speed, the aircraft's structure must support its own weight without any help from aerodynamic lift. In this situation, the weight of the various components making up the aircraft are transmitted from component to component and eventually through to the undercarriage and tyres.

Consider a typical light aircraft, weighing **2000 lbs** (**907 kg** or, more scientifically, **8900 Newtons**), whose wing area is **170 ft²** (**15.8 m²**), in two different situations: in flight and on the ground. In steady, straight flight, the wing loading (Weight/Wing Area) is **12 lbs/ft²** (or 563 Newtons/ m²), whereas, on the ground, the tyres will be supporting a load of around **1684 lbs/ft²**, (12 lbs/in² or 28 Newtons/cm²).

During taxying manoeuvres, thrust and braking loads are superimposed on the ground loads. These loads, occurring along the longitudinal axis, normally arise as a result of take-off, landing and braking, which means that the undercarriage must be strong, but with weight kept to a minimum, particularly as it is of no use to us once airborne. The aircraft designer, then, must produce a strong, lightweight undercarriage whilst maintaining minimum safety standards.

Side Loads on the Undercarriage.

Excessive side loads on the undercarriage, can cause damage to both undercarriage and tyres. Side loads can be imposed on the undercarriage through taxying the aircraft too fast or attempting to turn the aircraft through too tight an angle, but it is take-off and landing, particularly in crosswinds, which impose the greatest side loads. This is one of the reasons why limits are set on the maximum permissible crosswind for take-off and landing.

Crosswind

When taking off in a crosswind, keep straight with rudder and apply sufficient into wind aileron to prevent the upwind wing from lifting first.

Crosswind limits for take-off are determined by the manufacturer and published in the Pilot's Operating Handbook and Checklist.

Figure 14.18 Side loads are imposed on the undercarriage during crosswind takeoffs and landings.

Initially, during a crosswind take-off, the weight of the aircraft on the undercarriage will help to resist any sideways movement. But as speed increases and the wings start to generate lift, the into-wind wing may start to rise which will cause a side load on the undercarriage.

A lifting wing may be counteracted throughout the take-off run by applying a measure of aileron into wind in order to keep the wings level while maintaining direction by application of opposite rudder to resist the aircraft's tendency to weathercock into wind.

LANDING WITH CROSSWIND.

Not only taking off but also landing with a crosswind can cause excessive side loads on an aircraft undercarriage, therefore a maximum crosswind limit for landing will also be imposed. It is important that the side loads are kept to a minimum at the point of touchdown which is one reason why you will learn various crosswind landing techniques during flight training.

Tail Wheel Aircraft.

Throughout the various chapters of this Principles of Flight book, the aircraft to which we have referred, to illustrate the many different topics we have covered, have, for the most part, possessed tricycle undercarriages. Tricycle undercarriage aircraft now represent, by far the majority of aircraft in service. However, many tail wheel aircraft, or tail draggers, as they are popularly known, are still flown. *(See Figures 14.19 & 14.20.)*

Figure 14.19 Maule M-7.

In the air both types are flown by the pilot using the same techniques but, on the ground, their handling characteristics are quite different.

Figure 14.20 Spitfire Mk 24.

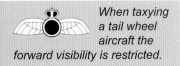
When taxying a tail wheel aircraft the forward visibility is restricted.

The tail wheel aircraft has its Centre of Gravity (C of G) behind the main wheels. This C of G position tends to make the aircraft unstable during ground movement. If a tail wheel aircraft were to start to swing during the take-off run, the amplitude of the swing would tend to increase, and, unless carefully controlled, could lead to the aircraft entering a ground loop. Tail wheel pilots soon learn that any swing on take-off must be prevented or promptly corrected by use of rudder.

DESIGN LOADS AND SAFETY FACTORS.

Having looked in some detail at the speed, weight and loading limitations to which aircraft are subjected, it is may be of interest to conclude this chapter by considering how a designer approaches the issue of load limits.

Aircraft designers are able to calculate the effects that flight forces will have on an aircraft's structure, during the initial conception of a new aircraft. Manufacturers, therefore, design and construct an aircraft so that it has adequate strength to withstand the loads which it is expected to bear in fulfilling the role for which it is designed.

You have already learned that even a touring aircraft may be stressed to bear positive loads which are up to 3.8 times the magnitude of its maximum operating weight. There is a regulatory requirement that Normal Category aircraft <u>must</u> be strong enough to bear a positive load factor of at least 2.5 (2.5g). Aircraft are stressed to withstand these load factors (referred to by such terms as **positive limit load factors**) as part of their normal operating envelope.

Aerobatic aircraft will be stressed to bear a typical positive load factor of 6, and a negative load factor of -3. Again these are designed limit loads. A military fighter aircraft may well be designed to withstand positive manoeuvres of up to 12g. (The Typhoon and the F- 22 both have design load factor limits of +9 and -3)

But despite the best forecasts of the designer, and making all the appropriate allowances for unexpected loads due to gusts, heavy landings etc, there still remain a number of incalculable circumstances against which designers have to guard. Obviously, if every eventuality were catered for, aircraft structures would become far too heavy; but to meet the unexpected, factors are applied to the highest loads envisaged during normal flight conditions.

These factors are called **safety factors**.

Aircraft are designed up to a level of structural strength defined by what is called the **ultimate design load**. Damage to the aircraft's structure, in the form of component deformation, will be likely at some point between the prescribed **maximum load limits** and the **ultimate design load**; but at the **ultimate design load** or beyond, the aircraft's structure is almost certain to fail.

The maximum design load will normally be increased by a **safety factor** of at least 1.5 over and above the aircraft's prescribed **maximum load limits** (the load limits of the manoeuvre envelope). Thus, an aircraft of the Normal Category whose **positive load factor limit** may be set at 3.8 should be able to absorb a load factor of at least +5.7 before the structure fails.

Aircraft components and complete airframes are tested by being subjected to repeated load reversals in test rigs in order to simulate the thousands of flying hours that an aircraft type might be expected to log in a normal in-service life. During the testing of a new aircraft type, the magnitude of the load reversals applied to the aircraft is increased progressively. If the structure fails prematurely, components are repaired up to the calculated **maximum design load**, which is the **design load limit** of the manoeuvre envelope **multiplied by a safety factor**. When this **maximum design load** has been established and tested to the satisfaction of the designers, loading continues until a major failure occurs. The load at which failure occurs is the **ultimate load** for the aircraft type and model.

From this testing, **safe life** periods are published for structural components, especially wing-spars, which determine the minimum number of flying hours which are statistically likely to elapse before major failure occurs.

It is interesting to note that most load-bearing metal components on an aircraft suffer from **fatigue** through continual load reversal, and will be given a definite **safe life**. The greater the amplitude of the reversals, and the more frequently they occur, the shorter will be the **fatigue life** of the component. Wooden components, however, notably the wooden spars of vintage aircraft, provided that they remain within their **elastic limit** have an indeterminate fatigue life. Wooden components are more likely to fail because of decomposing adhesive bonding, or even because of termite or rodent damage, rather than through fatigue. The wing spars on modern aircraft constructed of certain modern composite materials such as carbon fibres, bound together by epoxy resins, have the same indeterminate life as wooden spars.

Aircraft components made of wood or composite materials will fail, though, in the same way as metal components, if they exceed their design limit load. So, whatever the aircraft you fly, design load factors and airspeed limitations must be respected.

Representative PPL - type questions to test your theoretical knowledge of Flight and Ground Limitations.

1. If an aircraft is flown at its design manoeuvring speed V_A :

    a. it is possible to subject the aircraft to a load greater than its limit load during high 'g' manoeuvres
    b. it is not possible to exceed the limit load because the aircraft will stall before this is reached.
    c. it is only possible to subject the aircraft to a load greater than its limit load during violent increases in incidence, i.e. when using excessive stick force to pull-out of a dive
    d. it must be immediately slowed down if turbulence is encountered

2. V_{NE} is:

    a. the airspeed which must not be exceeded except in a dive
    b. the maximum airspeed at which manoeuvres approaching the stall may be carried out
    c. the maximum airspeed at which the aircraft may be flown
    d. the maximum speed, above which flaps should not be extended

3. The maximum allowable airspeed with flaps extended (V_{FE}) is lower than cruising speed because:

    a. flaps are used only when preparing to land
    b. too much drag is induced
    c. flaps will stall if they are deployed at too high an airspeed
    d. the additional lift and drag created would overload the wing and flap structure at higher speeds

4. What is the significance of the speed known as V_{NO}?

    a. It is the maximum speed at which abrupt movements of the controls will result in a stall, before the aircraft's positive load limit is exceeded
    b. It is the speed beyond which structural failure of the airframe will occur
    c. It signifies the upper limit of the normal operating speed range
    d. It signifies the airspeed which must never be exceeded

5. The stalling speed in a turn or in the pull-out from a dive is increased because:

    a. the angle of attack must be increased
    b. the load factor increases
    c. the aircraft's speed increases
    d. the pitch angle increases

6. V_s is:

    a.   the velocity-never-to-exceed
    b.   the maximum normal operating speed
    c.   the stall speed when the aircraft is subject to a Load Factor of 1
    d.   the stall speed when the aircraft is subject to no Load Factor at all

7.   The lower end of the white arc on the Airspeed Indicator marks:

    a.   the stall speed clean, in steady straight flight, at maximum all up weight, gear down and power off
    b.   the stall speed with flaps fully extended, in steady straight flight, at maximum all up weight, gear down and power off
    c.   the stall speed with flaps fully extended, at maximum all up weight, gear down and in a 2g turn
    d.   the stall speed with flaps in the take-off position, in steady straight flight, at maximum all up weight, gear down and power off

8.   The lower end of the green arc on the Airspeed Indicator marks:

    a.   the stall speed clean, in steady straight flight, at maximum all up weight, gear down and power off
    b.   the stall speed with flaps fully extended, in steady straight flight, at maximum all up weight, gear down and power off
    c.   the stall speed with flaps fully extended, at maximum all up weight, gear down and in a 2g turn
    d.   the stall speed with flaps in the take-off position, in steady straight flight, at maximum all up weight, gear down and power off

9.   The top end of the yellow arc on the Airspeed Indicator marks:

    a.   the maximum manoeuvring speed
    b.   the maximum normal operating speed
    c.   the design dive speed
    d.   the velocity never-to-exceed

10.   Above V_A:

    a.   the aircraft may stall before the positive limit load factor has been reached
    b.   when the aircraft stalls, the positive limit load factor will have been surpassed
    c.   structural damage to the airframe is highly likely at any speed
    d.   the aircraft may be flown in smooth air only

11.   The inertial forces acting on an aircraft is a function of:

     a.   The square of the aircraft's indicated airspeed, its mass and the manoeuvre radius

     b.   The aircraft's altitude

     c.   The square of the aircraft's true airspeed, its mass and the manoeuvre radius

     d.   The rate of turn only

12.   An aircraft's stall speed during a positive g manoeuvre is equal to the product of its straight flight, 1g, stall speed and:

     a.   The square root of the load factor

     b.   The cosine of the angle of bank

     c.   The sine of the bank angle

     d.   The number of g pulled in the manoeuvre

13.   In a steady, level turn, the load factor acting on an aircraft is equal to:

     a.   The indicated airspeed divided by 10, plus 7

     b.   The Cosine of the bank angle

     c.   1 divided by the Cosine of the bank angle.

     d.   The true airspeed multiplied by the square root of the straight flight stall speed

Question	1	2	3	4	5	6	7	8	9	10	11	12
Answer												

Question	13
Answer	

The answers to these questions can be found at the end of this book.

JAR-FCL PPL THEORETICAL KNOWLEDGE SYLLABUS

PRINCIPLES OF FLIGHT

The table below contains the principal topics and subtopics from the current outline syllabus for the theoretical examination in **Principles of Flight** for the **Private Pilot's Licence**, as published in **JAR-FCL 1**. Syllabuses may be modified, so always check the latest examination documentation from your **national civil aviation authority**, or from **JAR-FCL/EASA**.

In the United Kingdom, **Principles of Flight** is examined in the same paper as **Aircraft (General)**. In this series of volumes, **Aircraft (General)** is covered by the section on **Aeroplanes** in **Volume 6**.

PRINCIPLES OF FLIGHT	
The atmosphere:	composition and structure; ICAO standard atmosphere; atmospheric pressure.
Airflow around a body, sub-sonic:	air resistance and air density; boundary layer; friction forces; laminar and turbulent flow; Bernoulli's principle – venturi effect.
Airflow about a two dimensional aerofoil:	airflow around a flat plate; airflow around a curved plate (aerofoil); description of aerofoil cross section; lift and drag; C_l and C_d and their relationship to angle of attack.
Three-dimensional flow about an aerofoil:	three-dimensional flow about an aerofoil; aerofoil shapes and wing planforms; induced drag (downwash angle, vortex drag, ground effect; aspect ratio); parasite (profile) drag (form, skin friction and interference drag); lift/drag ratio.
Distribution of the four forces:	balance and couples; lift and mass; thrust and drag; methods of achieving balance.
Flying controls:	Flying controls; the three planes (pitching about the lateral axis; rolling about the longitudinal axis; yawing about the normal axis); effects of the elevators (stabilators), ailerons and rudder; control in pitch, roll and yaw; cross coupling, roll and yaw; mass and aerodynamic balance of control surfaces.
Trimming controls:	basic trim tab, balance tab and anti-balance tab; purpose and function; method of operation.
Flaps and slats:	simple, split, slotted and Fowler flaps; purpose and function; operational use; slats, leading edge; purpose and function; normal/automatic operation.
The stall:	stalling angle of attack; disruption of smooth airflow; reduction of lift, increase of drag; movement of centre of pressure; symptoms of development; aeroplane characteristics at the stall; factors affecting stall speed and aeroplane behaviour at the stall; stalling from level, climbing, descending and turning flight; inherent and artificial stall warnings; recovery from the stall.
Avoidance of spins:	wing tip stall; the development of roll; recognition at the incipient stage; immediate and positive stall recovery.
Stability:	definitions of static and dynamic stability; longitudinal stability; centre of gravity effect on control in pitch; lateral and directional stability; interrelationship, lateral and directional stability.
Load factor and manoeuvres:	structural considerations; manoeuvring and gust envelope; limiting load factors, with and without flaps; changes in load factor in turns and pull-ups; manoeuvring speed limitations; in-flight precautions.

351

ANSWERS TO PRINCIPLES OF FLIGHT QUESTIONS

Chapter 2   **The Atmosphere**

Question	1	2	3	4	5	6	7	8	9	10	11	12
Answer	a	d	c	b	c	b	a	b	c	b	d	c

Question	13	14	15
Answer	a	b	d

Chapter 3   **Lift**

Question	1	2	3	4	5	6	7	8	9	10	11	12
Answer	d	b	c	c	a	b	d	a	c	b	b	d

Question	13	14	15	16	17	18	19	20	21	22	23	24
Answer	a	c	d	c	c	d	c	d	b	c	b	d

Chapter 4   **More About Airflow and Aerofoils**

Question	1	2	3	4	5	6	7	8	9	10	11	12
Answer	c	b	c	a	a	a	a	d	c	d	b	b

Question	13	14
Answer	b	d

Chapter 5   **Drag**

Question	1	2	3	4	5	6	7	8	9	10	11	12
Answer	b	d	c	c	a	c	d	a	d	b	c	d

Question	13	14
Answer	d	b

Chapter 6   **The Lift Drag Ratio**

Question	1	2	3	4	5
Answer	a	b	c	a	d

Chapter 7   *Weight*

Question	1	2	3	4	5	6	7	8	9	10
Answer	c	d	a	c	b	c	a	c	d	b

Chapter 8   *Propeller Thrust*

Question	1	2	3	4	5	6	7	8	9	10	11	12
Answer	d	d	b	c	b	b	c	d	c	d	a	c

Question	13	14	15	16	17	18	19	20	21	22	23	24
Answer	b	b	a	d	d	c	b	b	d	c	d	b

Chapter 9   *The Four Forces Including Turning Flight*

Question	1	2	3	4	5	6	7	8	9	10	11	12
Answer	a	b	a	b	a	b	c	b	b	d	d	b

Question	13	14	15	16
Answer	a	a	c	c

Chapter 10   *Lift Augmentation*

Question	1	2	3	4	5	6	7	8	9	10
Answer	c	b	b	d	b	b	c	a	b	d

Chapter 11   *Stability*

Question	1	2	3	4	5	6	7	8	9	10	11	12
Answer	c	c	d	c	d	b	c	a	b	c	a	c

Question	13	14	15	16	17	18	19	20	21	22	23	24
Answer	d	b	a	d	a	a	b	b	a	a	b	c

Question	25	26	27	28	29
Answer	d	c	c	d	a

Chapter 12 **Flight Controls and Trimming**

Question	1	2	3	4	5	6	7	8	9	10	11	12
Answer	b	a	a	a	d	c	c	b	a	c	d	a

Question	13	14	15	16	17	18	19	20	21	22	23	24
Answer	c	b	d	d	c	b	a	d	a	a	c	b

Question	25	26	27	28	29	30	31	32	33	34
Answer	b	a	d	d	b	a	d	d	d	b

Chapter 13 **Stalling and Spinning**

Question	1	2	3	4	5	6	7	8	9	10	11	12
Answer	c	b	a	b	d	c	d	b	c	d	b	b

Question	13	14	15	16	17	18	19	20	21	22	23
Answer	d	b	b	d	d	b	c	a	a	b	a

Chapter 14 **Flight and Ground Limitations**

Question	1	2	3	4	5	6	7	8	9	10	11	12
Answer	b	c	d	c	b	c	b	a	d	b	c	a

Question	13
Answer	c

Index

A

B

C

SKILLS · FOR · FLIGHT

Aeroplane Performance

<u>**AEROPLANE PERFORMANCE**</u>

CHAPTER 1
INTRODUCTION

INTRODUCTION.

Figure 1.1 Take-off.

The section on **Mass and Balance** in the **Aeroplanes** volume of this series of text books emphasised the need for a pilot to ensure that his aircraft was properly **loaded**, whether be it with passengers, baggage or fuel, so that both the **centre of gravity** and the **all-up mass** (or **weight**) remains within prescribed limits. With the **centre of gravity position** and **all-up mass** within limits, the pilot can be confident that the aircraft will be controllable and not susceptible to overstress, during flight.

This section on **Aircraft Performance** is devoted to explaining how the performance of a correctly-loaded aircraft must be matched with the environment in which it will fly; that is to say, the **dimensions of the airfield and runways** and the **prevailing amospheric and meteorological conditions**. For instance, if the aircraft is loaded to its maximum authorised mass, and the centre of gravity is within limits, but the runway is not long enough for the aircraft to get airborne, then the aircraft's load will have to be reduced. In other words, the total mass of the aircraft and the published performance figures for the aircraft must be matched to the space available to the aircraft to operate in (e.g. the **surface dimensions and conditions of runways**, and the **obstacles** surrounding an aerodrome) and to the **meteorological conditions** prevailing in that space.

The consequences for a pilot of failing to take into account the performance of his aircraft, and the physical and meteorological conditions prevailing at an aerodrome he intends to use, are potentially serious. His aircraft may fail to get airborne, fail to clear obstacles on the climb-out, or over-run the runway, on landing.

There are very strict requirements for calculating the performance of public transport aircraft. However, these rules are not normally applicable to light aircraft operations. Nevertheless, the United Kingdom Civil Aviation Authority (UK CAA) strongly recommends that the safety factors which apply to public transport flights should be applied to general aviation flights too.

The CAA strongly recommends that public transport safety factors should be applied to private flights.

UK CAA Safety Sense Leaflet No 7 contains valuable advice from the UK CAA on **Aeroplane Performance** in respect of light aircraft.

Under JAR-FCL/EASA performance regulations, light, single-engined piston aircraft are classified as **Category B aircraft**. (In the former UK-only Categorisation System, the Performance Group of this class of aircraft is **E**.) The performance figures for **Category B aircraft** provided by the manufacturer are known as **gross performance figures**.

The most simple way to define the expression **"gross performance figures"** is to say that the figures assume that an aircraft is new, and that it is flown from a hard runway by a professional test pilot, in ideal conditions. When these **gross performance figures** are **factored** to allow for an in-service aircraft flown by an average pilot, the **gross performance figures** are adjusted to give what are known as **net performance figures**. **Net performance figures** define lower performance than **gross performance figures**.

The CAA strongly recommends that **net performance figures** should be applied to general aviation flights.

The CAA-approved performance charts for any given aircraft contain **unfactored data.** Consequently, the UK CAA recommends that a **safety factor** of **1.33** be applied to published **take-off performance** figures obtained from performance documentation. The CAA likewise recommends that a safety factor of **1.43** be applied to the manufacturer's published landing figures.

This section on **Aircraft Performance**, then, examines how pilots should interpret the performance figures for aircraft, published in an aircraft's **Flight Manual,** or **Pilot's Operating Handbook**, and in other performance documentation. The performance documents applicable to any given aircraft are specified in the aircraft's **Certificate of Airworthiness**.

Performance figures in light aircraft manuals do not usually include any safety factors.

As we have discussed, the performance figures contained in the above documents are **gross performance figures**. This section will teach you how to interpret those figures in order to predict the performance of your aircraft in **actual and expected flight conditions**. You will learn, therefore, how to take the **gross performance figures** for your aircraft and turn them into more realistic **net performance figures**.

It is the pilot's legal obligation, in accordance with Article 38 of the Air Navigation Order, to assure himself that his aircraft can deliver the required performance to carry out safely any planned flight.

It is the pilot's legal obligation, in accordance with Article 38 of the Air Navigation Order, to assure himself that his aircraft can deliver the required performance to carry out safely any planned flight. The pilot, therefore, must always study carefully the performance data that apply to his aircraft **and apply any mandatory limitation published by the CAA.** He should also give serious consideration to applying any **CAA recommended safety factors** to aircraft performance figures.

Figure 1.2 Landing.

4

CHAPTER 2
TAKE-OFF

TAKE-OFF.

An aircraft's take-off performance is dependent on several variables which include:

- **Aircraft mass (or weight).**
- **Aerodrome pressure altitude.**
- **Air temperature.**
- **Air Humidity.**
- **Wind strength and direction.**
- **Runway length and slope.**
- **Nature of runway surface (including contaminants).**
- **Flap settings.**

Definition of "Take-Off".
The **take-off** stage of flight is defined as being from brakes-off until the aircraft reaches a defined **screen height** following **lift-off**. For light aircraft this **screen height** is 50 ft.

After **lift-off**, a specific speed needs to be gained at the **screen height**. This is called the **take-off safety speed** which must be at least **20%** greater than the stalling speed (V_S). The **take-off safety speed**, then, must be greater than **1.2 V_S**.

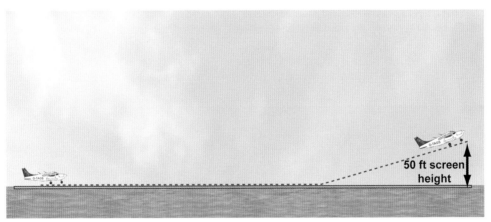

Figure 2.1 The take-off stage of flight for a light aircraft: from brakes-off until the aircraft reaches 50 feet.

Take-Off.
The take-off can be divided into the two parts. The first is the **take-off roll** or **take-off run** which is the distance travelled while the aircraft is still on the ground, in other words, from **brakes-off** to **lift-off**. When calculated for a particular aircraft on a particular day, this distance is called the **Take-Off Run Required (TORR)**.

The second part of the **take-off** is the **initial climb** which is the distance covered from **lift-off** until the aircraft reaches the **screen height of 50 feet**. The combined length of the **take-off run** and **initial climb** is known as the **take-off distance**. When **take-off distance** is calculated for a particular aircraft on a particular day, **take-off distance** is called the **Take-Off Distance Required**.

Pilots need to make sure that the **Take-Off Distance Required** does not exceed the **Take-Off Distance Available**, at the airfield in use. This may seem an obvious statement, but many incidents have occured which suggest that this important consideration is often forgotten.

We will now examine the various distances relevant to the take-off.

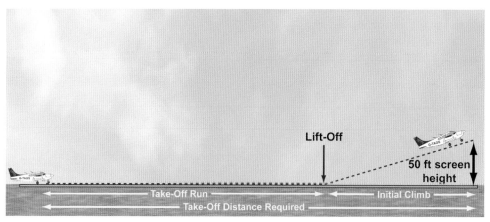

Figure 2.2 Take-Off Distance Required.

Take-Off Run.

Take-Off Run Available (TORA).

The **take-off run available (TORA)** is defined as being **the length of runway which is declared available by the appropriate authority and suitable for the ground run of an aircraft taking off**. Generally speaking, the **TORA** is the total length of the runway from **threshold** to **threshold**, excluding any **stopway**.

Take-Off Run Available is the length of runway available for an aircraft's ground run, threshold to threshold, excluding any stopway or clearway.

Figure 2.3 Take-Off Run Available - The length of runway suitable for the ground run of an aircraft on taking off.

Stopway.

Some runways have a **stopway** at either or both ends of the **TORA**. The **stopway** is an extension to the runway, able to support the weight of an aircraft, which is to be used to bring an aircraft to a stop in the event of an abandoned take off, and may not be used for any other purpose. The **stopway** is not included in the length of the **TORA**. The **TORA** plus any length of **stopway** is called the **Accelerate Stop Distance Available** or **ASDA**. The **ASDA** is sometimes also known as the **Emergency Distance Available (EMDA or EDA)**.

> The Stopway is an extension to the runway for emergency use only.

> That part of the take-off strip which indicates the Take-Off Run Available and the Stopway is called the Accelerate-Stop Distance Available or the Emergency Distance Available.

Figure 2.4 ASDA (Acceleration Stop Distance Available) = TORA + Stopway

Clearway.

The term **clearway** is defined as an area beyond the end of the runway, in the direction of take off, under the airport's authority, which is clear of any significant obstacles and suitable for an aircraft to make its initial climb to the **screen height** *(See Figure 2.5)*. Note that a **clearway** may include the **stopway** but need not be a surface in any way suitable to bear the weight of an aircraft; in fact, the **clearway** could be over water.

> The Clearway is an area beyond the end of the TORA under the airport's authority, clear of obstacles.

Take-Off Distance Available.

The **TORA** plus any **clearway** gives a distance known as the **Take-Off Distance Available (TODA)**. If a runway possesses neither **stopway** nor **clearway**, **TODA** and **ASDA** are the same as **TORA**. For many small aerodromes, the **TODA** is declared to be the same distance as the **TORA**. Always check this fact in the **Aerodrome Section (AD)** of the **AIP**.

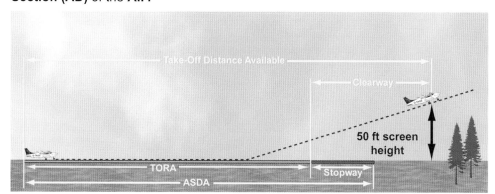

Figure 2.5 The declared distances.

> The Take-Off Distance Available (TODA) is defined as the TORA plus any clearway available.

For any given runway, the **TODA**, **ASDA** and **TORA,** together with the **Landing Distance Available (LDA)** *(See Chapter 4)*, are known as the **declared distances**.

Take-Off Distance Required.

Based on the **take-off performance** of his aircraft, a pilot must be able to calculate the **Take-Off Distance Required** for the aircraft in prevailing meteorological conditions for a given runway state. Having calculated **Take-Off Distance Required** and applied the necessary **correction factors** and **safety factors**, the pilot must be able to see a healthy margin between the **Take-Off Distance Required** and the **Take-Off Distance Available**. Calculating **Take-Off Distance Required** is the subject of the rest of this chapter.

TAKE-OFF PERFORMANCE.

In considering the factors which influence **take-off performance**, it will help you to recall two equations that you met in the **Principles of Flight** section of this book: the **lift equation** and the equation derived from **Newton's 2nd Law** linking the **thrust force** developed by the engine-propeller combination (or jet engine) with the **mass** of the aircraft and the **acceleration** that the aircraft is capable of achieving. These equations are as follows:

$$\text{Lift} = C_L \, \tfrac{1}{2} \, \rho v^2 S \ \dots \dots (1)$$

and

$$\text{Thrust (T)} = \text{mass (m)} \times \text{acceleration (a)} \ \dots \dots (2)$$

The latter equation, following simple mathematical transposition, may be written as

$$a = \frac{T}{m} \ \dots \dots (3)$$

Furthermore, it is straightforward, using Newton's **equations of motion**, to derive a third equation relating **velocity, v, acceleration, a,** and **distance, S**:

$$s = \frac{v^2}{2a} \ \dots \dots (4)$$

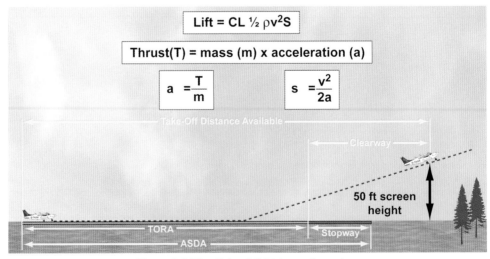

Figure 2.6 The Take-Off Distance formulae.

Let us consider the **lift equation** first for the moment of **lift-off**. In order to **lift off**, the **lift** produced by the wings must equal the total (all-up) **weight** of the aircraft. The **lift equation** tells us that If we assume fixed values of C_L, **coefficient of lift** (a number which accounts for a **wing's shape** and **angle of attack**), ρ, **air density**, and **S**, **effective wing area**, the aircraft will **lift off** at a given **airspeed, v**. Remember that, in the lift equation, **v** represents the aircraft's **true airspeed**. The aircraft, therefore, accelerates along the runway until it reaches a **true airspeed, v**, at which **lift** equals the aircraft's **weight**. If the aircraft is allowed to continue accelerating, the aircraft will literally fly off the ground. However, at the **take-off speed, v**, published in the **Pilot's Operating Handbook** as an **indicated airspeed**, not as a **true airspeed**, the pilot normally eases back on the control column, increasing C_L (by increasing **angle of attack**) and, thereby, further increasing **lift** and positively "unsticking" the aircraft from the ground. After **lift-off** in a light aircraft, it is normal piloting practice to lower the nose very slightly to allow the aircraft to accelerate rapidly to the **take-off safety speed**.

The **distance** required by the aircraft to reach its **take-off speed** is dependent, among other factors, on the **net average thrust** developed by the engine-propeller combination, and the **mass** of the aircraft. The expression **net thrust** means the **total thrust** produced by the propeller **minus aerodynamic drag** and wheel **drag**. The expression **average thrust** means the average value of the propeller's thrust force generated during the take-off run, the instantaneous value of thrust decreasing with increasing forward speed for a fixed-pitch propeller. In the equation , **a = T/m**, as we have seen, **a** is acceleration, **T** is the net, average thrust developed during the take-off run, and **m** is the aircraft's mass.

Remember that **in a constant gravitational field** such as that of the near-Earth region where aircraft fly, **a given mass will always have the same weight**, so although **mass** and **weight** are two very different concepts, they may be considered as being of equal value for our purposes in this section on **Aircraft Performance**.

It is straightforward to see, from **Equation (3)**, that if thrust, **T**, is increased, acceleration, **a,** is increased, too. With higher acceleration, the aircraft will, of course, reach its **take-off speed** sooner. The equation also shows us that for a given average, net thrust, **T,** if mass, **m,** is increased, **a** will decrease, causing the aircraft to take longer to reach its **take-off speed**.

Finally, **Equation (4)** links acceleration, **a**, with **take-off ground speed, v,** and the **take-off distance**, **s**, required to reach that **speed**. It is fairly easy to see from **Equation (4)** that, if acceleration, **a**, is reduced, distance, **s**, increases for any given **take-off ground speed, v**. Increasing **a** will, on the other hand, decrease **s**. Of course, the **groundspeed** for any given **airspeed** depends on the **headwind** or **tailwind component**, discussed later in this chapter.

Having looked briefly at some useful equations which should help you understand how various factors affect aircraft performance on take-off, we now go on to look at the factors themselves.

So, **thrust, acceleration, take-off speed**, and **take-off distance** are all vital to an aircraft's **take-off performance**. We will now examine the various factors which affect that performance.

FACTORS AFFECTING TAKE-OFF PERFORMANCE.

The principal factors affecting an aircraft's take-off performance are as follows:

- Aircraft Mass/Weight.
- Air Density (Aerodrome Elevation, Temperature, Humidity).
- Wind Strength and Direction.
- Runway Gradient (Slope).
- Runway Surface Conditions.

Aircraft Mass/Weight.
In general, an increase in an aircraft's mass will lead to a decrease in take-off performance and *vice versa*.

As we have just seen, **increasing an aircraft's mass** for a given average net **thrust force** developed by the propeller will **decrease acceleration** and **increase distance required to achieve take-off speed**.

Greater mass means greater weight, so **increasing mass** will put a greater load on the aircraft's wheels and **increase wheel drag**.

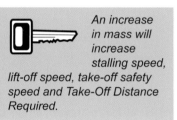
An increase in mass will increase stalling speed, lift-off speed, take-off safety speed and Take-Off Distance Required.

Increased weight means that **more lift will have to be generated** by the wings to lift the aircraft off the ground. The **lift equation** shows us that for a given wing shape and angle of attack, C_L, air density, ρ, and wing area, **S**, **greater lift requires a higher take-off speed**. The higher take-off speed, for a given acceleration, will take longer to achieve and require **increased distance**. But, of course, we have already seen that an **increase in mass** not only **reduces acceleration** for a given **thrust**, but also, because the greater **mass** increases wheel **drag**, it actually reduces **net thrust**, thereby further decreasing **acceleration** and, in consequence, further increasing the **distance** to reach the higher take-off **speed**.

You will recall from **Chapter 13 of Principles of Flight** that an increase in **weight** causes an increase in the aircraft's **stalling speed** from straight flight, which is the **stalling speed** quoted in the **Pilot's Operating Handbook**. The straight flight **stalling speed** is, of course, closely related to an aircraft's **lift-off speed**. The aircraft will **lift-off** as soon as the **straight flight stalling speed** is achieved and just exceeded, which is why the aircraft must be accelerated to the **take-off safety speed** as expeditiously as possible. Consequently, as an increase in **weight** increases the **lift-off speed** and the closely related **straight flight stalling speed**, the **take-off safety speed** must increase, too.

Finally, the **increase in mass and weight reduces the aircraft's angle and rate of climb**, thereby **increasing** the overall **Take-Off Distance Required** to reach the **screen height of 50 feet**.

It can be calculated that an increase in aircraft mass of 10% will increase the overall Take-Off Distance Required by 20%, in other words, by a factor of 1.2.

Of course, decreasing the aircraft's **mass** will reduce the lift-off speed, give the aircraft greater acceleration, and decrease the distance required to achieve take-off speed. Decreasing **mass** will also improve both angle and rate of climb and, thus, decrease the overall **Take-Off Distance Required**.

Air Density.

In general, a decrease in an air density will cause a decrease in take-off performance and lead to an increase in the Take-Off Distance Required.

Air density is a function of **airfield elevation (altitude), air temperature, air pressure** and the **humidity of the air**.

Considering the above factors separately:

- The higher an airfield is situated, the lower will be the air density.
- The higher the air temperature, the lower will be the air density.
- The lower the air pressure, the lower will be the air density.
- The higher the humidity of the air, the lower will be its density.

The relationships between **air density, altitude, temperature, pressure** and **humidity** are explained in **Chapter 2** of the **Principles of Flight** section of this Volume.

Reduced **air density** will have an adverse effect on take-off performance in the following principal areas:

- Propeller thrust will be degraded.
- Engine performance will be degraded.
- The lift force required to counterbalance the aircraft's weight will be generated at a higher true airspeed.
- Directly related to the above point, the indicated take-off airspeed, quoted in the **Pilot's Operating Handbook**, will be reached at a higher true airspeed.
- The initial climb performance will be degraded.

- **Propeller Thrust. Propeller thrust** is generated by imparting a rearwards acceleration to a **mass** of air. The magnitude of the **thrust** force is a function of the rate of change of momentum imparted to the air passing through the propeller disk. Rate of change of momentum is a function of a mass and acceleration. The lower the **air density** the smaller the **mass** of air which is accelerated rearwards and the lower the **thrust force**. The lower the **thrust force**, the lower the **acceleration** and the longer the **distance required to achieve take-off speed**.

- **Engine Performance.** The **power** developed by an internal combustion engine depends, among other things. on the **mass** of air drawn into the cylinders. **Mass is equal to density multiplied by volume.** The lower the **air density**, the lower the **mass** of the volume of air inducted into the cylinders of the aircraft's engine and the lower will be the engine's **power output**. This factor will further reduce the **thrust** generated by the propeller.

- **Lift Force.** From the lift equation, $\textbf{Lift} = \textbf{C}_\textbf{L}\ \tfrac{1}{2}\ \rho\textbf{v}^2\textbf{S}$, for a given value of $\textbf{C}_\textbf{L}$ and **S**, you can see that if **air density**, ρ, decreases, the **lift force** will require **v**, the aircraft's true airspeed, to increase in value before **lift** is equal to the aircraft's **weight** in order to achieve **lift-off**. As a decrease in **air density** already leads to a degradation in engine **power** and propeller **thrust**, the lower resultant **acceleration** will mean that there is a significant increase in **time** and **distance** required to reach the higher true **take-off speed**.

An increase in altitude, temperature or humidity will decrease air density and increase Take-Off Distance Required.

In conditions of low air density, the reduction in engine power and the decrease in lift for a given true airspeed will increase Take-Off Distance Required.

- *Indicated Take-Off Speed.* With decreasing **air density, the indicated lift-off speed**, quoted in the Pilot's Operated Handbook, **remains nevertheless unchanged** because **indicated airspeed** is a measure of **dynamic pressure**, expressed by the term, ½ ρv^2. The **dynamic pressure** required to cause a given **airspeed indication** on the **Airspeed Indicator** will be the same in all circumstances, **indicated airspeed** is the same as true airspeed, only when **air density** has its ICAO Standard Atmosphere sea-level value. But as **air density** decreases, the magnitude of the **dynamic pressure**, ½ρv^2, for a given **true-air speed**, decreases, too, and the difference between the true airspeed and the corresponding **indicated airspeed** will grow. Therefore, the lower the **air density**, the higher the **true airspeed** for any given **indicated airspeed**, and the greater the **Take-Off Run** and the **Take-Off Distance Required**.

- *Initial Climb Performance.* A decrease in **air density** will degrade both **angle and rate of climb**, thus increasing the distance required to achieve the **screen height of 50 feet**, following lift off. The reasons for the degradation in **climb performance** will be explained in the next chapter.

A decrease in air density, then, will cause a degradation in all the principal aspects of an aircraft's take-off performance, despite the fact that there will be a small decrease in drag force for any given true airspeed.

A decrease in air density will, therefore, increase the Take-Off Distance Required. Conversely, in conditions of **high air density, Take-Off Distance Required will be reduced** compared to that required in conditions of low **air density**.

Consequently, if, on a hot, humid day, you are considering operating from an airfield whose elevation is high, think carefully about the effect of this combination of conditions on your aircraft's performance.

Accounting for Air Density in Performance Calculations.

For every 1 000 feet increase in altitude the Take-Off Distance Required increases by 10%, or a factor of 1.1. Similarly, for every rise in temperature of 10°C, Take-Off Distance Required increases by 10%, or a factor of 1.1.

Be aware that when applying these factors to the Take-Of Distance Required, if more than one factor has to be applied (for instance, if temperature, airfield elevation and mass are all high) all factors are multiplied together. So if the airfield elevation is 1 000 feet above the assumed elevation in your aircraft performance figures and the all-up mass is 10% higher than the assumed mass, you must multiply the Take-Off Distance Required in the published figures by 1.1 and then again by 1.2. Then, of course, you should apply the CAA's recommended take-off safety factor of 1.33.

Later on in this Chapter, you will learn how to use a take-off distance graph to calculate the **Take-Off Distance Required** for different physical and meteorological conditions prevailing at a given airfield on any given day. Always remember that the **elevation (altitude)** of the airfield asked for in the graph will be the **pressure altitude** of the airfield; that is, **its altitude (elevation) measured from a pressure datum of 1 013.2 millibars or hectopascals**. In order to find the **pressure altitude** of the airfield you are operating from, simply select **1 013** on your aircraft's altimeter subscale while it is parked.

Temperature information is usually entered separately into aircraft performance graphs, but occasionally **air density** has to be accounted for by a pilot having to calculate **density altitude**. **Density altitude** is simply **pressure altitude** corrected for **air temperature**. Calculations of **density altitude** are easy to perform using a stantdard **flight navigation computer**. (See **Volume 3** of this series: **Navigation and Radio Aids**.)

Wind Strength and Direction.

Headwinds.

An aircraft will lift off at a certain indicated air speed quoted in the Pilot's Operating Handbook. Consequently, if a stationary aircraft is pointing into a wind of, say, 15 knots, it will already register an indicated airspeed of 15 knots and be 15 knots closer to its lift-off speed, even though its ground speed is zero. An aircraft whose lift-off speed is 60 knots will, therefore, only have to accelerate to a ground speed of 45 knots in order to get airborne. Therefore, when taking off **into wind**, the aircraft reaches its lift-off speed in a shorter distance, than if the wind were calm or blowing from a different direction.

Following lift-off, the aircraft's angle of climb relative to the ground is also steeper, when climbing **into wind**, than if the wind were calm. This is because the aircraft's initial angle of climb, which is always close to its maximum angle of climb, is achieved at a given airspeed. Obviously, when flying into a **headwind**, the corresponding ground speed is lower, so a given climb gradient is always steeper relative to the ground when flying into a **headwind**.

Taking off into a headwind decreases the groundspeed of an aircraft at lift-off and decreases the Take-Off Distance Required.

With a **headwind**, the **50 ft screen height** will, consequently, be achieved over a shorter distance than in calm conditions. The stronger the **headwind**, the shorter will be the **Take-Off Distance Required**, as shown in *Figure 2.7*.

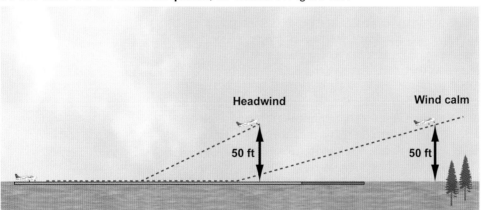

Figure 2.7 Headwinds reduce ground speed for a given indicated air speed and increase initial climb angle, decreasing Take-Off Distance Required.

When calculating **Take-Off Distance Required** in a **headwind**, the UK CAA recommends that, as a **safety factor, only 50% of the observed headwind component strength be used** in the calculation, in order to take into account changes in wind strength and direction. Some take-off performance graphs may have this **safety-factor** already built in. It is the pilot's responsibility to confirm whether that is the case or not.

Tailwinds.

If an aircraft were to take off with a **tailwind** of, say, 5 knots, the aircraft would have to accelerate to 5 knots ground speed before its airspeed began to register. At 5 knots groundspeed, with a 5 knot **tailwind**, the aircraft's airspeed would be zero. Airspeed is the critical factor in generating lift force, **so with a tailwind the aircraft will evidently have to accelerate to a groundspeed which is greater than the take-off airspeed, thus making the ground run longer.**

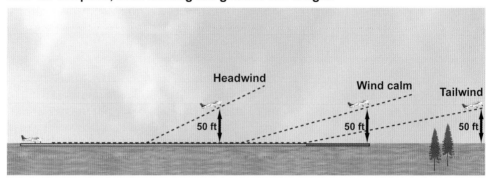

Figure 2.8 Tailwinds increase the ground speed for a given indicated air speed and reduce the initial climb angle. Take-Off Distance Required is, thus, greater in a tailwind.

Likewise, after lift-off, the aircraft's groundspeed will remain 5 knots above its airspeed, and, as an aircraft's achievable angle of climb performance is relative to the air in which the aircraft is flying and not to the ground, with a **tailwind** the aircraft's gradient of climb will be shallower with respect to the ground. **The aircraft's obstacle clearance performance will, thus, be degraded in a tail wind** and the horizontal distance required for the aircraft to reach the 50 feet screen height will be greater. **Take-Off Distance Required, then, will be greater in a tailwind.** *(See Figure 2.8.)*

Even a light **tailwind** will increase the **Take-Off Distance Required** very significantly, and obstacle clearance may be degraded to such an extent that a safe take-off may not be able to be carried out. **For a 5 knot tailwind, Take-Off Distance Required is increased by about 25% (increased by a factor of 1.25). In a 10 knot tailwind Take-Off Distance Required increases by about 155% (increased by a factor of 1.55).**

When calculating **Take-Off Distance Required in a tailwind**, it is recommended that that, as a **safety factor, 150% of the observed tailwind component strength be used** in the calculation in order to take into account changes in wind strength and direction.

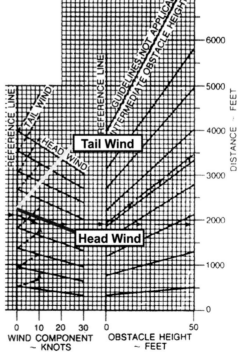

Figure 2.9 Most performance graphs include 50% / 150% wind safety factors.

Crosswinds.

The wind rarely blows down the runway centre-line, so very frequently a given wind will have a **crosswind component** as well as a **headwind/tailwind component**. When entering **headwind** into any take-off calculation, pilots must ensure that they make an accurate assessment of the wind speed and direction and use **the component of the wind which acts along the centre line of the runway, <u>against</u> the direction of take-off**. For example, a **crosswind** blowing at **90°** to the runway centre-line will give an aircraft **no beneficial headwind component** at all, whereas it may well cause the pilot difficulties of controllability during the take-off run because of the tendency of an aircraft to weathercock into wind and for the into-wind wing to lift.

Calculating Headwind Component.

Pilots can calculate **headwind components** for **any given wind direction and strength**, using a **flight navigation computer**. The CD-ROM in the **Navigation & Radio Aids** volume of this series teaches you how to do that. As a rough guide to assessing **headwind components**, however, pilots may use the diagram at *Figure 2.10*.

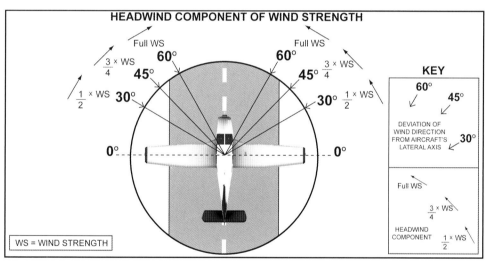

Figure 2.10 The "Clock" System of estimating Headwing Component. Angles are measured from the aircraft's lateral axis.

Notice that **wind angles** are measured with respect to the aircraft's **lateral axis** or with respect to **a line cutting the runway centre line at 90°**. The system illustrated may be memorized by comparing the factors of **headwind component** to the division of an hour of time. **30°** may be compared to **30 minutes**; **30 minutes** is **half an hour**, and so **30° of crosswind, measured from the aircraft's lateral axis**, gives a **headwind component** of **half the wind strength**. Similarly, **45°** gives ¾ **of the wind strength** as the **headwind component**, and any angle greater than **60°** will effectively give the **full wind strength** as the **headwind component**. This system is not 100% accurate, mathematically, but it is very close to that, and may be used to estimate **headwind components** with a fair degree of accuracy if you do not have a computer or calculator with you.

Tailwind components in a **crosswind** may be estimated in the same manner.

Calculating Crosswind Component.

Pilots can calculate the **crosswind component** of **any given wind direction and strength** using **a flight navigation computer** or they may reasonably accurately assess the **crosswind component** using the diagram at *Figure 2.11*.

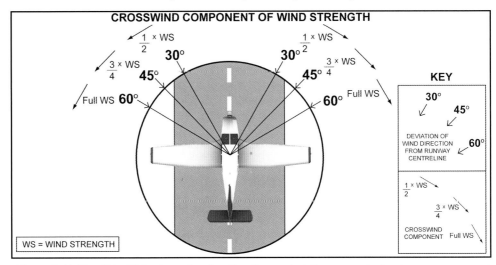

Figure 2.11 The "Clock" System of estimating Crosswind Component. Angles are measured from the aircraft's longitudinal axis.

Notice that, here, **wind angles** are measured with respect to the **aircraft's longitudinal axis** or with respect to the **runway centre line**. As you have just learned, the wind directions may be compared to the division of an hour of time. **30°** may be compared to **30 minutes**; **30 minutes** is **half an hour**, and so **30° of headwind, measured from the aircraft's longitudinal axis or the runway centre line**, gives a **crosswind component of half the wind strength**. Similarly, **45°** gives ¾ **of the wind strength** as the **crosswind component**, and any angle greater than **60°** will effectively give the **full wind strength** as the **crosswind component**.

Turbulence and Windshear.

Turbulence and **windshear** will also adversely affect take-off performance.

Firstly, from a practical piloting point of view, in **turbulent conditions** it is often advisable, during the take-off run, to hold the aircraft on the ground for a slightly longer period of time to provide a better margin above the stall. This will also increase controllability after lift-off, but the penalty is that it will increase the take-off run, too, as well as the overall **Take-Off Distance Required**.

The possibility of **turbulence** and **windshear** must be taken into consideration when working out take-off distances. **Windshear** is a change in wind velocity (speed and/ or direction) over a very short distance. The presence of **windshear** can cause sudden fluctuations in airspeed. Hangars, buildings and areas of trees all influence the direction of the wind near them. In **turbulent conditions, windshear** and **gusts** may be significant in the lee of obstructions. The vertical components of this type of turbulence will affect climb angle and rate of climb, either beneficially or adversely. The great danger of the presence of **turbulence** and **windshear** is that the effects are **unpredictable**.

Runway Slope.

Runway Slope affects take-off distance because, if **slope** is present, a component of the aircraft's weight will act along the runway, down the **slope**.

If an aircraft takes off on a runway which **slopes** upwards, a component of the aircraft's weight will act <u>against</u> the direction of motion of the aircraft, reducing the net thrust force developed at the propeller, decreasing acceleration and increasing the take-off run. Obviously the **Take-Off Distance Required** (to read the 50 feet screen height) will also be increased.

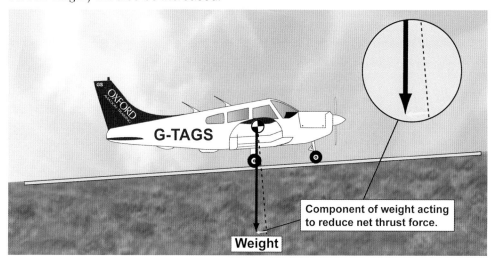

Figure 2.12 Upslope reduces acceleration owing to a component of weight acting backwards against thrust. This increases the Take-Off Distance Required.

Conversely, if an aircraft takes off on a **downwards sloping runway**, a component of the aircraft's weight will act <u>in</u> the direction of take-off, thereby adding to the thrust force developed by the propeller. **Taking off on a down-slope, then, will increase acceleration, reduce the take-off run and decrease the overall Take-Off Distance Required.**

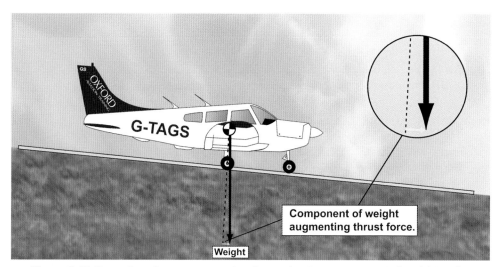

Figure 2.13 Downslope increases acceleration owing to a component of weight acting forwards to augment propeller thrust force. This reduces Take-Off Distance Required.

For every **1%** of up-slope the **take off distance** is increased by **5%**, or a factor of **1.05**.

No factor is applied for the advantage of a downwards-sloping runway for take-off. A down-slope should be regarded as a bonus when taking off.

Calculating Runway Slope.

The **gradient of a slope** can be calculated if certain information is available. If a pilot knows the difference in height between the two ends of a runway, the **gradient of slope** may be found by dividing the difference in height by the runway length (taking care to work in the same units of measurement). For example, a **2 500 feet (760-metre)** long runway which is **50 feet (15 metres)** higher at one end than the other has a **slope gradient** of approximately **0.02**, or a **2%**.

Runway Surface.

Most **take-off performance graphs and tables** assume that certain **"associated conditions"** apply to the airfield and aircraft which are the subjct of the **takc-off performance calculations.** One of those **associated conditions** is, invariably, that the aircraft is operating from a **level, paved, dry surface**. This is the case for the section of graph that we illustrate in *Figure 2.14*. If the **runway surface** conditions differ from these assumptions, allowance must be made for that difference, in take-off calculations.

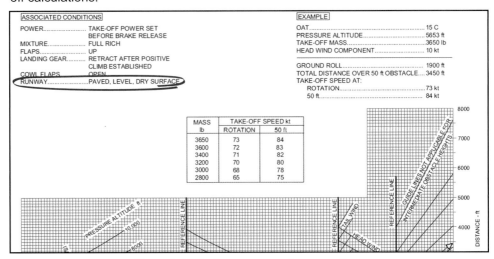

Figure 2.14 Performance graph assumptions.

Even on a hard, paved runway, a wet surface will cause an increase in wheel drag. An aircraft taking off on a wet runway will, therefore, accelerate less rapidly leading to an increase in the **take-off run** and in the overall **Take-Off Distance Required**. Any puddles of water on the runway would have a very significant retarding effect on an aircraft's acceleration. **Taking off through standing water should be avoided**.

Of course, many small airfields have grass strips. Even **dry grass** will **increase wheel drag** compared to a take-off on a paved or asphalt runway, again leading to an increase in the **take-off run** and overall **Take-Off Distance Required**.

Dry grass can increase Take-Off Distance Required by up to 15% compared to a paved runway. If **dry grass** is as long as **8 inches (20 cm)**, Take-Off Distance

Required is increased by 20%. Long, wet grass will cause a much greater increase in the take-off run, depending on the length and wetness of the grass and the weight and wheel size of the aircraft.

Soft ground or snow will cause an even greater increase in **Take-Off Distance Required**.

Summary of Correction Factors.

The following table at *Figure 2.15*, taken from **UK CAA Safety Sense Leaflet No 7, 'General Aviation Aircraft Performance'**, summarises the **correction factors** that you have learned so far, and which should be applied to **take-off calculations** in order to allow for conditions which depart from the **associeted conditions** assumed by **take-off performance graphs**. Note that when more than one **correction factor** applies, each new factor involves a further **multiplication**. The table at *Figure 2.15* also includes **correction factors** to be applied to **landing calculations**, as well as **overall safety factors** to account for the fact that graphs contain **unfactored data**.

CONDITION	TAKE-OFF		LANDING	
	INCREASE IN TAKE -OFF DISTANCE TO HEIGHT 50 FEET	FACTOR	INCREASE IN LANDING DISTANCE FROM 50 FEET	FACTOR
A 10% increase in aeroplane weight, e.g. another passenger	20%	1.20	10%	1.10
An increase of 1,000 ft in aerodrome elevation	10%	1.10	5%	1.05
An increase of 10°C in ambient temperature	10%	1.10	5%	1.05
Dry grass* - Up to 20 cm (8 in) (on firm soil)	20%	1.20	15%[+]	1.15
Wet grass* - Up to 20 cm (8 in) (on firm soil)	30%	1.3	35%[+]	1.35
			Very short grass may be slippery, distances may increase by up to 60%	
Wet paved surface	-	-	15%	1.15
A 2% slope*	Uphill 10%	1.10	Downhill 10%	1.10
A tailwind component of 10% of lift-off speed	20%	1.20	20%	1.20
Soft ground or snow*	25% or more	1.25 +	25%[+] or more	1.25 +
NOW USE ADDITIONAL SAFETY FACTORS (if data is unfactored)		**1.33**		**1.43**

Notes: 1.   * Effect on Ground Run/ Roll will be greater.

2.   [+] For a few types of aeroplane e. g. those without brakes, grass surfaces may decrease the landing roll. However, to be on the safe side, assume the INCREASE shown until you are thoroughly conversant with the aeroplane type.

3.   Any deviation from normal operating techniques is likely to result in an increased distance.

Figure 2.15 Factors to be applied to account for surfaces which are not hard, dry or level. When more than one factor is applied, each new factor involves a new multiplication.

Flap Setting.

As you learnt in the **Principles of Flight** section of this volume, **deployment of flap reduces the stalling speed** and, as a corollary, will also enable an aircraft **to lift off at a lower indicated airspeed**. This can mean a shorter ground run.

Care must be taken, however, to use the manufacturer's recommended **take-off flap setting** because **deployment of flap always increases drag as well as lift**, and

Compared to a flapless take-off, use of the manufacturer's recommended take-off flap setting will shorten the Take-Off Run Required but reduce the initial angle of climb, and may increase Take-Off Distance Required.

so use of inappropriately large **flap** settings may actually increase the **ground run** to lift-off. The manufacturer's recommended **take-off flap setting** will always be a small setting. For instance, **recommended take-off flap setting for the Cessna 152 is 10°**.

But even when the recommended **flap** setting is used, the **lift/drag ratio** will be degraded, and there will be a corresponding **reduction in the angle and rate of climb**. Consequently, even though use of **take-off flap** will shorten the **ground run**, the distance to the **50 feet screen height**, that is **the Take-Off Distance Required, may not be decreased**. *(See Figure 2.16.)*

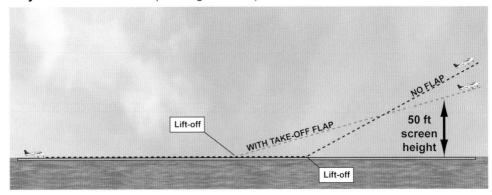

Figure 2.16 Take-off flap will reduce take-off run but may increase overall Take-Off Distance Required.

The actual effect of using **take-off flap** will depend on several factors such as the **flap setting** itself, engine power and propeller thrust. As we have mentioned, if **flap** is used on take-off it should always be with the setting recommended in the **Pilot's Operating Handbook (POH)**, but you must never forget to check any supplement included in the **POH**. Depending on runway surface conditions, runway length and prevailing meteorological conditions, a light aircraft may reach the **50 feet screen height** earlier by taking off without deploying **flap**.

Wing Contamination.

The presence of **insects, ice, rain drops** and **snow** on the wings of an aircraft, especially at the leading-edge, can have a significantly adverse effect on the generation of lift. Laminar flow aerofoils are particularly badly affected by **wing contamination**. All **contamination**, but especially **ice** and **snow,** will also increase an aircraft's **weight**. Consequently, take-off speed will be higher and **Take-Off Distance Required longer with contaminated wings**.

Figure 2.17 Wing contamination will degrade an aerofoil's lift-generating properties and increase Take-Off Distance Required. Ice and snow will also significantly increase weight.

Tyre Pressure and Wheel Contamination.

The **take-off run** will be longer if the aircraft's **tyre pressures** are below the recommended level. **Accumulated mud and/or grass** around wheel axles will also increase **rolling resistance** and lengthen the take-off run. Wheels fitted with spats may experience significant rolling resistance if the spats are packed with **mud, grass** or **slush.**

ENGINE FAILURE AFTER TAKE-OFF.

Though modern engines are very reliable, engines may **fail** or suffer from **loss of power** at any time. **The pilot must always be especially aware for the possibility of total or partial loss of power during the take-off run and initial climb.**

TAKE-OFF DECISION POINT.

A prudent pilot should know the point during the take-off run where the aircraft can be safely brought to a halt in the event of insufficient acceleration, engine failure, or such malfunctions as the loss of the Airspeed Indicator.

TAKE-OFF DISTANCE GRAPHS AND TABLES.

Take-Off Distances Required can be calculated by referring to either **tables** or **graphs**. In the following pages, we will cover **take-off calculations** using a representative **take-off distance graph** (*Figure 2.18*) typical of those available for most light aircraft.

Note that the **take-off performance data** contained in this type of graph are **unfactored**. Therefore, the **take-off performance** obtained from the graph will be expressed in **gross performance figures**, which assume that both the aircraft and engine are new, and that the aircraft is being flown in ideal conditions by a highly experienced pilot. Consequently, when a **Take-Off Distance Required** has been calculated from the **graph**, it is prudent to apply the recommended **overall safety factor** of **1.33** in order obtain **net take-off performance figures** which take into account any degradation in performance in an older aircraft being flown by an inexperienced pilot, in less than ideal conditions.

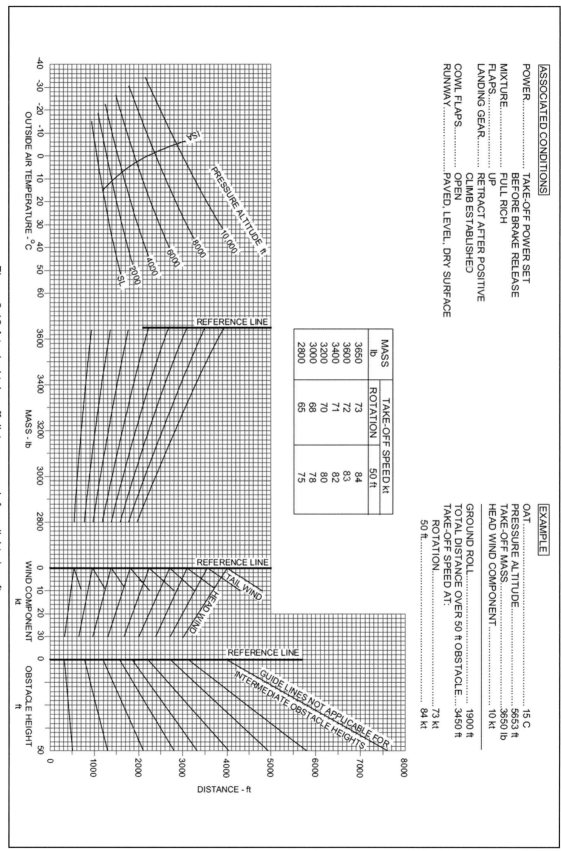

Figure 2.18 A typical take-off distance graph for a light aircraft.

Information Given at the Top of the Take-Off Distance Graph.

Before beginning any calculation of **Take-Off Distance Required** for prevailing runway and meteorological conditions and aircraft mass, do not fail to note the conditions assumed by the data in the **take-off distance graph**, as listed under the title **"Associated Conditions"**, usually positioned at the top of the graph. (*See Figure 2.19.*)

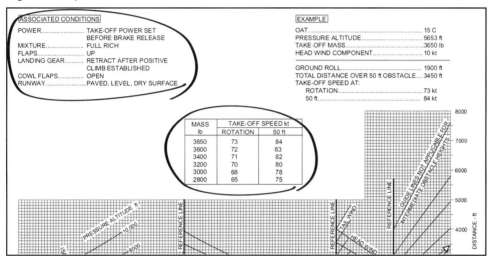

Figure 2.19 Associated Conditions and Take-Off Speeds assumed by the Take-Off Performance Graph.

You will see, immediately, that the graph assumes that **take-off (full) power will be applied before brakes-release, mixture will be fully rich, no flap will be deployed, landing gear will be retracted** after a positive rate of climb is established, and that the **runway is level and has a paved, dry surface.**

If there is any difference between the assumed and actual conditions for your aircraft type and runway conditions, **correction factors**, including the types already discussed, must be applied. These **correction factors** are summarised in the table at *Figure 2.15*. For instance, if the runway has a **dry grass surface** and a **2% up-hill slope**, any **Take-Off Distance Required** extracted from the graph would have to be multiplied by a factor of **1.2** and then again by **1.1** (Remember, all **correction factors** applied must be multiplied together.)

You will note that the information on the graph at *Figure 2.19* also includes details of **rotation speeds** and **take-off safety speeds** (speeds to be achieved at the **screen height of 50 feet**) for several different values of **take-off mass**. These speeds must be adhered to during the actual take-off, because they are the speeds which have been assumed in the construction the graph.

In the top right hand corner of the graph, you will notice that an **example calculation** has been carried out. Never make the mistake of using this example calculation to apply to your own aircraft. Always carry out the calculation using the figures for <u>your</u> aircraft and for the conditions prevailing at the airfield at the time of your planned take-off.

Using the Take-Off Distance Graph Itself.

Now let us take a closer look at the **Take-Off Distance Graph**, itself. The graph in *Figure 2.18* is divided into four vertical sections each of which has a different scale at its base.

1   The section at the extreme left contains curves representing the **pressure altitude** of the airfield. Remember, the **pressure altitude** of the airfield is the airfield's vertical distance above the ICAO Standard Atmosphere (IAS) sea-level pressure of **1 013.2 millibars (hectopascals)**. You can find the **pressure altitude** of the airfield you are operating from by selecting **1 013** on your aircraft's **altimeter subscale** while you aircraft is on the ground. The scale at the base of this first section of the graph is graduated in **degrees Celsius** and allows you to enter the **prevailing outside air temperature**. Pressure altitude and **temperature** information together, permits the required **air density** data to be entered into the graph.

2   The next section of the graph contains curves representing aircraft **all-up mass** which can be entered using the horizontal scale at the base of the section, graduated in **pounds (lb)**.

3   The next section contains lines representing **headwind and tailwind components** against the scale at the base of the section, graduated in **knots**. You should note that in some graphs the **50% headwind factor** and **150% tailwind factor** may have already been applied. But you should check the Performance section of the aircraft's **Flight Manual** or **Pilot's Operating Handbook** to confirm this fact.

4   The next section of the graph allows you to enter the height in feet of any obstacles in the initial climb-out path.

5   Finally, the **vertical scale at the extreme right of the graph** enables you to read off the **Take-Off Distance Required** in feet, **assuming that the associated conditions prevail which are listed at the top of the graph.**

When the **Take-Off Distances Required** has been read from the graph, **correction factors** will need to be applied, if relevant. And, of course, the UK CAA recommended **overall safety factor of 1.33 should be applied.**

Example Calculation.

We will carry out our own **example calculation**, using the graph at *Figure 2.20* which refers to a **PA-28-161**. The information in this **Take-Off Distance Required** graph is formatted slightly differently to the graph at *Figure 2.18*, and contains no obstacle section, but it is typical of the type of graph you might find in an aircraft's **Flight Manual** or **Pilot's Operating Handbook**.

Let us assume that we wish to take off from an airfield with a grass strip, **1 025 metres** long, aligned **05/23** on a day when the outside air temperature is **12° Celsius**. Having prepared our aircraft for take-off, we calculate its all-up mass as **2 250 lb**. We observe the wind as blowing from about **270° Magnetic** at **15 knots**. The airfield **QNH** is **1 003**. By setting **1 013** on the aircraft's **altimeter subscale,** we note that at our **airfield elevation of 250 feet**, the **pressure altitude is 550 feet**.

The runway-in-use is **23** so, from the observable wind, we calculate that the **headwind component** is about **10 knots**.

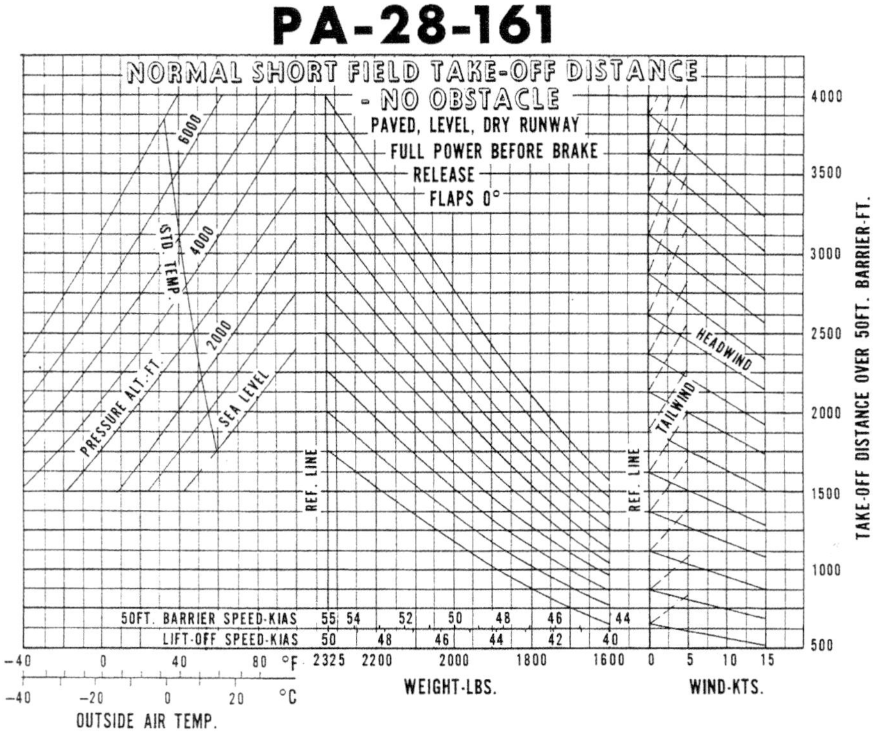

PA-28-161

NORMAL SHORT FIELD TAKE-OFF DISTANCE
- NO OBSTACLE
PAVED, LEVEL, DRY RUNWAY
FULL POWER BEFORE BRAKE
RELEASE
FLAPS 0°

Example: Departure airport pressure altitude: 550 ft	Distance over 50 ft barrier: 1375 ft
Departure airport temperatures 12°C	Lift-off speed: 48
Weight: 2250 lbs	Barrier speed: 53
Wind: 10 kts headwind	

Figure 2.20 Short field take-off distance graph for a PA-28-161 Warrior.

We now have enough information to calculate the **take-off distance we require**. We note from the **associated conditions** on the **Take-Off Distance Required** graph that the **runway is assumed to be paved, level and dry,** and that it is further assumed that **full power is applied before brake-release** and that **no take-off flap is used**. Our runway is level, but it is a grass runway.

The runway that we will be using grass is short and the ground is dry. We note, therefore, that we must apply a **correction factor** to allow for the grass surface, <u>after</u> we have extracted the **Take-Off Distance Required** from the graph.

We will take a decision and the use of flaps depending on the overall **Take-Off Distance Required** and the **Take-Off Distance Available**.

We now begin our calculation, as indicated at *Figure 2.21, overleaf*. On the graph, our working is shown by the red lines.

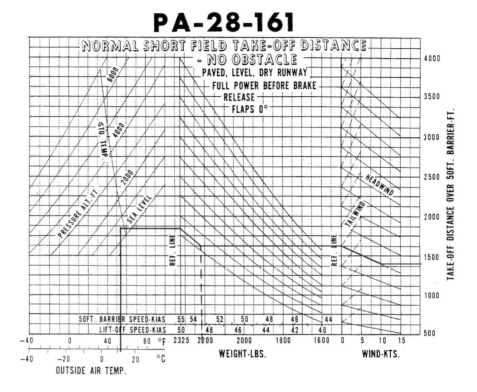

PA-28-161

Example:

Departure airport pressure altitude: 550 ft	Distance over 50 ft barrier: 1375 ft
Departure airport temperatures 12°C	Lift-off speed: 48
Weight: 2250 lbs	Barrier speed: 53
Wind: 10 kts headwind	

Figure 2.21 Calculation of Take-Off Distance Required.

On the left-hand side of the graph, we locate the horizontal **temperature scale** at the foot of the graph and draw a vertical line from the **12° C** mark until the line meets a point among the **pressure altitude lines** corresponding to **550 feet**, the **pressure altitude** of our airfield. There is no **550 feet line**, so we have to interpolate, choosing a suitable point between the **sea-level** and **1 000 feet** lines.

We then draw a horizontal line from the **550 feet** point to the next **vertical reference line** which marks the beginning of the **weight/lift-off speed/screen height safely speed section** of the graph. From that **reference line**, we follow the slope of the nearest **weight-line** down to a point which corresponds to our calculated **take-off weight of 2 250 lbs**, read from the horizontal scale at the foot of the graph.

We note, reading vertically downwards to the **lift-off speed/screen height safely speed scales**, that our **lift-off speed** at **2 250lb** will be just over **48 knots**, and that our **screen height safety speed** should be **53 knots**.

Drawing, now, a further horizontal line towards the **vertical reference line** which marks the beginning of the **wind section of the graph**, we extend our line downwards parallel to the nearest **headwind line** to a point which corresponds to **10 knots** on the horizontal scale at the foot of the graph. In this example our line coincides with a chart drawn headwind line. This will not always happen.

From that point we conclude the graph part of our calculation by drawing a horizontal line to meet the **vertical scale** at the extreme right-hand side of the graph which gives the **Take-Off Distance Required**. We read from that scale that the **take-off distance that we require is 1 375 feet**, provided all of the assumed conditions apply.

Finally, we complete the calculation for our particular take-off by applying any **correction factors** which must be applied to allow for any deviation from the **assumed conditions**.

These **correction factors** are summarised in the table at *Figure 2.15*. Our take-off strip is **short dry grass**, so we need to multiply **1 375 feet** by **1.2** to give us **1 650 feet**.

The last action that we need to take is to multiply **1 650 feet** by the **recommended overall safety factor of 1.33 for the take-off**, in order to account for the fact that the graph's data assumes ideal conditions and a new and perfectly maintained aircraft flown by an expert pilot. This concluding calculation gives us a **Take-Off Distance Required** of **2 195 feet**. This is the distance we must compare with the **Take-Off Distance Available** at our airfield.

We note from the **UK AIP, Aerodrome Data Section**, that at our airfield, both the **Take-Off Run Available**, and the **Take-Off Distance Available** for Runway **05/23** is **1 025 metres**, which is **3 362 feet**. We, therefore, feel confident that we can make a safe take-off, that we will be able to initiate the take-off run normally, without having to apply full power against the brakes, and that we will be well within our safety margins by taking off without any flap deployed.

If we had found that the **Take-Off Distance Required** exceeded the **Take-Off Distance Available**, we would have to reduce weight by taking on less fuel or off-loading baggage and/or passengers. If we still wished to fly we would then need to carry out a new calculation for **Take-Off Distance Required (TODR),** at the revised weight, and compare the new **TODR** with the **Take-Off Distance Available**.

TAKE-OFF DISTANCE TABLES.

Sometimes, the data a pilot requires for calculating **Take-Off Distance Required** is given in tabular form. One such table is shown in *Figure 2.22*. The interpretation of these tables is straightforward.

Weight (Kgs)	Takeoff Speed KIAS	Takeoff Speed (MPH)	Press Alt Ft	0°C (32°F) Metres GND RUN	0°C (32°F) Metres 50 FT	10°C (40°F) Metres GND RUN	10°C (40°F) Metres 50 FT	20°C (68°F) Metres GND RUN	20°C (68°F) Metres 50 FT	30°C (86°F) Metres GND RUN	30°C (86°F) Metres 50 FT	40°C (104°F) Metres GND RUN	40°C (104°F) Metres 50 FT
	LIFT OFF	Clear 50ft											
998	56	63	SL	230	419	255	464	282	512	311	564	341	618
	(64)	(73)	2000	273	495	304	549	336	606	370	667	407	732
			4000	326	587	362	651	401	719	442	791	485	868
			6000	391	698	434	774	479	854	529	940	581	1031
			8000	469	832	520	922	575	1010	634	1120	697	1229
907	53	60	SL	183	336	203	372	224	411	247	452	272	496
	(61)	(69)	2000	218	397	241	440	267	486	294	535	323	587
			4000	260	471	288	522	319	576	351	635	386	696
			6000	311	560	345	621	382	685	420	754	462	828
			8000	373	668	414	740	458	817	504	899	554	983
816	50	57	SL	142	263	158	292	174	322	192	355	211	389
	(58)	(66)	2000	169	312	187	345	207	381	229	419	251	460
			4000	202	369	221	409	247	452	273	497	300	546
			6000	241	439	268	486	296	537	326	591	359	649
			8000	290	523	321	580	355	640	392	704	430	773

Figure 2.22 Take-off performance information presented in tabular format.

Representative PPL - type questions to test your theoretical knowledge of Take-off.

1.   If the density of the atmosphere is reduced, the take-off distance required will be:

   a.   increased
   b.   decreased
   c.   unaffected
   d.   reduced with a wind

2.   What effect will a higher aircraft mass have on the rotate speed and take off safety speed?

   a.   It will decrease both speeds
   b.   It will increase rotate speed and decrease take off safety speed
   c.   It will increase both speeds
   d.   It will decrease rotate speed and increase take off safety speed

3.   That part of a runway surface which is used for normal operations during take off, excluding any clearway or stopway, is referred to as:

   a.   the Take-Off Run Available (TORA)
   b.   the Accelerate-Stop Distance Available (ASDA)
   c.   the Take-Off Distance Available (TODA)
   d.   the Emergency Distance Available (EMDA)

4.   Complete the following statement as accurately as possible using one of the options a), b), c) or d).

   If the density of the air increases the effect will be:

   a.   to increase the take-off distance required
   b.   to increase the take-off run
   c.   to decrease the take-off distance required
   d.   to decrease the indicated airspeed at lift-off

5.   Complete the following statement as accurately as possible using one of the options, a), b), c) or d).

   The main reason for taking off into wind is to:

   a.   increase the take-off distance required
   b.   decrease the take-off distance available
   c.   increase the ground speed of the aircraft at lift-off
   d.   decrease the ground speed of the aircraft at lift-off and to decrease the Take-Off Distance Required

6.   Complete the following statement as accurately as possible using one of the following options: a), b), c) or d).

        During take-off, the use of the manufacturer's recommended take-off flap setting:

        a.   compared to zero flap, will increase the length of the take-off run and obstacle clearance performance
        b.   compared to zero flap, will decrease the take-off run required but reduce obstacle clearance performance
        c.   compared to zero flap, will increase the indicated airspeed at which the aircraft can lift-off
        d.   compared to zero flap, will ensure a steeper angle of climb after lift-off

7 .   Complete the following statement accurately using one of the options: a), b), c) or d).

        When the density of the atmosphere is relatively low, the resulting reduction in:

        a.   thrust and drag has no apparent effect on the take-off distance required
        b.   both lift and engine power will require a longer take-off distance
        c.   drag will permit the use of greater flap angles
        d.   drag offsets the loss of engine power giving improved acceleration

8.   The horizontal distance covered during take-off, from brakes-release to the 50 feet screen height, and which includes any stopway or clearway, is referred to as:

        a.   the Take-Off Run Available (TORA)
        b.   the Accelerate-Stop Distance Available (ASDA)
        c.   the Take-Off Distance Available (TODA)
        d.   the Emergency Distance Available (EMDA)

9.   That part of a take-off strip which includes the Take-Off Run Available and the stopway, is referred to as:

        a.   the Take-Off Run Available (TORA)
        b.   the clearway
        c.   the Take-Off Distance Available (TODA)
        d.   the Accelerate-Stop Distance Available (ASDA) or Emergency Distance Available (EDA)

10.   What name is given to the distance which comprises Take-Off Run Available (TORA) and any clearway?

       a.   Emergency Distance Available (EMDA)
       b.   Take-Off Distance Required (TODA)
       c.   Accelerate-Stop Distance Available (ASDA)
       d.   Take-Off Distance Available (TODA)

11.   A 15 knot wind at 60° off the runway heading gives a headwind component of approximately:

       a.   8 knots
       b.   14 knots
       c.   12 knots
       d.   3 knots

12.   A 15 knot wind at 60° off the runway heading gives a crosswind component of approximately:

       a.   8 knots
       b.   14 knots
       c.   12 knots
       d.   3 knots

Question	1	2	3	4	5	6	7	8	9	10	11	12
Answer												

The answers to these questions can be found at the end of this book.

CHAPTER 3
CLIMB

INTRODUCTION.

An aircraft's ability to achieve a satisfactory **angle and rate of climb** is an important aspect of its overall performance. It is obviously efficient to be able to **climb rapidly** to the pilot's chosen cruising altitude, but it is also desirable that an aircraft should be able to **climb steeply** in order to achieve safe **obstacle clearance performance** as well as to keep noise pollution to a minimum. We will begin by examining **angle of climb**.

ANGLE OF CLIMB.

Figure 3.1 depicts an aircraft in un-accelerated straight and level flight. **Lift** balances **weight** and **thrust** balances **drag**, so all four forces are in **equilibrium**. Airspeed and altitude are constant.

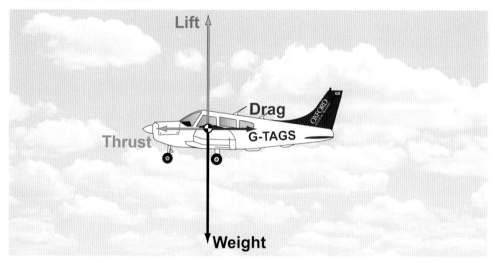

Figure 3.1 Straight and level flight with the four principal flight forces in equilibrium.

If the pilot now eases back on the control column, without increasing thrust, the disposition of forces will be as shown in *Figure 3.2*.

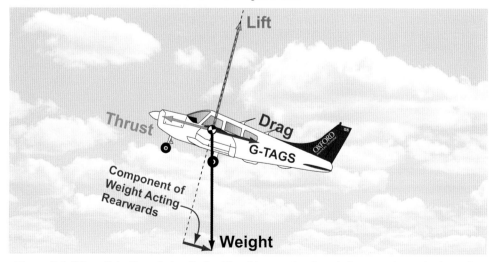

Figure 3.2 If the pilot attempts to climb without increasing thrust, the aerodynamic drag plus the component of the aircraft's weight acting rearwards are now greater than thrust. The aircraft will, therefore, lose speed.

Figure 3.2 shows that the aircraft will begin to climb, but **a component of the aircraft's weight now acts rearwards** along the longitudinal axis in the same direction as the **aerodynamic drag**. This component is called **weight apparent drag**. The rearward acting forces are now, consequently, greater than the forward acting thrust force. The end result, depending on the pitch altitude selected by the pilot, would be either that the aircraft continues to climb at a lower airspeed, or the aircraft may stall.

In order to maintain his **original speed in the climb**, therefore, the pilot opens the throttle to increase the thrust developed at the propeller and so balance the **rearwards acting weight component** of the aircraft (**the weight apparent drag**). The **extra thrust** that the pilot has applied is **excess thrust** that the engine has available over and above the thrust required to maintain level flight **at the same speed**. (*See Figure 3.3.*)

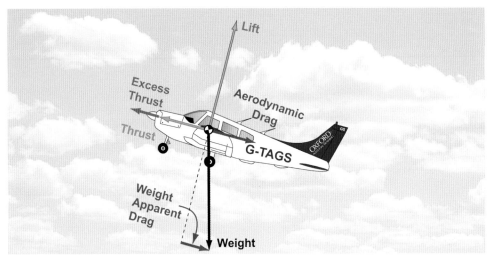

Figure 3.3 Forces in a steady climb showing excess thrust balancing weight apparent drag.

You have learnt in **Principles of Flight** that in order to maintain level flight, the thrust required from the propeller must exactly counteract **aerodynamic drag**. In level flight, then, any **extra thrust** which is available from the engine-propeller combination can be used to climb the aircraft, if the pilot wishes.

The greater the amount of excess thrust available, the greater can be the angle of climb.

It follows then that, for a given airspeed, the greater the excess thrust available in the engine-propeller combination, over and above the thrust required to maintain level flight at that airspeed, the steeper the aircraft will be able to climb <u>at that airspeed</u>. The steepest angle of climb will be achieved by climbing at full throttle at the level flight speed at which the extra thrust available for the climb is at a maximum.

This principle is depicted by *Figure 3.4* which shows two aircraft, each at its **maximum angle of climb**; (Note, though, that the force arrows are not drawn to scale.) The aircraft on the left has attained a steeper **angle of climb** because, for its **speed**, weight and configuration, in the climb, it had more **excess thrust available at that speed** when it was in straight and level flight.

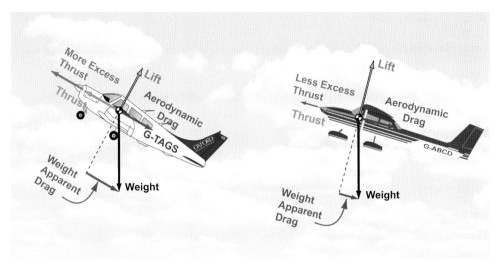

Figure 3.4 The steepest angle of climb will be achieved by climbing at full throttle at the level-flight speed at which the excess thrust available is a maximum.

There are several factors then which affect how much **extra thrust** is **available** for the climb, over and above the thrust required for level flight. The speed factor has already been mentioned, and we discuss speed in more detail, below. Other factors which affect **angle of climb** are **aircraft weight, aircraft configuration** (e.g. deployment of flaps and undercarriage), **air density** and, as far as the **angle of climb relative to the ground** is concerned, the strength of **headwind** component. These latter factors will mentioned latter in this chapter.

Speed and Best Achievable Angle of Climb.
Let us look at some final points about the relationship between **speed** and **angle of climb**.

As we have seen the **angle of climb** at a given **speed** is a function of the **excess thrust available** from the engine-propeller combination over and above the **thrust required to fly straight and level at that speed**. There will of course be only one level flight speed at which the **excess thrust**, still able to be developed by the propeller, is at a **maximum**. This will be the aircraft's **best angle of climb speed**, known as **V$_X$**.

Jet-powered aircraft will achieve their **best angle of climb** at a speed where drag is minimum. (Jet fighters capable of producing more thrust than they weigh, such as the Harrier, can, of course, climb vertically, and actually accelerate in the vertical climb.)

But, as you learnt in **Principles of Flight**, in the case of an aircraft driven by a **fixed-pitch propeller**, the amount of **thrust produced decreases with airspeed** because propeller-blade angle of attack also decreases with airspeed. An aircraft with a **fixed-pitch propeller**, therefore, produces its **maximum thrust** at a **lower airspeed than the speed for minimum drag**. By the time such an aircraft has reached minimum drag speed, thrust has decreased considerably, even though engine power has increased. **Therefore, the speed for maximum angle of climb (V$_X$) for a simple light aircraft is lower than the speed for minimum drag**.

The graph at *Figure 3.5* depicts the relationship (for a representative light aircraft) between the **speed in level flight** and two other parameters: the **thrust required to maintain level flight at that speed** and the **total thrust available from the** propeller at that speed. The **thrust required** curve is taken from the total drag curve for the aircraft because, as you already know, **thrust required to maintain level flight must be equal to drag**.

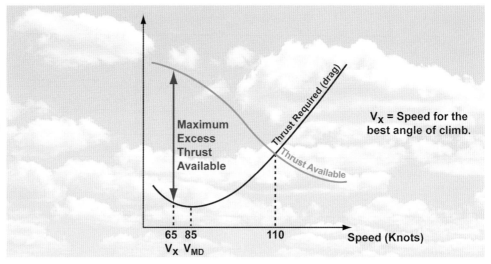

Figure 3.5 Climb angle or gradient is dependent on Excess Thrust Available. Maximum excess thrust available will give maximum angle or gradient of climb. V$_X$ is defined as the speed for best angle or gradient of climb.

Examining the graph, we see that the **maximum amount of excess thrust available for the climb** is found where the distance between the thrust available and the thrust required curves is the greatest, The corresponding speed on the graph's horizontal axis is the speed, **V$_X$** at which the **greatest angle of climb is achieved when full throttle is applied**. **V$_X$**, then, is the speed to fly for the **best angle of climb**.

In a light aircraft such as the **Cessna 152**, **V$_X$** will be about **65 knots**.

At any other speed than **V$_X$**, you can see that the **excess thrust available** reduces; so for any other speed than **V$_X$** the angle of climb will also reduce.

Forces in the Climb.
In a **steady climb**, at **constant angle of climb** and **constant speed**, the forces of **thrust**, **drag**, **lift** and **weight** are in **equilibrium**, just as they are in level flight. However, in the climb, the **weight and aerodynamic drag** of the aircraft are balanced by **a combination of lift and thrust**. (*See Figure 3.6.*) An interesting phenomenon that you should note is that, because, in a steady climb, the **total thrust** is greater than **aerodynamic drag, the lift force, itself, is** <u>less</u> **than the aircraft's weight**.

For a light aircraft, at typical light aircraft **angles of climb**, the **lift** will be only a little less than the **weight**. And, of course, as the climb is initiated with the nose of the aircraft raised to the climbing attitude as full power is applied, the **lift** force will momentarily increase. **But as soon as the aircraft is established in the climb, lift reduces to a little below the value of weight.**

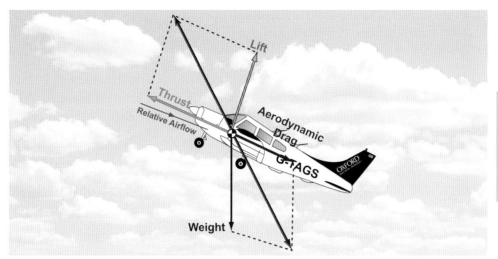

Figure 3.6 Equilibrium in a steady climb, at constant speed. Total thrust is greater than aerodynamic drag, and lift is less than weight.

> *The lift generated by an aircraft in a steady climb, at constant airspeed and power setting will be less than the aircraft's weight.*

As the **angle of climb** steepens, the more the **lift** force reduces with respect to **weight**. (For a Harrier jet fighter **in a vertical climb**, it is **thrust** alone which balances both the aircraft's **weight** and **aerodynamic drag**, the **lift** force playing no role at all.)

Other Factors Affecting Angle of Climb.

Weight.

The greater an aircraft's **all–up weight**, the greater the **lift** required to maintain level flight at any speed. The **lift formula, Lift = C_L ½ $\rho v^2 S$**, teaches us that for a given airspeed and at constant density, the increase in **lift** required to support a heavier aircraft can only be obtained by increasing C_L. Unless flap is lowered, which may not be practical or safe, C_L can be increased only by increasing **angle of attack**. An increase in **angle of attack** will increase **induced drag**, and so, at any given speed, **more thrust is required to maintain level flight than for a lighter aircraft**. Consequently, there will be less **excess thrust available** in level flight for the aircraft to **climb**. The **angle of climb** achievable at any speed will, thus, reduce. It follows that, **when an aircraft is heavily loaded, the best angle of climb achievable will be less steep than the best angle of climb for a more lightly loaded aircraft**.

For any given **climb angle**, an increase in **weight** will also increase the **rearwards acting weight component** (i.e. the **weight apparent drag**), requiring increased **"excess" thrust** to balance it. Therefore, for a given value of **maximum excess thrust available** from the propeller, which is <u>already</u> reduced for a heavier aircraft, **the best climb angle achievable will be further reduced compared to a lighter aircraft**.

> *Increasing the aircraft's all-up weight will reduce the best angle of climb.*

Figure 3.7, overleaf, shows that the overall effect of increasing **weight** is that the **thrust required curve** moves up and to the right, whereas the **thrust available curve** remains unchanged. The graph confirms, then, that, at any given straight and level flight speed, the **excess thrust available for the climb reduces**, and that the best achievable **angle of climb** at that speed will be shallower than for a lighter aircraft. The graph for the heavier aircraft also shows that the speed at which **maximum excess thrust** is available, increases compared to a lighter aircraft.

Consequently, the speed for the best angle of climb is higher for a heavy aircraft than for a lightly-loaded aircraft.

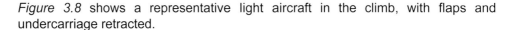

Figure 3.7 At increased aircraft weight, the thrust required curve moves up and to the right. The thrust available curve remains unchanged. For all speeds, excess thrust available for the climb reduces. V_X, the speed for the best angle of climb, increases.

To summarise, then, **a heavier aircraft will have a shallower best angle of climb than a more lightly loaded aircraft, and the speed at which the reduced best angle of climb is achieved is higher.**

Aircraft Configuration.

The angle of climb is also affected by the **configuration** of the aircraft. By **configuration**, we mean whether **flaps** and **undercarriage** are extended or not.

Figure 3.8 shows a representative light aircraft in the climb, with flaps and undercarriage retracted.

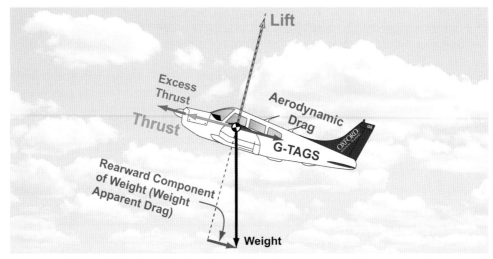

Figure 3.8 A aircraft in the climb, with undercarriage and flaps retracted.

If the undercarriage and flaps are extended, the **parasite drag** of the aircraft and, thus, its **total drag**, at any given speed will increase. Consequently, at any given speed, there is a reduction in **excess thrust available** from the propeller at that speed, and the best achievable **angle of climb** at that speed will also be reduced (*See Figure 3.10.*)

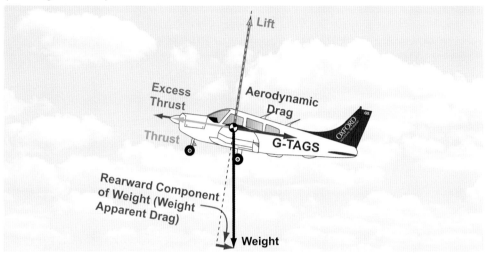

Figure 3.9 An aircraft in the climb with flaps and undercarriage extended.

If we look again at the graph for **thrust available** against **thrust required**, for **flaps and undercarriage extended**, we see that the **thrust required curve** which is based on the **drag curve**, has moved upwards, and to the left. The consequence of this change is although the excess thrust available has deceased, the speed at which **maximum excess thrust** is **available** for the climb, V_X, has also decreased.

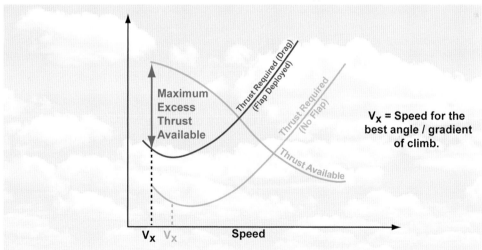

Figure 3.10 When parasite drag is increased, the thrust required curve moves upwards, best climb angle is reduced, and V_X is lower.

With the undercarriage and/or flaps extended, V_X is lower and the best achievable **climb angle** is shallower. A pilot might conclude, therefore, that, on take-off, it would be prudent not to deploy **flaps** so that the climb angle is as steep as possible. However, **flaps** do have a beneficial effect on take-off performance in the sense that they reduce the lift-off speed and the length of the take-off run. Consequently, **flaps** are often used for take-off, but are retracted in stages as soon as it is safe to do so, in order to increase the **angle of climb** as soon as possible.

The **Pilot's Operating Manual** should be consulted for flap retraction speeds.

Density.

As you have already learnt in the chapter on **Take-Off**, both **propeller thrust** and **engine power** are affected by the **density of the air** in which an aircraft flies. A decrease in **air density** will reduce **propeller thrust** available.

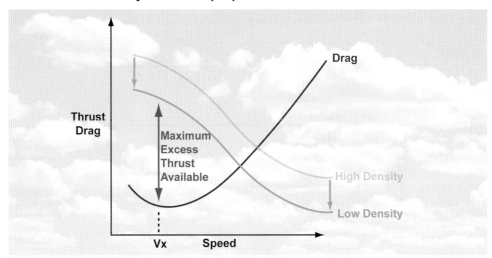

Figure 3.11 A decrease in air density will reduce propeller thrust, and reduce the excess thrust available..

From the graph, you can see that the **decrease in air density**, reduces excess thrust available, and results in the **angle of climb being reduced at all airspeeds**. You should note that **indicated airspeed** for the best **achievable angle of climb** will remain unchanged because **indicated airspeed** is a function of $\frac{1}{2}\rho v^2$, the **dynamic pressure**. The **true airspeed, for V_X however, will increase**.

In order to take into consideration **air density** when calculating your aircraft's performance, a pilot needs to know the aircraft's **density altitude**. **Density altitude** is **pressure altitude** (i.e. vertical distance from the **1013.2 millibar (hectopascal) pressure** datum line) corrected for **air temperature**. Calculations of **density altitude** are easy to perform using a standard **flight navigation computer**. (See **Volume 3** of this series **Navigation and Radio Aids**.)

Normally, however, when using **take-off performance graphs**, **air temperature** and **pressure altitude** information is entered into the graphs separately. In this way, **air density** is taken into account.

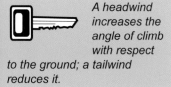

A headwind increases the angle of climb with respect to the ground; a tailwind reduces it.

Wind Speed and Direction.

Up until now in this Chapter, we have been considering **angle of climb** with respect to the air in which the aircraft is flying. But any aircraft's **angle of climb with respect to the ground** is also affected by **wind speed and direction**, namely, the **headwind** and **tailwind component**. **Climb angle** with respect to the ground will steepen when flying into a **headwind** and be more shallow with **tailwind**. This topic has already been covered in Chapter 2: **Take-Off**. (*See Figure 3.12.*)

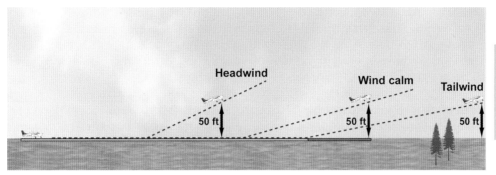

Figure 3.12 Relative to the ground, headwinds increase climb angle and tailwinds decrease climb angle.

The best rate of climb will cause the aircraft to gain the maximum height in the least amount of time.

RATE OF CLIMB.

Achieving the best possible **angle of climb** is of great importance when considering an aircraft's **obstacle clearance performance**. But, often, following take-off, a pilot's principal concern is to climb to the **cruising altitude** as **rapidly** as possible. If this is so, then the pilot is more concerned with achieving the best **rate of climb**, rather than the best **angle of climb**.

There is an important difference between **rate of climb** and **angle of climb**. The **rate** at which an aircraft gains height depends both on the **angle of (or gradient) of his flight path** <u>and</u> on its **forward speed along that path**. As you may imagine, an aircraft may climb slowly at a fairly steep angle or at high speed at a fairly shallow angle. For any given aircraft, however, there is **one combination of speed and angle of climb**, in other words of **speed along a climbing flight path**, which will permit the aircraft to increase its height by the greatest amount in a given amount of time. This will be the aircraft's best **rate of climb**.

Figure 3.13 attempts to depict the concept of **best rate of climb**. The vertical axis represents gain of height in feet, and the horizontal axis represents airspeed. The speeds on the horizontal axis, below each aircraft, represent the airspeed at which that aircraft is flying. The aircraft on the middle sloping line, climbing at 75 knots, has made the greatest gain of height even though the aircraft on the left is climbing at a steeper angle, at a lower speed, and the aircraft on the right is climbing at a higher

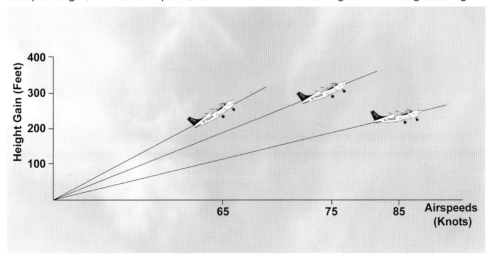

Figure 3.13 Climb performance at different speeds.

airspeed, but at a shallower angle. The speed at which the middle aircraft is climbing represents the **best rate of climb of speed**. We can assume that all aircraft are climbing **at full power**, so the **pitch attitude** of the middle aircraft is the attitude which, **at full power**, gives the **angle of attack** required to attain the **best rate of climb speed**.

Rate of Climb is a Function of Excess Power Available.

We have learnt that **angle of climb** is a function of **excess thrust**. The diagram which illustrates the concept of **angle of climb** is a force diagram, which resolves forwards and rearwards acting forces. (*See Figure 3.4.*) However, **rate of climb** is a question of both **thrust** to achieve a given **gradient of climb** and **speed along that gradient**. **Rate of climb**, then, is a function of **excess thrust multiplied by velocity**. In other words, **rate of climb** is a function of **excess horsepower**. You may recall from your **Physics** lessons that **power is the rate at which work is done**.

Work = Force × Distance

Power   = $\dfrac{\text{Work}}{\text{Time Taken}}$

Power   = $\dfrac{\text{Force × Distance}}{\text{Time Taken}}$

Power = Force × Speed

And, as force produced by a propeller is known as thrust,

Power = thrust × speed

To lift an aircraft weighing **2000lbs** to **4000ft** requires **2000 × 4000 = 8 000 000 ft-lbs of work**. For a **2000lb** aircraft to climb to **4000ft** in **8 minutes** would require work to be done at the rate of **1 000 000 foot-lb/min**. Now **33 000 ft-lbs/min** is defined as **One Horse Power**; so the power required to lift a **2000lb** aircraft to **4000ft** in **8 mins** is **$\dfrac{1\,000\,000}{33\,000}$**. **30.3 Horse Power**, approximately.

To summarise, then, the aircraft's **maximum rate of climb** is achieved at a **gradient** that is **slightly less steep** than that giving its **maximum angle of climb**, but at **slightly higher airspeed**.

As we have said, an aircraft's **maximum rate of climb** is achieved at an airspeed in level flight, at which there is a **maximum amount of excess thrust horsepower** available for the climb.

Figure 3.14 is a representative graph of **thrust horsepower available** and **thrust horsepower required** to maintain level flight at any given true airspeed.

The maximum amount of excess power available for the climb occurs at the speed at which the distance between the two curves is the greatest. If we wish to calculate the achievable vertical speed of an aircraft, we may use the equation:

Vertical Speed (feet/min)   = $\dfrac{\text{33 000 × Excess Power Available}}{\text{Weight of aircraft}}$

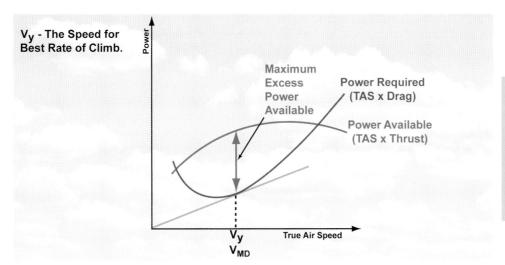

V$_y$ - The Speed for Best Rate of Climb.

Maximum Excess Power Available

Power Required (TAS x Drag)

Power Available (TAS x Thrust)

Power

V$_y$

V$_{MD}$

True Air Speed

The speed for maximum rate of climb is the speed at which there is the maximum excess of power available over power required for level flight at that speed. This speed is known as V$_Y$.

Figure 3.14 The speed for maximum rate of climb is the speed at which there is the maximum excess of power available over power required for level flight at that speed. This speed is known as V$_Y$.

For instance, in the case we have just considered of the aircraft weighing **2000lbs** climbing to **4000ft** in **8 minutes**, which required an excess thrust horsepower of **30.3 HP**, the equation may be written as:

$$\text{Vertical Speed (ft/min)} = \frac{33\,000 \times 30.3}{2000}$$
$$= \mathbf{500\ ft/min}$$

Which is what we would expect as **4000 ft** is reached in **8 minutes**.

The Power Available and Power Required Curve.

The method of deriving the **power available curve** in the graph at *Figure 3.14* requires a knowledge of power output of the internal combustion engine which goes beyond the scope of this book. The power **available curve** is basically an expression of power available after the power losses arising from the inefficiency of the propeller have been deducted from engine power output.

The **power required curve** is derived from the **total drag curve** for the aircraft. Total drag at any aircraft speed is multiplied by the speed, itself, to give the power required to overcome drag and to maintain level flight. You may ask yourself why the **power required graph** in *Figure 3.14* indicates that high power must be delivered by the engine-propeller combination at low speeds as well as at high speeds. The explanation is that, at low speeds, the aircraft is flying at high angles of attack, resulting in high values of **induced drag** despite the low speed. At high speeds, angle of attack is small, but, of course, **parasite drag** is very high because airspeed is high and because **parasite drag** increases with the square of the airspeed.

When the **power available curve** is above the **power required curve**, level flight is possible, and, as we have seen, at the speed where the vertical distance between the two curves is the greatest, the **rate of climb will be a maximum if full throttle is applied and a pitch attitude selected to maintain that speed**.

The outside portions of the graph, beyond the two intersections of the **power available** and **power required curves**, indicate speeds at which level flight is impossible because, at those speeds, whether high or low, more power is required for level flight than the engine can deliver. The two intersections of the two power curves also reveal that full throttle is required to achieve not only the <u>highest</u> level flight speed attainable but also the <u>lowest</u> possible level flight speed.

The Speed for Maximum Rate of Climb.

The speed for **maximum rate of climb** is found by dropping a vertical line from the point at which a straight line drawn from the origin of the two axes touches the **power required curve** at a tangent. **The speed for the best rate of climb is known as** V_Y. V_Y is also the speed for **minimum drag** V_{MD}. *(See Figure 3.15).*

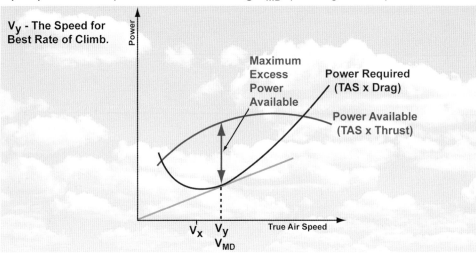

V_Y is the speed at which to fly to obtain the best rate of climb. V_Y for the PA-28 Warrior, up to 5000 feet, is 75 knots indicated air speed.

Figure 3.15 The best rate of climb speed, V_Y, is also the speed for minimum drag, V_{MD}.

You should note that because **thrust** and **power** are not the same thing, the airspeed at which **maximum excess thrust** is available (V_X) is not the same as the airspeed where **maximum excess thrust horsepower** is available (V_Y). Remember that **thrust from a fixed-pitch propeller is maximum at full throttle with the aircraft stationary.** By the time V_{MD} is reached, **propeller thrust** will have begun to decrease, so **maximum excess thrust** available occurs at a lower airspeed than V_{MD}. V_X for the **PA28-161 Warrior** is **65 knots.** V_Y for the **PA28-161 Warrior** is **75 knots.**

The manufacturer's recommended best rate of climb speed is often slightly higher than V_Y so that the airflow over the engine is sufficient for effective cooling.

V_Y, then, is the speed to fly when seeking to achieve the **maximum height gain in the shortest possible time**. Nevertheless, some Pilot's Operating Manuals may give a speed slightly higher than V_Y as an aircraft's **best rate of climb speed** because a slightly higher speed ensures a more satisfactory cooling effect on the engine at the high power settings and relatively low speeds used in the climb. If a pilot sees that cylinder head temperature and engine-oil temperature are approaching their upper limits in the climb, he should increase speed.

Factors Affecting Rate of Climb.

Aircraft Weight.

The higher an aircraft's all-up weight (mass) the lower the rate of climb.

As you have already learnt, the greater an aircraft's **all–up weight**, the greater the **lift** required to maintain level flight at any speed. At a given speed, unless flap is lowered (and we will assume here that it is not), **lift** can be increased only by increasing **angle of attack**. An increase in **angle of attack** will increase **induced drag**, and so, at any given speed, **more thrust is required to maintain level flight than for a lighter**

aircraft. If more **thrust** is required to maintain a given speed then more **power** is required, too, leaving less **excess power** available to achieve a desired **rate of climb**. This situation holds for all speeds; **consequently, an increase in weight will cause a decrease in the maximum rate of climb**. Conversely, a decrease in weight will improve **rate of climb**, at all speeds.

Also, as we have seen in the diagrams illustrating angle of climb, a climb at any angle with a heavier aircraft will lead to an increase in the weight component acting rearwards (the so-called **weight-apparent drag**). As the **maximum rate of climb** is achieved at a given combination of speed of climb and angle of climb, **weight apparent drag** will always be a factor. **An increase in weight apparent drag leaves less power available for the climb, again decreasing rate of climb at all speeds**.

The following equation for **rate of climb** that you met earlier in this chapter:

Rate of climb in feet per minute = 33000 × Excess Power Available
Weight

clearly shows that **an increase in weight decreases rate of climb**. The calculation that we made earlier to illustrate the use of this equation involved a **2000 lb** aircraft with an **excess of power available** of **30.3 Horsepower**, climbing **4000 feet in 8 minutes**, at a rate of climb of **500 feet per minute**. If we increased the aircraft's weight to **2 300 lb**. the equation shows us that rate of climb will decrease. Substituting the new figures into the equation, we obtain:

Rate of climb in feet per minute = 33000 × 30.3 = 435 feet per minute
2 300

At higher aircraft weights, then, the power required (drag × speed) for level flight is greater, for any airspeed. Minimum **drag**, and **power** required to balance that **drag**, is higher at the **greater weight**, and, in fact, **as weight increases**, the **power required curve** moves up and to the right, as depicted in *Figure 3.16*.

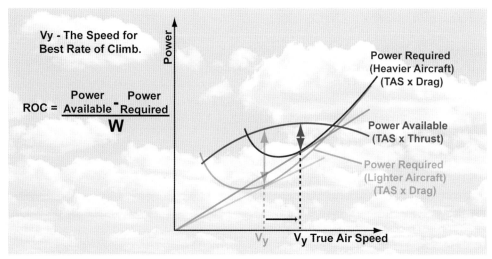

Figure 3.16 An increase in weight moves the power required curve up and to the right. Excess power available, and, thus, rate of climb reduce at all speeds.

The graph for the higher weight illustrates clearly that there is less excess power available for the climb, at any speed; so the maximum rate of climb decreases and V_Y, the speed for the best achievable rate of climb at the higher weight, increases.

Aircraft Configuration.

Let us now consider **the effect of flap on the rate of climb**. We have already seen in our treatment of angle of climb, that **deployment of flap increases drag at any speed** and, therefore, will reduce the amount, excess thrust and **excess power** available for the climb, at all speeds. Consequently, when flaps are deployed, the **power required curve**, which as you have learnt is derived for the **total drag curve**, will move upwards and to the left. (*See Figure 3.17.*)

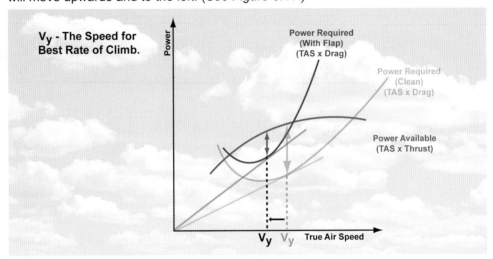

Figure 3.17 The extension of flap and/or undercarriage leads to an increase in parasite drag, causing the power required curve to move up and to the left.

The graph clearly illustrates that the maximum excess power available, and, thus, maximum achievable rate of climb, decreases with flaps lowered. Furthermore, V_Y, the speed for the best <u>achievable</u> rate of climb is lower than for a clean aircraft.

Altitude and Atmospheric Density.

With increasing altitude, air density decreases.

The effect of reduced air density is to <u>increase</u> the power required for level flight, at any given airspeed, but <u>decrease</u> the power available.

So, reducing **air density** will cause the **power required** and **power available curves** to close up, as shown in *Figure 3.18, opposite.*

Figure 3.18 shows clearly that, with decreasing **air density**, the **excess power available** for the climb is reduced, at all speeds. We can deduce, then, that **reduced air density (increasing altitude) will cause the maximum rate of climb to decrease**. If an aircraft's engine is fitted with a turbo-charger, the decrease in climb performance with altitude can be delayed, but most light training aircraft are not turbo-charged.

> With flap deployed, an aircraft's rate of climb and angle of climb will be reduced.

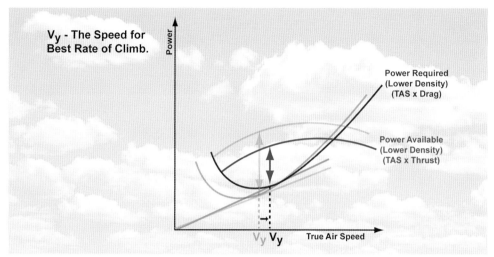

Figure 3.18 A reduction in density reduces the power available and increases the power required, therefore decreasing the Excess Power Available and the Rate of Climb. The Airspeed V_Y for the best <u>achievable</u> Rate of Climb is higher.

You can also see from the graph that **speed for the best achievable rate of climb is higher at the lower density**. However, it is important to grasp that the speeds used in the **power available/power required graphs** are **true airspeeds**, whereas the speed that the pilot reads from his **ASI** is **indicated airspeed**. **At lower air densities, the indicated airspeed for best rate of climb, which is, itself, a function of the air density element of dynamic pressure (dynamic pressure = ½ ρv^2), will decrease.**

The indicated airspeed for the best achievable rate of climb will decrease with increasing altitude, but the true airspeed increases.

As an aircraft climbs, therefore, the pilot who strives to maintain the **best rate of climb** perceives that he must fly at constantly reducing indicated airspeeds in order to optimise performance. **In practice, though, a single recommended climbing speed is used within specific height bands.** For example the **best rate of climb** for the **PA28-161 Warrior's** is obtained at **75 kts** up to **5000 ft**, at **70 knots** up to its operating ceiling of **10 000 ft**, and then at **65 knots** to its service ceiling of about **15 000 feet**.

Absolute Ceiling and Service Ceiling.
Closer examination of the power curves reveals that, with increasing altitude (it is the corresponding reduction in air density, of course, which is decisive), the minimum possible true airspeed for level flight increases whereas the maximum level flight speed decreases. Eventually, then, an altitude is reached where there is only one possible speed for level flight. At this altitude excess power is nil, and therefore the rate of climb is zero. (*See Figure 3.19, overleaf.*)

The altitude at which **rate of climb** reduces to zero is the aircraft's **absolute ceiling**. If an aircraft were to reach its **absolute ceiling**, it could carry out no manoeuvres. This fact, and because it would take a very long time for the aircraft to struggle up to its **absolute ceiling**, makes the **absolute ceiling** fairly meaningless for practical purposes. Therefore, in the **Pilot's Operating Handbook**, it is usual to see the aircraft's **service ceiling** referred to. An aircraft's **service ceiling** is the altitude at which the aircraft's **maximum rate of climb** reduces to **100 feet per minute**. The **service ceiling** for the **PA28-161 Warrior** is around **15 000 feet**.

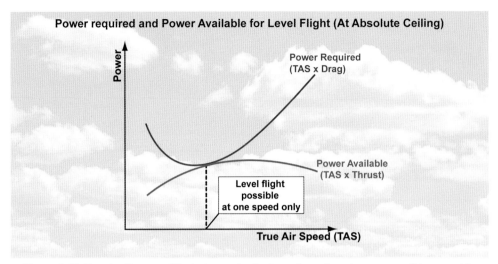

Figure 3.19 Eventually , an altitude is reached where there is only one possible speed for level flight and where the rate of climb has reduced to zero. This altitude is the aircraft's absolute ceiling.

There is, of course, no necessity for the pilot always to climb the aircraft at the **best rate of climb speed** or the **best angle of climb speed**. There may be no operational or flight safety reason for a pilot to gain altitude as quickly as possible. A pilot may choose, for instance, to climb en route after having set the heading for the first leg of a cross country flight. This type of climb is often called a **cruise climb**. In the **cruise climb**, the nose of the aircraft will be lower than for **best angle or rate of climb**, giving the pilot a better view ahead. For the Warrior the recommended **cruise climb speed** is **90 knots**, with full power selected.

CALCULATING AN AIRCRAFT'S CLIMB PERFORMANCE.

The calculations of the actual **climb performance** that a pilot can expect on a given day, flying from a known airfield, are carried out using the **performance tables or graphs** in the **Pilot's Operating Handbook (POH)** for the aircraft to be flown. Using the information from the **POH**, a pilot may calculate such values as expected **rate of climb**, **fuel consumed in the climb** to a given height or cruising altitude, and **horizontal distance covered** in the climb.

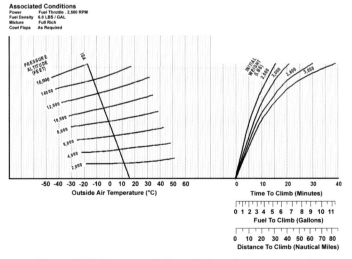

Figure 3.20 A representative climb performance graph.

In the example overleaf, we are going to calculate the values that we have just mentioned using a representative **climb performance graph** of the type represented in *Figure 3.20*. Note that the **time to height** gives us an **average rate of climb**, while the **horizontal distance covered** would enable us, if we wished, to calculate the **mean angle of climb**.

Note, too, that no wind information can be entered into the graph. Therefore, any estimation of angle of climb would have to assume zero wind, and be adjusted to allow for prevailing wind conditions.

As with most **performance graphs**, the **climb graph** assumes that atmospheric conditions are those of the **ICAO Standard Atmosphere (ISA)**. Furthermore, the **climb graph** is **unfactored**. You will recall that the term **unfactored** means that the graph makes no allowance for varying degrees of pilot proficiency or for any mechanical or aerodynamic deterioration of the aircraft. The climb graph also assumes that the climb will be made at **full throttle**, with **mixture fully rich**.

The method used to calculate the desired performance figures from the **climb graph** is first to consider standard values for the **cruise altitude** to which we wish to climb. So the first variables to consider are the **cruise pressure altitude** and the **outside air temperature** at the **cruising altitude**. We are, thus, effectively considering the **density altitude** to which we wish to climb. These considerations give us the **air density** conditions at the required altitude.

In following this graphical method, the assumption is that the aircraft is climbing from sea-level; (**ISA sea-level conditions prevailing**, of course.). Consequently, it is necessary to amend the performance figures extracted from the graph in the case of a climb begun from an airfield situated at a level other than **ISA sea-level**. This is done by subtracting from the first set of figures, values for the altitude of the airfield from which the aircraft took off.

Example of a Climb Calculation using a Climb Performance Graph.
We will assume that we wish to take-off from an airfield whose **pressure altitude** we have already calculated to be **4 000 feet**; (i.e. **4 000 feet** above the **1013.2 millibars** (hectopascals) pressure datum). Our aircraft's **all-up weight** is to be **3 650 lb** and the **outside air temperature** is **20° Celsius**. We wish to climb to **Flight Level 100** where the **temperature** is forecast to be **0° Celsius**. We immediately realize that we do not have to calculate a **pressure altitude** for a **Flight Level**. **All Flight Levels are measured from the Standard Pressure Setting**. So, **Flight Level 100** is **10 000 feet** above the **1013.2 millibars** (hectopascals) pressure datum.

We wish to calculate **how long** it will take us to climb to **FL 100**, **how much fuel we will use** and what **horizontal distance we will cover in the climb**. We will begin by entering the values for the conditions prevailing at **Flight Level 100**, the level to which we wish to climb. The process we are using is illustrated on the **climb performance graph** at *Figure 3.21, opposite*.

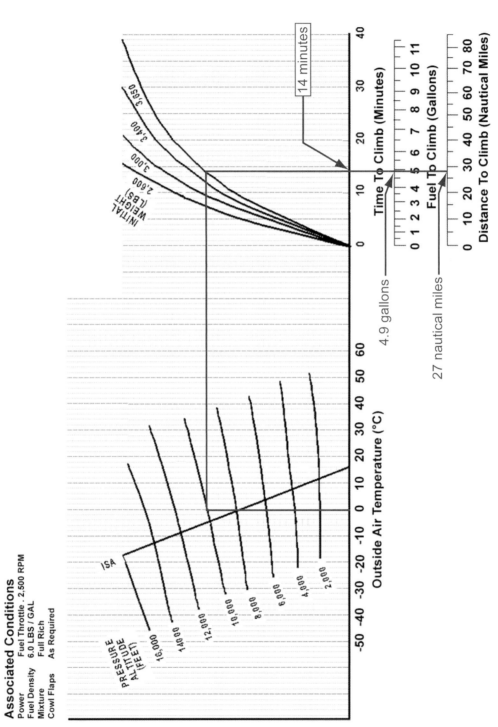

Figure 3.21 Time taken, fuel used and distance covered from sea level to a pressure altitude of 10 000 feet (Flight Level 100).

Locating the **temperature** forecast for **Flight Level 100, 0° Celsius**, we draw a line vertically upwards until we meet the curve of the **10 000 feet pressure altitude**. From that point, we draw a horizontal line across to meet the curve for our aircraft's **weight** of **3650 lb**. We are fortunate to have on the graph a curve for that precise value, but if our aircraft had weighed, say, 3 500 lbs, we would have ended our horizontal line about half way between the 3650 lb curve and the 3 400 lb curve. Finally, in Stage One of our calculation, we drop a vertical line down from the point where the horizontal line meets the **3650 lb curve** and note where the vertical line intersects the scales for **Time To Climb**, **Fuel To Climb** and **(Horizontal) Distance To Climb**.

As you see from *Figure 3.21*, **Time To Climb** is **14 minutes**, **Fuel To Climb** is **4.9 gallons** and **(Horizontal) Distance To Climb** is **27 nautical miles**.

However, the above figures assume that we wish to climb from sea-level (i.e. ISA sea-level) to Flight Level 100. But we know that the **elevation** of the airfield from which we will be taking off lies at a **pressure altitude of 4 000 feet**. Therefore, we must subtract from the values already extracted from the graph, the corresponding values for a climb from **sea-level** to **4000 feet**.

Noting that the **temperature** at the airfield is **20° Celsius**, we extract from the climb graph the values that we need, using the same method as previously. From the Graph we see that a hypothetical climb from **ISA sea-level** to a **pressure altitude of 4 000 feet** would, in our aircraft, require **5 minutes** and **2 gallons of fuel** while covering **11 nautical miles horizontally**.

Finally, then, in order to obtain our figures for a climb from a **pressure altitude of 4 000 feet** to a **pressure altitude of 10 000 feet**, we subtract the second set of figures from the first, giving us a **Time To Climb of 9 minutes, Fuel To Climb of 2.9 gallons** and **(Horizontal) Distance To Climb of 16 nautical miles**.

Example of a Climb Calculation using a Climb Performance Table.

You may find that the climb performance figures pertaining to your aircraft are available only in **tabular form**, though **tables** are more commonly found in examination papers than in **Pilot's Operating Handbooks**. A representative table containing flight performance figures is depicted overleaf in *Figure 3.21.*

FUEL, TIME and DISTANCE TO CLIMB

Associated Conditions
Weight: 2440 Lbs, **Flaps:** 0°, **Full Throttle**
Mixture leaned as per maker's instructions
79 Knots, indicated airspeed. No Wind

FOR TRAINING PURPOSES ONLY

Pressure Altitude Feet	ISA Temp °C	From Sea Level		
		Time in Minutes	Fuel used Gallons	Distance
Sea Level	15	0	0	0
1000	13	2	0.4	2
2000	11	4	0.7	5
3000	9	6	1.5	8
4000	7	8	1.8	11
5000	5	10	2.0	14
6000	3	13	2.5	17
7000	1	16	3	21
8000	-1	19	4	27
9000	-3	24	5	34
10 000	-5	30	6	42

Figure 3.21 Climb performance figures in tabular format.

Let us see how we derive climb performance information from this type of **table**.

First of all we notice that we cannot enter any information into the **table**, we must read figures directly <u>from</u> the **table**. We may, however, **interpolate** (i.e. make estimations based on given figures) for pressure altitudes which do not coincide with those given. For example, **a time to height from ISA sea-level to a pressure altitude of 4 500 feet** may be deduced to be **9 minutes**; (lying between 8 minutes for a climb to 4 000 feet and 10 minutes for a climb to 5 000 feet).

We note also that the table contains standard **ISA** temperatures against pressure altitudes, so we cannot allow for temperature deviations from standard.

The table contains several associated conditions, assuming an aircraft **weight** (mass) of **2440 lbs**, **no flap deployed**, a climb with **throttle fully open, mixture leaned in accordance with the maker's recommendations, no wind**, and a **best indicated airspeed for the climb of 79 knots**. We take note of these conditions, knowing that we have to make allowance for any variation from the conditions stipulated.

So, let us assume that we wish to estimate **how long** it would take us to climb from an airfield lying at a **pressure altitude** of **1000 feet**, on a given day, to a **pressure**

altitude of **6 000 feet**. We wish to know, too, **how much fuel** we will consume in the climb and what **horizontal distance** we would cover, assuming no wind.
Firstly, we can read directly from the chart the figures for a climb to **6 000 feet** from **sea-level**. **Time** would be **13 minutes, fuel consumed** would be **2.5 gallons, and horizontal distance covered** would be **17 miles**.

But we are taking off from an airfield lying at a pressure altitude of 1000 feet. Therefore, we must <u>subtract</u> the figures for a hypothetical climb from sea-level to 1000 feet from the above figures for the climb from sea-level to 6 000 feet. From the graph, we see that **time to height, fuel consumed** and **horizontal distance covered** for the **hypothetical climb from sea-level to 1000 feet** are **2 minutes**, **0.4 gallons** and **2 miles**, respectively. Consequently, we <u>subtract</u> these figures from the earlier figures to obtain the required information for a climb from the airfield to a **pressure altitude** of **6 000 feet**. We calculate, then, that **the climb we are planning will take 11 minutes, consume 2.1 gallons of fuel and cover a horizontal distance of 15 miles assuming zero wind.**

Figure 3.22 illustrates another type of table you may come across.

CLIMB PERFORMANCE

Associated Conditions **Gross Weight:** 2440 Lbs, **Full Throttle** **Lean Mixture per maker's instructions. 79 KIAS**	FOR TRAINING PURPOSES ONLY

	Rate of Climb - Feet per Minute Outside Air Temperature - °C				
	-20°	-10°	0°	10°	20°
Sea Level	850	790	730	670	610
2000	730	670	610	560	500
4000	620	550	490	430	370
6000	490	430	360	310	250
8000	370	300	250	190	150
10 000	250	180	150	70	20

Figure 3.22 Climb performance figures in tabular format.

This type of table enables you to calculate **rate of climb** at various **pressure altitudes** and **outside air temperatures**. Having noted all the associated conditions, especially the recommended indicated airspeed for the climb, let us assume that we need to find the **rate of climb at 3000 feet**, if the **outside air temperature is +10° C**. Remember, the altitudes in the table are pressure altitudes. Examining the table, we see that in the **+10° C** column (notated simply as **10° C**) we find **rates of climb of 560 feet per minute at 2 000 feet and 430 feet per minute, at 4 000 feet**. It seems logical, then, that in order to estimate the **rate of climb at 3 000 feet**, we should take the **mean value of the rates of climb at 2 000 feet and 4 000 feet**, because the **rate of climb at 3 000 feet** will be between the two rates of climb given by the table. That difference is **130 feet per minute**. Half of that difference is **65 feet per minute**. We know that **the rate of climb that we are looking for lies between 560 feet per minute and 430 feet per minute**. We can, therefore, **add 65 feet per**

minute to the lower value or subtract it from the higher value. Either way, we arrive at **495 feet per minute**, which seems to be a sensible answer.

Conclusion.

Do not underestimate the importance of knowing what your aircraft's **climb performance** will be in a given set of circumstances. **It is the angle of climb which is the critical parameter for flight safety**, especially when combined with take-off considerations at an airfield surrounded by obstacles which must be cleared on the climb-out.

If you are to take-off from an upward-sloping wet grass strip, on a hot day, at a high airfield, at near your aircraft's maximum weight (mass), and with obstacles in your climb-out path, **it is vital that you have an accurate idea of what will be the take-off run required and your initial angle of climb**. Getting your performance figures wrong in such circumstances could lead to catastrophe.

Representative PPL - type questions to test your theoretical knowledge of the Climb.

1. From the table shown, extract the rate of climb for an aircraft operating at 5 000 feet with an outside air temperature of 0° C.

CLIMB PERFORMANCE

| Associated Conditions
Gross Weight: 2440 Lbs, Full Throttle
Lean Mixture per maker's instructions. 79 KIAS | | FOR TRAINING
PURPOSES ONLY | | |

	Rate of Climb - Feet per Minute Outside Air Temperature - °C				
	-20°	-10°	0°	10°	20°
Sea Level	850	790	730	670	610
2000	730	670	610	560	500
4000	620	550	490	430	370
6000	490	430	360	310	250
8000	370	300	250	190	150
10 000	250	180	150	70	20

Figure 3.23 Climb performance figures in tabular format.

a. 555 feet per minute
b. 425 feet per minute
c. 490 feet per minute
d. 295 feet per minute

2. To gain the greatest amount of height in the shortest time, an aircraft should be flown at:

a. 60 knots
b. the best rate of climb speed (V_Y)
c. the best angle of climb speed (V_X)
d. at the speed for maximum endurance

3. The indicated air speed for the best rate of climb when climbing to an aircraft's service ceiling will tend to:

a. decrease then increase
b. remain the same
c. increase
d. decrease

4. What is the reason for increasing the speed in a prolonged climb?

a. to maintain the best rate of climb
b. to reduce the noise of the aircraft in sensitive areas
c. to increase the flow of air through the engine and keep it cool
d. to maintain the best angle of climb

5.   The best rate of climb is achieved:

        a.   when flying at the speed for maximum excess thrust available
        b.   when climbing into wind
        c.   when flying at V_X
        d.   when flying at the for maximum excess power available.

6.   Climbing at V_X will achieve:

        a.   the best time to height
        b.   the greatest increase in altitude in a given time
        c.   the maximum angle of climb
        d.   the maximum horizontal distance for a given vertical distance

7.   One effect of climbing an aircraft with flap selected would be:

        a.   an improved climb performance
        b.   a decreased co-efficient of drag
        c.   a decreased co-efficient of lift
        d.   a reduced rate and angle of climb

8.   Increasing the mass (and, therefore, the weight) of an aircraft will:

        a.   decrease the rate and angle of climb
        b.   increase the rate and angle of climb
        c.   increase the rate of climb and decrease the angle of climb
        d.   decrease the rate of climb and increase the angle of climb

9.   Climbing at V_Y will achieve:

        a.   the maximum angle of climb
        b.   the greatest increase in altitude in a given period of time
        c.   the maximum increase in height in the shortest horizontal distance
        d.   the best obstacle clearance performance

10.   An aircraft cruising at a pressure altitude 2 000 feet is cleared to climb to a pressure altitude 8 000 feet. Using the table, calculate the time taken in minutes, the fuel used in gallons and the horizontal distance flown in the climb, assuming zero wind.

FUEL, TIME and DISTANCE TO CLIMB

Associated Conditions
Weight: 2440 Lbs, **Flaps:** 0°, **Full Throttle**
Mixture leaned as per maker's instructions
79 Knots, indicated airspeed. No Wind

FOR TRAINING PURPOSES ONLY

Pressure Altitude Feet	ISA Temp °C	From Sea Level		
		Time in Minutes	Fuel used Gallons	Distance
Sea Level	15	0	0	0
1000	13	2	0.4	2
2000	11	4	0.7	5
3000	9	6	1.5	8
4000	7	8	1.8	11
5000	5	10	2.0	14
6000	3	13	2.5	17
7000	1	16	3	21
8000	-1	19	4	27
9000	-3	24	5	34
10 000	-5	30	6	42

Figure 3.24 Climb performance figures in tabular format.

a.   19 minutes, 4 gallons, 27 miles
b.   23 minutes, 4.07 gallons, 32 miles
c.   15 minutes, 3.3 gallons, 22 miles
d.   4 minutes, 0.7 gallons, 5 miles

11.   The lift produced by the wing of an aircraft in a steady climb maintaining a constant indicated airspeed will be:

a.   less than weight
b.   greater than weight
c.   equal to weight
d.   independent of weight

12.	How will an aircraft's maximum rate of climb be affected by selecting take-off flap?

a.	The maximum rate of climb will increase
b.	The maximum rate of climb will not be affected
c.	The maximum rate of climb will remain the same provided that the pilot chooses an appropriate power setting
d.	The maximum rate of climb will decrease

13.	What effect will a decreasing headwind component have on the best achievable angle of climb.

a.	The angle of climb will decrease
b.	The angle of climb will steepen
c.	The angle of climb will remain constant at all values of headwind component.
d.	The angle of climb is independent of the value of headwind component.

Question	1	2	3	4	5	6	7	8	9	10	11	12
Answer												

Question	13
Answer	

The answers to these questions can be found at the end of this book.

CHAPTER 4
EN-ROUTE PERFORMANCE

INTRODUCTION.

This chapter deals with the performance of an aircraft in the **en-route phase** of flight. The **en-route phase** of flight includes **climb to cruising altitude**, the **cruise** itself, and the **initial descent**. Chapter 3 covered the **climb** in detail, so, in this chapter, we will deal with the **cruise** and the **initial descent**. We begin with the **cruise**.

Cruise performance is generally measured in terms of an aircraft's **range, fuel consumption** and **endurance**. But, first of all, we will consider the forces acting on an aircraft in the **cruise**, assuming **straight and level flight, at constant speed**.

FORCES ACTING ON AN AIRCRAFT IN THE CRUISE.

You learnt in **Chapter 9** of the **Principles of Flight** section of this volume, that, for an aircraft to be in **steady, straight flight, all forces acting on the aircraft, and any turning moments to which the aircraft is subjected, must balance one another**. In other words, for **steady, straight flight, the forces, and moments** acting on the aircraft must be in a state of **equilibrium**.

Chapter 9 explained that because of the disposition of the principal flight forces of **thrust, drag, lift** and **weight**, and the movement of their lines of action during flight, the **turning moments** produced by the **thrust-drag force couple** and the **lift-weight force couple** are very rarely in balance. For instance, in *Figure 4.1, below,* both the **thrust-drag** and **lift-weight couples** reinforce each other to give a **nose-down pitching moment**. Consequently, in this case, a downwards-acting force must be generated by the **tailplane** or **stabilator** to achieve **equilibrium**. (*See Figure 4.1.*)

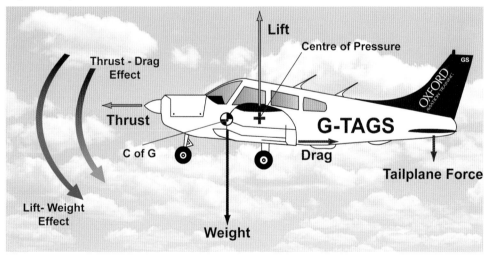

Figure 4.1 A tailplane force is required to balance the Thrust-Drag and Lift-Weight Couples.

The magnitude and direction of the **tailplane force** is under the control of the pilot through his manipulation of the control column in the fore and aft directions. The fact that the pilot has control over the **tailplane force** means that **equilibrium** may be maintained for all conditions of straight and steady flight, and, by trimming the aircraft correctly, the pilot can put the aircraft in **equilibrium** and fly it without having to apply any force to the control column.

Straight and level flight at constant speed, the flight condition for the cruise, is a special case of steady straight flight where altitude is maintained constant. So, in the cruise, all the forces acting on the aircraft will be in equilibrium. In straight and level flight at constant speed, **thrust** will be balanced by **drag**, and the **upwards acting forces** will be balanced by the **downwards acting forces**. The **tailplane force** may act upwards or downwards depending on aircraft type and flight condition, so the **upwards acting forces** may comprise **lift plus the tailplane force** or **lift minus the tailplane force** (as in the case in *Figure 4.1*) and the **downwards acting forces** may comprise **weight plus the tailplane force** (as in the case in *Figure 4.1*) or **weight minus the tailplane force**.

Any **tailplane force** which increases the total drag acting on the aircraft will have an adverse effect on performance. A **tailplane downforce**, because it acts in the same direction as **weight**, also adds to the aircraft's effective **weight** and requires the wings to produce extra **lift**, thus increasing **induced drag**. A decrease in **tailplane downforce**, on the other hand, will lead to a reduction in the **lift** force required to balance it, resulting in a corresponding reduction in **induced drag**.

Any tailplane force required to maintain an aircraft in equilibrium will generate increased drag. A tailplane down-force will also increase an aircraft's effective weight. Any tailplane force, then, will reduce range and endurance.

But, as we have already learned, **any increase in drag requires more power and thrust to be generated to maintain level flight at any speed**. Consequently, any amount **of tailplane force**, acting either upwards or downwards, required to maintain an aircraft in **equilibrium**, will affect **range**, **endurance** and **rate of fuel consumption**. **An increase in tailplane force will always reduce range and endurance, and increase rate of fuel consumption**.

As you learnt elsewhere, in **Volume 5** on **Aeroplanes and Mass & Balance**, the position of the **centre of gravity** of the aircraft, along the aircraft's longitudinal axis, will affect the amount of **tailplane force** required to maintain **equilibrium** at any speed, because, since the aircraft rotates about its **centre of gravity** when it manoeuvres, the tailplane's **moment arm** changes in length with changing **centre of gravity** position. The position of the **centre of gravity** will, therefore, affect an aircraft's **range** and **endurance**. The exact effect of **centre of gravity** position depends on aircraft type, especially whether an aircraft is low or high wing. But, generally speaking, for the type of aircraft depicted in *Figure 4.1*, a forward **centre of gravity** position even though it lengthens the tailplane's **moment arm** will mean that more **tailplane force** is required to maintain **equilibrium**, leading to greater **induced drag** and, thus, a more detrimental effect on **range** and **endurance**. A rearward **centre of gravity** position on the aircraft in *Figure 4.1* will require less **tailplane force**, leading to reduced **induced drag** and fewer consequent performance degradations in the **cruise**.

However, despite the theory, for practical purposes the general aviation pilot is rarely in a position to consider **centre of gravity** position in terms of its effect on **cruise performance**. **The pilot's main concern is that the centre of gravity of the aircraft remains within its prescribed fore and aft limits, for the duration of any planned flight**.

PERFORMANCE AND POWER CONSIDERATIONS IN THE CRUISE.

As we have discussed, the essential condition for straight and level flight at constant airspeed is that the forces acting on the aircraft should be in **equilibrium**. Among other things, for straight and level flight at constant airspeed, the **total drag** generated by the aircraft must be balanced by an **equal and opposite thrust** from the propeller-engine combination. As we learnt in the chapter on **climb**, we may consider **drag** being balanced by either the **thrust** force produced by the propeller, or by the **power available** from the propeller-engine combination. In terms of aircraft **en-route performance**, it is the power requirements that we need to consider.

The **power required** to overcome the **drag** generated by an aircraft at any **true airspeed** is found by multiplying the drag force by the true airspeed. The rationale behind this method of calculating **power required** was covered in the chapter on **climb**, but basically, because **power is defined as work done per unit time**, **power** may be calculated as follows:

Work Done = Force × Distance

$$\textbf{Power} = \frac{\textbf{Work Done}}{\textbf{Time}}$$

$$\textbf{Power} = \frac{\textbf{Force × Distance}}{\textbf{Time}}$$

$$\frac{\textbf{Distance}}{\textbf{Time}} = \textbf{Speed}$$

Therefore, **Power = Force × Speed**

The standard unit of **power**, in science, is the **watt**, in other words, the **Joule per second**. These units are obtained by multiplying **force in Newtons** by **speed in metres per second**. But in aviation, we still talk about **power** in terms of **Horsepower**. **One Horsepower** is developed when **33 000 pounds (lb) are raised through one foot in one minute**, or if **550 lb are raised through one foot in one second**. If the **drag**, measured in **lb**, produced by an aircraft flying at a given **airspeed** is multiplied by that **airspeed**, converted to **feet per minute**, and then divided by **33 000**, the number of **horsepower** required to balance that **drag** is found. The actual calculation is not important to us at this level of study, but that is the method used to calculate how much **horsepower** is required to keep an aircraft flying straight and level, at constant speed.

In order to calculate how much **thrust horsepower** can be delivered by an aircraft's propeller at any **airspeed**, we take the **thrust in lb** able to be produced by the propeller at that speed, multiply the **thrust** by the **speed** itself, in **feet per minute**, and then divide by **33 000**.

A graph of **power available** from the engine-propeller combination and **power required** for level flight, against **true airspeed**, can be established for any aircraft. A graph of this type, identical to the one you meet in **Chapter 3**, is depicted at *Figure 4.2.*

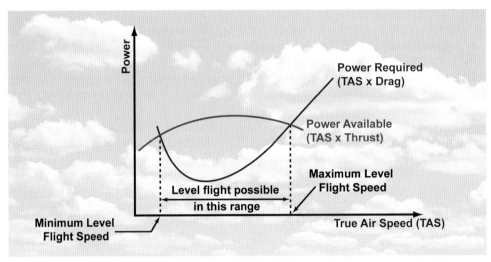

Figure 4.2 A graph of power required for level flight and power available from the propeller-engine combination, against true airspeed.

Any engine-propeller combination fitted to an aircraft can deliver a given maximum amount of **thrust horsepower** at given **airspeeds**. This information is given by the **power available curve** in *Figure 4.2*. Similarly, the **total drag** generated by the aircraft at the various speeds requires a **given amount of thrust horsepower** to overcome that **drag** in order for the aircraft to maintain straight and level flight. This information is given by the **power required curve** in *Figure 4.2*.

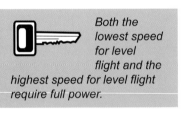

Both the lowest speed for level flight and the highest speed for level flight require full power.

You will notice that the curves intersect each other in two places. An aircraft is able to maintain straight and level flight at speeds on the horizontal axis between the two intersections. In other words, **wherever the power available curve is above the power required curve, level flight can be maintained**. The speed corresponding to the intersection on the left is the slowest speed at which level flight is possible; the **power required** for level flight at that speed corresponds exactly to the **power available** from the engine-propeller combination. That **power** can only be delivered at **full throttle**. Consequently you can see that for an aircraft to fly level at the slowest possible speed, the pilot must open the throttle fully. If the aircraft is flown at a speed slower than the speed indicated, the aircraft will descend.

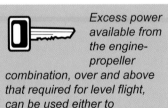

Excess power available from the engine-propeller combination, over and above that required for level flight, can be used either to accelerate or climb the aircraft.

The right hand intersection of the two curves corresponds to the highest level flight speed attainable by the aircraft. Again the **power required** at that speed corresponds exactly to the power **available** and will require full throttle to deliver. If the pilot attempts to fly faster than this speed, the aircraft will descend.

Full power is required at the slowest speed for level flight because **low speed requires high angles of attack which generate high levels of induced drag** which must be balanced by the engine delivering **all the power it has available**. At the highest speed attainable, **angle of attack is very small, but, as the speed is high, parasite drag is high** which again requires **full power**.

At all speeds between the minimum and maximum level flight speeds, there is **power available** from the engine-propeller combination over and above the power required, and the aircraft is flying at less than full throttle. **This excess power available can be used either to accelerate the aircraft in level flight or to climb the aircraft.**

ENDURANCE.

An aircraft's endurance is a measure of its ability to remain airborne for a given maximum time. To remain airborne for as long as possible, the aircraft must consume fuel at as low a rate as possible. **Rate of fuel consumption** is a function **of power required**, and **fuel consumption** will be a minimum when the **power required** to maintain level flight is a minimum. **Minimum rate of fuel consumption, then, will be achieved at the speed for minimum power.** The **minimum power speed** is the speed that corresponds to the **lowest point on the power required graph**, and may be labelled as V_{MP}. (*See Figure 4.3*) V_{MP} for the **PA28-161 Warrior** is about **65 knots**.

For a propeller driven aircraft the speed for maximum endurance is minimum power speed, V_{MP}.

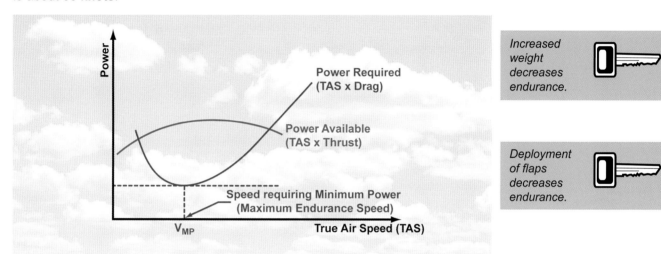

Increased weight decreases endurance.

Deployment of flaps decreases endurance.

Figure 4.3 The level-flight speed which requires minimum power (V_{MP}) is the speed for maximum endurance.

Any **increase in weight** or **deployment of flaps**, both of which will **increase drag** for any given level-flight speed, will require **more power to maintain level flight** and **decrease an aircraft's endurance (the amount of time that an aircraft can fly)**.

RANGE.

Most often, pilots are concerned to be able to cover the maximum distance for minimum fuel consumption. **The maximum distance an aircraft can fly for a given quantity of fuel consumed is called the aircraft's range.** Several factors, not the least being wind speed and direction, affect an aircraft's **range**. The first factor we will consider is engine power.

Power and Range.

The speed for maximum endurance is not the speed to use when we wish to fly as far as possible. In other words, maximum endurance speed is not the **speed for maximum range**. To achieve maximum distance on a given quantity of fuel, we must fly at a speed which gives us the best <u>compromise</u> between speed and fuel consumption. This speed is that at which the ratio between **speed achievable** and **power required** is the least. **In order to find the speed at which the power/speed ratio is most favourable, a line is drawn from the origin of the axes of the power available - power required graph to touch the power required curve at a tangent** (*see Figure 4.4*). A vertical line dropped from the tangent to the curve, to intersect the horizontal axis, allows us to read **the speed for maximum range** directly. If the gradient of the straight line were to meet the curve at any other point than the tangent (it would then, of course, cut the power required curve in two places), the line would be steeper and, therefore, the **power/airspeed** ratio would be less favourable.

Though it is beyond the scope of this book, it can be shown that the **speed for maximum range** for any propeller-driven aircraft is also the **speed for minimum drag**, often represented as V_{MD}. **Minimum drag** occurs at the **best lift/drag ratio** with the aircraft flying at an angle of attack of about 4°.

You will note that the speed for maximum range (minimum drag), V_{MD}, is a little higher than the speed for maximum endurance (minimum power), V_{MP}.

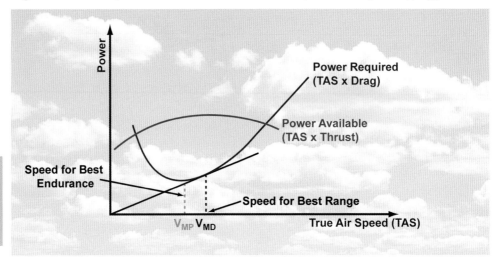

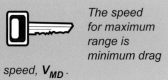

The speed for maximum range is minimum drag speed, V_{MD}.

Figure 4.4 The speed at which the aircraft achieves the most advantageous compromise between speed and power required is the speed for maximum range. This is also the speed for minimum drag.

FACTORS WHICH EFFECT FLYING FOR RANGE.

The key point about flying for **maximum range** in a propeller-driven aircraft is that the aircraft flies at the **speed for minimum drag**; that is, at the **speed and angle of attack for the most favourable lift/drag ratio**. This **angle of attack** is about **4°** in a typical general aviation aircraft, and, as we have seen, in the **PA28 Warrior**, the **speed for this angle of attack**, giving **best lift/drag ratio and maximum range**, is 75 kts. At this **speed and angle of attack**, the aircraft is flying at its most efficient, aerodynamically speaking.

There are **four principal factors** which affect an aircraft's **range** and **speed for maximum range**: **aircraft mass (weight)**, **aircraft configuration**, **altitude** and **wind speed and direction**. By aircraft **configuration** we mean whether the **flaps** and/or **undercarriage** are deployed or not. We will examine these four factors, one by one.

Aircraft Weight.

As we have seen, in order to achieve **maximum range** the aircraft must fly at the **speed for minimum drag**. It must also, however, fly at **minimum load**. If greater **load** is carried, the **maximum achievable range** will <u>decrease</u>, while the **speed** at which **the lower maximum range** is achieved will <u>increase</u>.

Increasing an aircraft's **weight** means that the wings of the aircraft must generate extra **lift** to support the higher **weight**. Consequently, as an aircraft's **weight** increases the aircraft must fly faster to maintain any given **angle of attack**, or it must fly at a greater **angle of attack** for any given **airspeed**.

An increase in **lift** at any speed results in an increase in **induced drag** at that speed. **More power** will be required to overcome the **extra drag**, the greater power will **raise fuel consumption**, and so **the best power required/speed ratio will be less favourable** at a higher aircraft weight than at a lower weight. **Consequently, maximum range will be less at the higher weight**.

On the other hand, the **angle of attack** for the best **lift/weight ratio** remains unaffected by **weight** and will remain at about **4°**. As we have just stated, **a heavier aircraft must fly faster to maintain a given angle of attack**. Therefore, **the speed for maximum achievable range will increase**.

The effect of increasing **weight** just described means that the **power required curve** in our graph moves up and to the right. The **speed for maximum range** is, as before, given by dropping a vertical line from the tangent to the **power required curve** formed by a straight line drawn from the origin of the graph's axes, and reading the new **maximum range (minimum drag) speed, V$_{MD}$**, from the horizontal axis. (*See Figure 4.5*.)

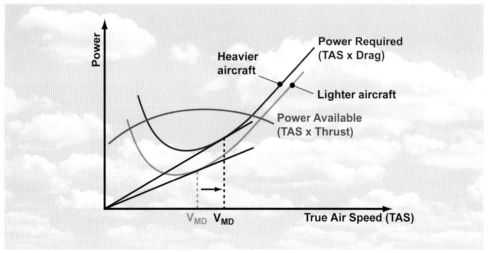

Figure 4.5 At higher weights, lift and drag increase and the power required to overcome the drag increases. The power required curve moves up and to the right. Maximum range decreases and the speed for best achievable maximum range increases.

Aircraft Configuration.

If **flaps** and/or **undercarriage** are deployed, there is a significant increase in **drag**. Considering **flaps** alone (most light aircraft having fixed undercarriages anyway), when they are lowered more **lift** and associated **drag** is generated at **lower speeds**.

Drag and **power required** are higher at all **speeds** because of the increase in the **coefficient of drag, C_D**, engendered by the change in the effective shape and camber of the wing cross section (aerofoil). Consequently, **the value of minimum drag will increase, and require increased power to balance that drag. Increased power means a higher rate of fuel consumption and a decrease in maximum range** compared to a more lightly loaded aircraft.

Selecting any angle of flap increases drag by a greater proportion than lift. Therefore, the best achievable lift/drag ratio will also be lower when flap is deployed.

The result of all the above considerations is that the **power required curve** moves upward and to the left, as shown in *Figure 4.6.*

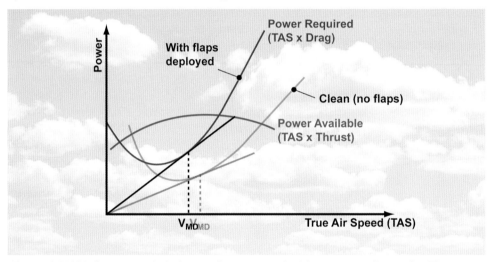

Figure 4.6 With flaps extended, drag and power required increase at all speeds. The power required curve moves up and to the right. Maximum range decreases and the speed for best achievable maximum range increases.

The **speed for maximum range** is, as before, given by dropping a vertical line from the tangent to the power required curve formed by a straight line drawn from the origin of the graph's axes, and reading the new **maximum range (minimum drag) speed, V_{MD}**, from the horizontal axis. You will see that the best attainable **power/speed ratio** is less favourable than for a "clean" aircraft, and that the speed which gives the best **power/speed ratio** (i.e. the speed for the **maximum attainable range**) is lower than for an aircraft with no **flap** deployed.

Altitude.
If we were considering the aircraft alone (i.e. its aerodynamic properties) and not the engine, we would get the same **maximum range** by flying at the same **indicated maximum range speed, (speed for best lift/drag ratio)** whatever **altitude** we flew at. **Indicated airspeed** is a function of **dynamic pressure** ($\frac{1}{2} \rho v^2$), and so is **drag**, so (still considering the aircraft only) as long as we flew at indicated **airspeed** for best **lift/drag ratio**, the **drag** would be the same. One might naturally think that the **power required** to overcome the **drag** at that **speed** would also be the same. However, the **power required is not the same. Power required is a function of true airspeed, not indicated airspeed**, and, as you know (see **Chapter 4** of **Principles of Flight**),

the higher an aircraft flies the greater is its true airspeed for a given indicated airspeed, and the greater the power required at that airspeed. Also, at the **higher altitude, air density is lower** which further **increases the power required** for level flight while **reducing the power available** from the engine.

In order to get the maximum range from an aircraft, both the aircraft and the engine must be operated to best advantage. It follows, then, that the correct **altitude** to fly is the **altitude** at which the **indicated minimum drag (maximum lift/ drag ratio) airspeed** is also the **true airspeed** which permits the engine-propeller combination to operate at its most efficient. This reasoning explains why some **Pilot's Operating Handbooks** (but not all) give an **altitude** alongside the aircraft's **maximum range speed**. If the aircraft is flown at higher **altitudes** than the optimum **altitude**, more and more **power** will be required to achieve the speed **for minimum drag (best lift/drag ratio).**

Therefore, to maximize range at high **altitude** we must either reduce **speed**, meaning we are using the aircraft less efficiently, aerodynamically speaking, or open the throttle fully (or maybe enrichen the mixture), meaning that we are using the engine uneconomically.

Consequently, for all aircraft there is a best altitude at which to fly for range. That **altitude** is determined by the efficiency of the engine-propeller combination, not by the aerodynamic properties of the aircraft which would be equally as efficient at all altitudes.

In practice, for light, piston-engine powered aircraft with a fixed-pitch propeller and without a supercharger, which tend to operate at low altitudes, the best height for maximum range at those low altitudes is not very critical.

Wind considerations are usually far more critical to a light aircraft's best achievable range.

Reducing air density reduces an aircraft's overall performance.

Maximum range speed is the speed for the best lift/drag ratio, unless flying at high altitude when power considerations have to be taken into account.

Effects of Wind on Range.
Wind of any **strength** and any **direction** will affect an aircraft's **range**.

When no **wind** is blowing; that is, when the **wind** is calm, an aircraft's **true airspeed** will be the same as its speed over the ground. Speed over the ground is known as **groundspeed**.

An aircraft flying with a the **wind** behind it, i.e. a **tailwind**, will have a higher **groundspeed** than an aircraft flying at the same **true airspeed** when no **wind** is blowing or if it is flying into a **headwind**. With a **tailwind**, the **speed of the wind** itself is added to the aircraft's **true airspeed** to give the aircraft's **groundspeed**. Consequently, with a **tailwind**, the aircraft is covering a greater distance for any given rate of fuel consumption, than if it were flying in calm conditions or against a **headwind**. **A tailwind, then, will increase an aircraft's range.**

An aircraft flying into a **headwind** will have a lower speed over the ground than an aircraft flying at the same **true airspeed** when the wind is calm, or if there is a **tailwind**. With a **headwind**, the **speed of the wind** itself is subtracted from the aircraft's **true airspeed** to give its **groundspeed**. Consequently, with a **headwind**, the aircraft is covering a smaller distance for any given rate of fuel consumption, than if it were flying in calm conditions or with a **tailwind**. **A headwind, then, will reduce an aircraft's range.**

When taking into consideration the effect of the **wind** on the fuel consumed over a given distance for a track that you have planned to fly on a cross-country route, you will very often find that the direction of the **wind** is such that it is blowing obliquely to your planned track, at a greater or lesser angle. A **crosswind** of this nature will mean that you will experience either a **headwind or tailwind component** when tracking along the ground. **Volume 3** of this series, **Navigation & Radio Aids**, teaches you how to take account of **crosswinds** to calculate your heading and **groundspeed**. **Wind strength and direction may change significantly over time and with altitude**. In flying cross-country, therefore, the pilot-navigator needs to be very aware of deviations in **wind strength and direction** from those forecast.

When flying into a headwind, the speed for maximum range will be a little higher than the speed derived from the power required – power available graph, and the speed given in the **Pilot's Operating Handbook**. The increased fuel consumption resulting from the higher power setting is compensated for by the fact that the higher speed will mean that less time is spent flying against the **headwind**, on the track concerned.

When flying with a tailwind, the speed for maximum range is lower than that given in the **Pilot's Operating Handbook**. The reduction in best range speed is lower so that the aircraft can benefit from the higher **groundspeed** and, at the same time, reduce fuel consumption. In a strong **tailwind**, the speed to choose for **maximum range** will probably be not far different from the speed for best endurance.

CRUISE PERFORMANCE GRAPHS.

In the **Pilot's Operating Handbook (POH)** for your aircraft, you will probably not find any theoretical treatment of flying the aircraft for **range** or **endurance**. The **POH** generally contains graphs of the type depicted in *Figures 4.7*, and *4.8*, allowing the pilot to carry out practical **range** and **endurance** calculations.

Endurance Graphs.
Figure 4.7 depicts a typical **endurance graph** for a light aircraft. The method of calculating **endurance** from the graph is similar to the method that you learnt in the previous chapter for extracting performance figures for the climb.

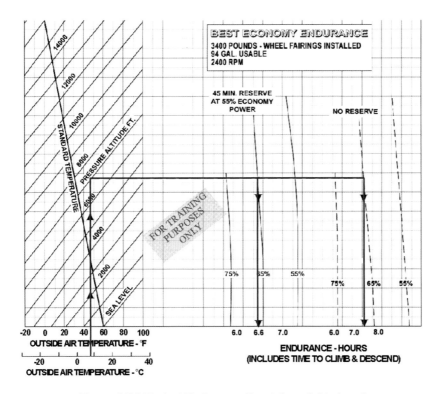

Figure 4.7 A Typical Endurance Graph for a light aircraft.

The red lines on the graph depict how **endurance** is extracted from the graph for a given set of atmospheric and aircraft parameters.

The example assumes that an aircraft is to cruise at a **pressure altitude of 7 000 feet** with an **outside air temperature of 7°C**. The power setting is assumed to be **2 400 revolutions per minute**, and the pilot wishes to have **45 minutes of reserve fuel** in his aircraft's tanks, at the end of the planned flight. Given these assumptions, *Figure 4.7* shows how the corresponding **endurance** is extracted from the graph. **Outside air temperature** and **pressure altitude** are entered at the left hand end of the graph by drawing a vertical line from the temperature scale to the curve representing the **pressure altitude**. A horizontal line is then drawn across to the curve representing **45 minutes reserve** (note that reserve figures assume the power setting to be **55% of maximum power**). A vertical line is dropped from this curve to cut the horizontal axis at a point which gives the aircraft's **endurance** in hours (**6.6 hours** in the example illustrated). The endurance given also takes into consideration the climb to height, and the descent.

Note that the example also shows that the **endurance with no reserves of fuel** would be approximately **7½ hours**.

Range Graphs.

Figure 4.8, below, depicts a typical **range graph** for a light aircraft. The method of calculating **range** from the graph is exactly the same as that used for the endurance graph.

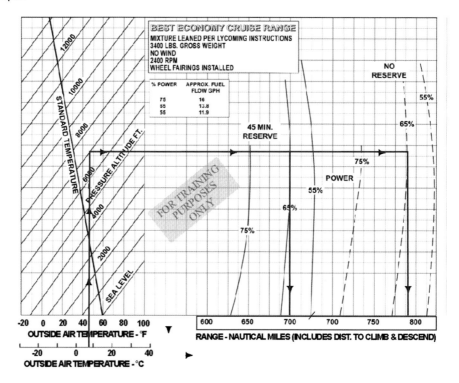

Figure 4.8 A typical range graph for a light aircraft.

The example assumes that an aircraft is to cruise at a **pressure altitude of 7 000 feet** with an **outside air temperature of 7°C** and **65% power** set.

You can see that, allowing for **45 minutes of reserve fuel**, the achievable range will be **700 nautical miles**, while, if **no reserve fuel** is assumed, the range will be **just over 780 nautical miles**.

When using **Cruise Performance Graphs**, be sure to follow the instructions in the **Pilot's Operating Handbook** carefully. Be sure, too, to take note of all the assumptions made in the calculations; the assumptions will most probably need to be taken into consideration to refine the figures extracted from the graphs.

THE DESCENT.

The descent may be regarded as the final part of the en-route of flight.

There are two ways of assessing the **descent performance** of an aircraft: **angle of descent**, sometimes called **descent range**, or **rate of descent**, sometimes called **descent endurance**.

Angle of Descent (Descent Range).

Figure 4.9 depicts an aircraft in level, cruising flight at constant speed, with the four principal flight forces in **equilibrium**. As you have learnt, one of the main conditions for level flight at constant speed is that **thrust** must balance **drag**.

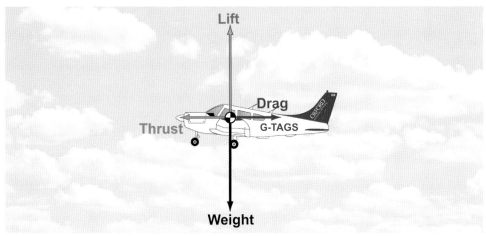

Figure 4.9 In straight and level flight at constant speed, the four principal flight forces are in equilibrium.

In order to initiate a **steady descent**, **thrust** is normally reduced by the pilot reducing power. **Drag** now exceeds **thrust**. In order to keep the flight forces in **equilibrium** and maintain **speed**, the nose of the aircraft must be lowered until the **forwards-acting component of the aircraft's weight** increases the forwards-acting forces to the point where the **aerodynamic drag** is again **balanced**. The aircraft is now descending at the same constant speed that it had in level flight, with all flight forces again in **equilibrium**.

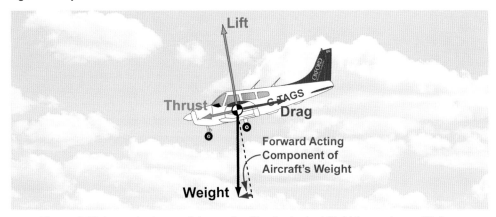

Figure 4.10 A constant-speed descent, with all principal flight forces in equilibrium.

79

If the pilot closes the throttle further, propeller **thrust** is again reduced, and the aircraft's nose must be lowered even more so that the **forwards-acting component of weight** can maintain the flight forces in **equilibrium** and maintain **speed**. This action will further steepen the descent angle. **In fact, the greater the margin of drag force over the thrust force, the greater will be the descent angle**.

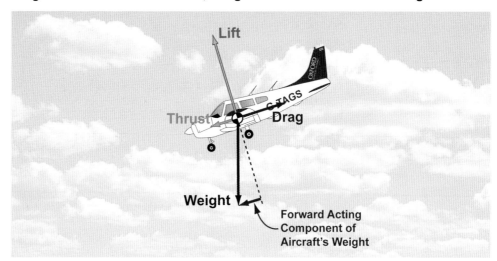

Figure 4.11 The more thrust is reduced, the greater must be the forward-acting component of weight in order to balance aerodynamic drag, and the steeper will be the descent required to maintain a given speed.

Obviously, to descend at a shallower descent angle while maintaining cruising speed, the pilot should reduce power by only a small amount. To descend more steeply while maintaining cruising speed, power should be reduced further.

Glide Angle.

Even though modern engines are extremely reliable, a pilot should always be prepared for an engine-failure. If an engine-failure should occur while on a cross-country flight, an important consideration for the pilot is that he should quickly identify a suitable field in which to land. In order to give himself the greatest chance of finding and reaching a suitable field, the pilot should aim to fly the aircraft at its best (shallowest) **glide angle**. By doing this, a greater distance will be covered, before the aircraft descends to ground level.

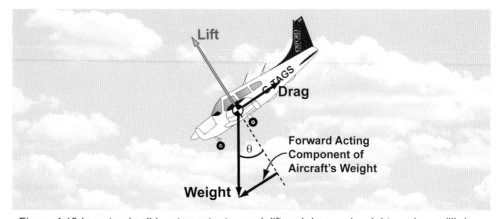

Figure 4.12 In a steady glide, at constant speed, lift and drag and weight are in equilibrium. The only propulsive force is the forward-acting component of the aircraft's weight.

When the engine fails, there is, of course, no thrust force produced by the propeller. So the only forces acting on an aircraft in the **glide**, following engine failure, are **lift**, **drag** and **weight**. **In a steady glide at constant speed, these three forces must be in equilibrium**. The **weight** of the aircraft is supported by the **resultant of the lift and drag** forces, and the only propulsive force acting on the aircraft is the **forwards-acting component of the weight force**. (*See Figure 4.12.*) **In a glide, at constant airspeed, this forwards-acting component of weight is equal and opposite to the aerodynamic drag.**

It is simple to prove mathematically that the angle θ between the **lift vector** and the **resultant of the lift and drag vectors** is equal to the **angle of glide** of the aircraft with respect to the ground, assuming zero wind.

Best glide performance is achieved by flying the aircraft at the speed for maximum lift/drag ratio.

The angle θ will be a minimum, and, therefore, the aircraft's glide angle shallowest (i.e. giving maximum range) when the ratio of lift to drag is highest.

Therefore an aircraft's best glide performance is achieved when it flies at the speed for the best lift/drag ratio.

Now, the **best lift/drag ratio** is achieved when **drag is a minimum** (lift having to remain constant). **So an aircraft's best angle of glide performance is achieved at the speed for minimum drag, V_{MD}.**

To achieve maximum gliding range the aircraft should be flown at minimum drag speed, V_{MD}.

On most light aircraft, the **speed for minimum drag** is achieved at an angle of attack of about **4°**. V_{MD} will be given in the **Pilot's Operating Handbook**. For the **PA28-161 Warrior**, V_{MD} is **75 knots**, giving a **maximum lift/drag ratio of 10:1** and a **best glide angle** of about **7°**.

In still air, then, from **3 000 feet** above ground level, a Warrior flying at its **best glide speed of 75 knots** would cover about **5 nautical miles**. You may remember that V_{MD} is also the speed for **maximum range in the cruise**, because at the **best lift/drag ratio** the wing is operating at its most efficient.

Factors Affecting Glide Angle.

Flaps.
Flaps increase drag at any speed. So lowering **flaps** will always degrade the **lift/drag ratio** and, thus, steepen the **glide angle**. **Flap**, then, must not be deployed when gliding for range, but deployment of **flap** is advantageous when the **glide** needs to be steepened, such as for the final approach to land.

Speed.
As we have just discussed, the **speed for minimum drag, V_{MD}**, in other words, the **speed for the best lift/drag ratio**, gives an aircraft its **best glide performance**. Flying faster than V_{MD} will steepen the glide angle. Flying slower than V_{MD} will also steepen the glide angle, because at speeds lower than V_{MD} the **lift/drag ratio** is less favourable. Therefore, when flying at V_{MD}, **never raise the nose to try to "stretch" the glide**. You will only steepen the **glide** by raising the nose and you may also cause the aircraft to stall. **Many accidents have been caused by attempting to "stretch" the glide.**

Flying at V_{MD}, best lift/drag ratio, gives an aircraft its shallowest glide angle. Flying at any other speed will steepen the glide. Therefore, when at V_{MD}, never raise the nose to try to stretch the glide.

Wind.

Wind has a significant effect on **glide angle and range.** *Figure 4.14* shows **descent angle** and **descent range** in conditions of **zero wind**, a **headwind** and a **tailwind.** In zero wind, given its **maximum lift/drag ratio** of **10:1**, a Warrior will glide approximately **5 nautical miles** from **3 000 feet** above ground level.

Angle of descent is measured relative to the volume of air in which the aircraft is flying. Consequently, **relative to the ground, a headwind steepens the glide angle** and **decreases gliding range.** In a **headwind the speed for best gliding range is increased slightly** to reduce the amount of time the aircraft remains exposed to the **headwind.** Conversely, **a tailwind will decrease the glide angle with respect to the ground and increase the gliding range. In a tailwind the speed for best glide is reduced slightly** to increase the aircraft's exposure to the beneficial effect of the **tailwind.**

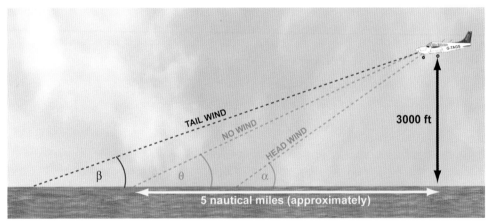

Figure 4.13 Headwind increases glide angle and decreases range. Tailwind decreases glide angle and increases range. With its 10:1 lift/drag ratio, clean, a Warrior will glide about 5 nm from a height of 3 000 feet.

THE EFFECT OF AIRCRAFT WEIGHT ON GLIDE ANGLE.

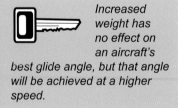

Increased weight has no effect on an aircraft's best glide angle, but that angle will be achieved at a higher speed.

Increasing an aircraft's weight has no effect on the glide angle. The **glide angle** is dependent only on the **lift/drag ratio** and is independent of **weight.** In a heavier aircraft (*see Figure 4.13*) there is an increase in both the **lift** and **drag** forces which act on the aircraft during the descent. But the <u>**ratio** of **lift to drag**</u>, and, hence, the **glide angle**, will remain the same. However, the increase in **lift** and **drag** required to balance a heavier aircraft's **weight** in the glide, can only be generated by an increase in **speed.** This higher **speed** is produced by the greater value of the **forwards-acting weight component. Thus, increased weight has no effect on an aircraft's best glide angle, but best glide is achieved at a higher speed.**

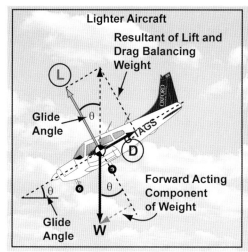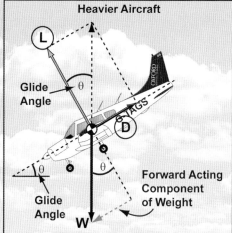

Figure 4.14 Weight has no effect on glide angle; glide angle depends on lift/drag ratio alone. However, a heavier aircraft will glide at a faster speed.

RATE OF DESCENT (DESCENT ENDURANCE).

The best way to consider **rate of descent** is to think of it as being the opposite to rate of climb.

You will recall that maximum rate of climb is achieved by flying at the speed at which the difference between the power required to maintain level flight and the thrust horsepower available from the engine-propeller combination is the greatest. At that speed, the maximum amount of excess power is available for climbing the aircraft, and flying at that speed with full power applied (full throttle for a fixed-pitch propeller) will give a pilot the maximum rate of climb.

The speed for best rate of climb, then, is the speed at which the difference between the power required for level flight and the power available from the engine is a maximum. This speed is known as V_{MD}. V_{MP}, for the **PA28-161 Warrior** is **65 knots**.

When an aircraft is descending at a given speed, it should be evident that more power is required at that speed for level flight than the engine is developing. The bigger the difference between the required power and the power the engine is developing, the greater is the rate of descent. Consequently, with the throttle closed, in order to keep this difference as small as possible we need to fly at the speed for minimum power. This speed is known as V_{MP}. Therefore, to maximise descent endurance (and achieve the maximum rate of descent) we must fly at V_{MP}.

You should note, however, that at any given descent airspeed, the desired rate of descent can be selected by the pilot by increasing or reducing power.

Note, too, that whereas wind has a significant effect on angle of descent, **wind has no effect on rate of descent**.

However, at a selected, constant airspeed in the descent, increasing and decreasing power will increase and decrease the angle of descent, respectively.

Representative PPL - type questions to test your theoretical knowledge of En - Route Performance.

1.   If the centre of gravity of an aircraft is moved rearwards, the effect is:

   a.   a stronger lift/weight couple which requires a greater tail-plane to maintain the aircraft in equilibrium
   b.   an increased range and endurance
   c.   a reduced range and endurance
   d.   a greater tail-load

2.   What speed must be flown to attain maximum cruise endurance?

   a. V_Y
   b.   Maximum Speed
   c. V_{MP}
   d. V_{MD}

3.   A wing contaminated by a small amount of ice will produce:

   a.   more weight and more lift
   b.   more drag, more weight and less lift
   c.   an increase in both lift and drag co-efficient
   d.   an increase in weight and decrease in drag

4.   When gliding for maximum range an aircraft with a greater weight will:

   a.   have a reduced glide range
   b.   have a shallower glide angle
   c.   have a faster gliding speed but the same glide angle
   d.   have a faster gliding speed and a reduced gliding range

5.   What speed, from *Figure 4.15*, should be flown for maximum range?

   a.   A
   b.   B
   c.   C
   d.   D

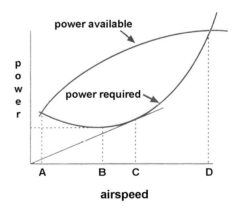

Figure 4.15 Power Curves for Q.5.

6.   The glide range will be maximised by flying at:

        a.   a relatively high angle of attack such as 10°
        b.   a relatively low angle of attack such as 4° which will give the best
                lift/drag ratio
        c.   a negative angle of attack
        d.   a high descent angle

7.   A pilot wishes to fly at a speed which will give him maximum range. He
        knows that he is flying in a tailwind. How will the speed selected by the
        pilot compare with the maximum range speed for still air quoted in the Flight
        Manual?

        a.   It will be decreased slightly
        b.   It will increased slightly
        c.   It will be the same as for still air
        d.   The speed will be greater by the value of the tailwind component

8.   What is the effect of a headwind on the glide angle and gliding range with
        respect to the ground?

        a.   Glide angle and glide range will remain the same as in still air
        b.   Glide angle and glide range will increase
        c.   Glide angle and glide range will decrease
        d.   Glide angle will increase and glide range decrease

9.   What is the maximum range speed for a piston engine aircraft?

        a. V_{MP}
        b. V_{MD}
        c.   At a lower speed than V_{MP}
        d.   At a speed less than V_{MD}

10.   The true airspeed of an aircraft which maintains a constant indicated airspeed
        will:

        a.   increase as altitude increase
        b.   remain constant as altitude increases
        c.   decrease as altitude increases
        d.   act unpredictably, as true airspeed has no connection with indicated
                airspeed

11. Examine the graph in *Figure 4.16*. Which of the speeds indicated by A, B, C or D should be flown for maximum endurance?

    a. A
    b. B
    c. C
    d. D

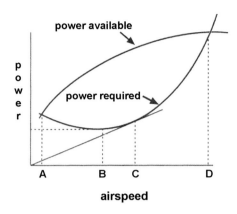

Figure 4.16 Power Curves for Q.11.

12. The Centre of Pressure of a given aircraft is aft of the aircraft's Centre of Gravity. During straight and level flight, any increase in the lift causing an imbalance in the equilibrium of forces is compensated for by:

    a. an upward force generated by the tailplane
    b. a downward force generated by the tailplane
    c. an increase in thrust
    d. a decrease in drag

13. Compared to gliding in still air, the effect of a tailwind will:

    a. increase the glide range but have no effect on the rate of descent
    b. decrease the glide angle and decrease the rate of descent
    c. have no effect on the glide range or the rate of descent
    d. increase the glide angle and increase the rate of descent

14. What would be the effect of an increase in temperature upon air density and aircraft performance?

    a. Increased density and reduced aircraft performance
    b. Increased density and increased aircraft performance
    c. Reduced density and an increase in aircraft performance
    d. Reduced density and reduced aircraft performance

15. In order to maximise glide range, the aircraft should be flown:

    a. at a high angle of attack to achieve V_Y
    b. at a low angle of attack to achieve V_{MP}
    c. at a negative angle of attack to achieve V_X
    d. at a low angle of attack to achieve V_{MD}

16.   What speed must be flown to attain maximum cruise range?

        a. V_X
        b.   Maximum speed
        c. V_{MD}
        d. V_{MP}

17.   If weight is increased, the range of the aircraft will be:

        a.   reduced
        b.   unchanged
        c.   increased
        d.   increased unless lift can be reduced

18.   An aircraft has a best lift/drag ratio of 9:1. What is the maximum distance it
        could glide from 4 000 ft above ground level, in zero wind conditions?

        a.   6 nautical miles approximately
        b.   7 nautical miles approximately
        c.   18 nautical miles approximately
        d.   9 nautical miles approximately

Question	1	2	3	4	5	6	7	8	9	10	11	12
Answer												

Question	13	14	15	16	17	18
Answer						

The answers to these questions can be found at the end of this book.

CHAPTER 5
LANDING

LANDING DISTANCE.

The **landing distance required** for an aircraft to touch down safely is measured from a point where the aircraft is **50 ft** above the threshold to the point at which the aircraft is bought to a full stop. (*See Figure 5.1.*)

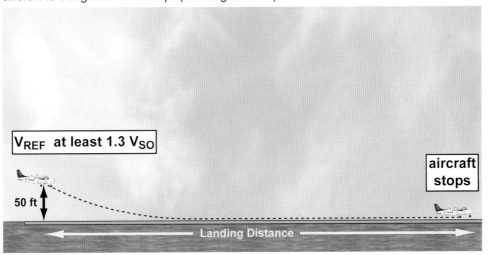

Figure 5.1 Landing Distance is measured from the 50 feet screen height to the point in the landing run where the aircraft is bought to a full stop.

The **50 feet** point is referred to as the **landing screen height** which is similar to the take off screen height. In the definition of **landing distance**, it is assumed that, at the **landing screen height**, the aircraft is flying at a reference speed, V_{REF}, of at least **1.3 times the aircraft's stalling speed**. V_{REF} gives the aircraft a **30%** margin of safety over its stalling speed, in the landing configuration. The stall speed in the landing configuration, with flaps lowered, is known as V_{SO}. So, if V_{SO} is **50 knots**, V_{REF} is **30%** greater than this; that is **65 knots**.

V_{REF} must be achieved, but excess speed on the approach will increase the landing distance required.

Pilots must be aware that although V_{REF} must be at least $1.3 \times V_{SO}$, if the speed exceeded V_{REF} significantly, the **landing distance** would also be increased by a significant margin. It is very important that a pilot should determine the correct approach speed for the conditions, and fly that speed as accurately as possible.

The Landing Distance Available.

The **landing distance** that an aircraft **requires** must not exceed the **landing distance available**. The **landing distance available (LDA)** at an airfield is defined as being **the length of runway suitable for landing**, taking into account any obstacles in the approach path. Usually, the **LDA** is the distance from one threshold of the runway to the other. (*See Figure 5.2, overleaf.*)

In a typical landing, landing flaps will have been selected at a suitable point on the approach, and with an airspeed of at least V_{REF} at the **50 feet screen height**, the throttle will normally have been closed. By following this procedure, the **landing distance required** will be kept to a minimum. There are, however, several factors which affect **landing distance required**, which we will now go on to examine.

Figure 5.2 The Landing Distance Available (LDA) at an airfield is defined as being the length of runway suitable for landing.

FACTORS AFFECTING THE LANDING.

Aircraft Mass.

Increased **mass** means that for any given true airspeed, the **momentum** of the aircraft will also be higher (**momentum = mass × velocity**). A body's **momentum** is often defined as a measure of how much **force** is required to stop the body moving. Therefore, **the higher an aircraft's momentum the greater the braking force required to bring the aircraft to rest.** As **braking force** is a function of the aircraft's brake assembly and is constant for any given set of runway conditions, **the greater the aircraft's mass, the longer will be the period of time during which the braking force must be applied and the longer will be the landing distance required**.

As you learnt in **Principles of Flight**, the greater the aircraft's **mass**, the greater will be its **weight**. You have also learnt that **the heavier an aircraft is, the higher will be its stall speed**. Therefore, as approach speed needs to be at least **1.3** times V_{SO}, a heavier aircraft will need to approach and touch down at a higher speed than a lighter aircraft. As we mentioned above, **momentum = mass × velocity**, so **the higher speed will impart greater momentum to the aircraft and increase the landing distance required**.

Of course, the heavier the aircraft, the greater will be the **load** acting on the undercarriage rolling assembly and the greater will be the **rolling resistance** once the aircraft is on the ground. However, this one beneficial effect on landing performance of increased **mass** or **weight** does not affect the aircraft anywhere near as much as its increased **momentum**.

The overall effect of increasing an aircraft's mass or weight, then, is to increase the landing distance required. As a rule of thumb, we may assume that the **landing distance required** increases by **10%** for every **10%** increase in the aircraft's **mass**. As a practical guide, for a light aircraft, a **10%** increase in **mass** equates approximately to carrying an extra passenger with luggage.

Reducing **mass** will, by counter argument, shorten the **landing distance required**.

The Landing Distance Available is the length of runway suitable for landing, taking into account any obstacles in the approach path.

Increased aircraft mass means increased momentum, increased V_{REF} and increased landing distance.

A 10% increase in aircraft mass will increase Landing Distance Required by 10%.

Air Density.

As you have learned from the **lift equation** in **Principles of Flight, Lift = C$_L$ ½ ρv^{2}S**, **lift** is directly proportional to **air density**, ρ. Thus, a decrease in **air density** will also decrease **lift**, and, for the reasons given below, lead to an increase in the **landing distance required**.

Air density, you will recall, decreases with increasing altitude and increasing temperature.

In lower air density, lift is reduced at any given value of true airspeed, v. Consequently, in order to maintain the **lift** necessary to support the aircraft in steady flight, whether that be straight and level flight or descending flight, such as on the approach to land, an aircraft will have to fly at a higher **true airspeed as air density** falls. Increased **speed** increases an aircraft's **momentum**, making it more difficult to stop, and, therefore, also increases, increasing the **landing distance required**.

You should be aware that it is particularly difficult for the pilot to detect conditions of low **air density**. **True airspeed, v**, must increase to maintain **lift** when **air density falls**; **indicated airspeed** is not affected by changing **air density**, being a measure of the **dynamic pressure**, ½ ρv^2. As ρ falls, **v** increases so that the expression, ½ ρv^2, remains constant, giving a constant **indicated airspeed**. Consequently, the pilot will get no clue from his **airspeed indicator** that **air density** is low.

In order, then, that a pilot may recognise that **air density** is low and, thus, be ready and prepared for longer **landing distances**, he needs to know what the **density altitude** is of the airfield from which he is operating. However, if he uses a **landing performance graph** to calculate the **landing distance required** for his aircraft, on a given day, he enters **pressure altitude** and **temperature** into the graph. As we learnt earlier in the chapter on **Take-Off**, these two factors used together will account for **air density**. But if a pilot has no access to **landing performance graphs** for his aircraft, he may calculate the **density altitude** of the airfield using a **flight navigation computer**. That calculation will tell the pilot whether or not **air density** is of a significantly high or low level. If **density altitude** is significantly different from the **pressure altitude** of the airfield, then the manufacturer's predicted **landing performance** will have to be modified.

For every 1 000 ft increase in altitude or 10ºC increase in temperature landing distance required will increase by approx 5%, or a factor of 1.05.

The drag equation, **Drag = C$_D$ ½ ρv^{2}S**, might <u>suggest</u> that if **air density** is low, the drag force acting on the aircraft will also be lower. However, although, in conditions of low **air density**, the aircraft lands at a higher **true airspeed**, for the reasons explained above, the **indicated airspeed**, a function of ½ ρv^2, will be the same whatever the density, because the reduction in ρ is compensated for by the increase in **v**. So, the **drag** force acting on the aircraft during the landing roll will also be the same. Only the higher **true airspeed** is critical; **so the longer landing run is the result solely of the increased momentum of the aircraft.**

High **humidity** also decreases **air density**. Therefore, **if you are operating from a hot, humid, high airfield, be aware of the effect of the prevailing conditions on your aircraft's performance.** For every **1 000 ft** increase in **altitude**, or **10°C** increase in **temperature**, **landing distance** will increase by approximately **5%**; that is, by a factor of **1.05**.

A headwind will decrease the landing distance required and a tailwind increase it. When applying wind to landing distance calculations, it is recommended that only 50% of a headwind should be assumed, but 150% of a tailwind.

Wind, Speed and Direction.

The speed and direction of the **wind** affects **landing distance required** because of the influence of **head and/or tailwind components**, on the ground speed of the aircraft. Just as for the take-off, it is essential that, when calculating **landing distance required**, the pilot calculates the strength of the **head and/or tailwind component** of the wind.

Headwinds will reduce the ground speed for any given indicated air speed and consequently reduce the landing distance required. Tailwinds, on the other hand, will increase ground speed for a given indicated air speed and increase the landing distance required.

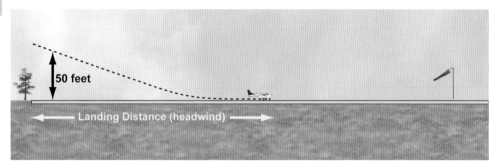

Figure 5.3a A landing with headwind.

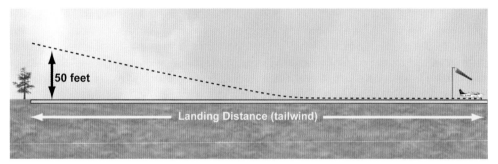

Figure 5.3b A landing with a tailwind.

Any tailwind component will significantly increase the landing distance required, so you must consider very carefully indeed whether a landing can safely be carried out, whenever a **tailwind component** is present. When calculating the **landing distance required**, it is highly recommended by the Civil Aviation Authority that you do not use the reported or observed, momentary **wind strengths** because **wind speed and direction** can vary greatly over a short time. The recommendation is to use **50% of the headwind component** and not less than **150% of the tailwind component**. Many performance graphs have these safety factors already applied.

There are two principal reasons why, whenever possible, the final approach and landing is made **into wind**. As you have already learnt, when landing **into wind**, the **ground speed** will be lower for a given touchdown **airspeed** by an amount equal to **the speed of the headwind component**. In this situation, **the landing distance required will be shorter**. Furthermore, an approach **into wind** gives a **steeper descent path** which, in turn, provides **better obstacle clearance performance**, and will reduce the **horizontal distance covered** during the **round-out and hold-off**. **Both these considerations reduce the overall landing distance required.**

Wind Gradient.

A landing, then, should wherever possible be made **into wind**. However, in **strong and turbulent wind conditions** a pilot must be aware of the effect of **wind gradient** on the performance of his aircraft. As far as the landing is concerned, the term **wind gradient** can be taken to mean *the progressive decrease in wind speed in the lower layers of air near the ground*. **Wind gradient** is most pronounced when a **strong, gusting wind** is blowing, especially if it is passing over **surface obstacles**. However, **wind gradients** may be present in light winds, too.

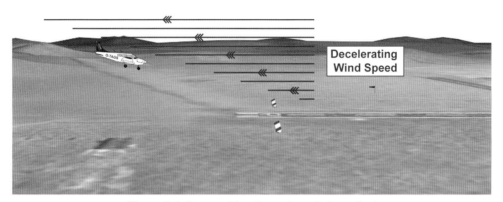

Figure 5.4 Approaching through a wind gradient.

Consequently, when an aircraft is approaching to land in a pronounced **wind gradient**, it is flying through layers of **decelerating wind speed**. (*See Figure 5.4.*) In this situation, the aircraft may suffer a sudden **reduction in indicated air speed**, and, therefore, **lift**, which will cause it to **lose height** suddenly. Sometimes, in very turbulent conditions, this **wind gradient** effect may be accentuated by the presence of downdraughts. Obviously, if the increase in **vertical descent speed** suffered by the aircraft were to occur unexpectedly, the aircraft may **undershoot** the runway badly and hit the ground firmly, causing damage to its structure and injury to its occupants.

So, if you suspect that **wind gradient** is present on the approach**, increase your approach speed** by a suitable amount (seek guidance from your instructor on this) and consider using **power** to arrest the extra rate of descent as the aircraft starts to sink. **Wind gradients** are invisible, but may be expected to be significant in **strong, gusting winds**. Often, pilots who have experienced a **wind gradient** will broadcast that fact over the RT, so listen out carefully for such reports when the wind is strong.

Runway Slope.
If a landing strip is not horizontal, the landing distance required will be affected.

An **uphill slope** to a landing strip will **decrease the landing distance required** because, when rolling uphill, a **component of the aircraft's weight acts rearwards, adding to the braking forces** acting on the aircraft. (*See Figure 5.5.*)

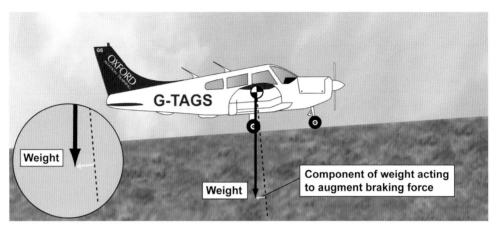

Figure 5.5 Upslope reduces the landing distance required owing to a component of the aircraft's weight acting backwards to augment braking.

Conversely, a **down-hill slope** to a landing strip will **increase the landing distance required** because, when rolling downhill, **a component of the aircraft's weight acts forwards, partially counteracting the braking forces** (rolling resistance and application of brakes) acting on the aircraft (*See Figure 5.6.*)

A down slope increases the landing distance required by 5% for every 1% of slope.

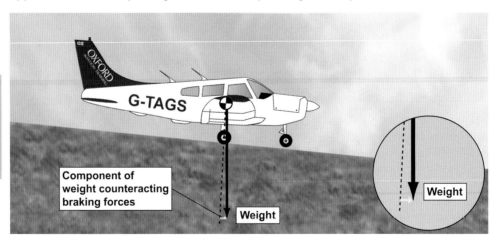

Figure 5.6 Downslope increases the landing distance required owing to a component of the aircraft's weight acting forwards, acting against the braking force.

For every **1%** of **down-slope**, the landing distance required is **increased** by approximately **5%**; in other words, landing distance is increased by a factor of **1.05**. Bear in mind that this is the factor which should be applied to the **landing <u>distance</u>**, that is, from a height of **50 feet** above the landing strip. The increase in the **landing run** will be proportionally greater.

Pilots should treat as a "bonus" any advantage gained from **landing on an up-slope** or **taking off on a down-slope**, and not include any allowance for these two latter circumstances in their performance calculations.

Runway Surface.

Most landing performance graphs assume that the aircraft is landing on a paved hard surface. If the surface of the landing strip is not paved, corrections must be applied to the calculated **landing distance required**.

Many small airfields have grass runways. Grass will increase the rolling resistance of the wheels, but, <u>more importantly</u>, will **<u>reduce</u>** the friction between the tyres and runway. This means that the brakes cannot be applied as firmly as on a paved surface, otherwise the wheels will lock and slip. Consequently, assuming that the wheel brakes are always used, landing on a grass surface will increase the **landing distance required**.

Dry grass of up to **8 inches (20 cm)** in height will increase the **landing distance** by **20%** or a factor of **1.2**, if brakes are used. However, assuming that brakes are not used, landing on grass will shorten the **landing run** and, thus, reduce the overall **landing distance required**, compared to landing on an asphalt surface without brakes.

A wet surface, either grass or paved, will reduce the **friction** between the wheels and the surface, preventing effective braking and increasing the **landing distance required**.

The following approximate factors will help you estimate the effect of different surfaces on **landing distance required**:

- On a **wet hard surface** the landing distance will be increased by **15%**, a factor of **1.15**.

- **Short dry grass** will increase the landing distance by **15%**, a factor of **1.15**, assuming that brakes are used.

- **Wet grass** will increase landing distance by **35%**, a factor of **1.35**.

- If there is **surface snow or slush**, the landing distance will increase by approximately **25%**, which is a factor of **1.25**.

A wet paved surface will increase the landing distance required by 15%, dry grass up to 20 cm by 20%, wet grass up to 20 cm by 35% and soft ground, snow or slush by 25%.

Use of Flap.

As you have learnt elsewhere, both in **Performance** and **Principles of Flight**, the **deployment of flap increases the total drag** acting on an aircraft, thereby **decreasing the lift/drag ratio**. Both these effects of flap influence the **landing distance required**.

The extent to which the use of **flap** increases **total drag** depends on the **angle of flap** selected.

The **drag equation (Drag = ½ C_D½ ρv^2 S)** shows us that **drag is directly proportional to C_D**. C_D, as you have learnt, is a measure, among other things, of **aerofoil profile** and **angle of attack**. Lowering **flap** modifies the **profile of the**

aerofoil, and will therefore alter the value of C_D. In general, then, we may conclude that **drag is proportional to the amount of flap selected**. Furthermore, because **lift** must remain constant for a given aircraft on a given flight (ignoring the change in weight resulting from fuel consumption), **as drag increases, the lift/drag ratio will decrease, and, in the approach at any given power setting, the descent angle will be steeper**.

If the pilot selects a large angle of **flap**, then, the increase in **drag** will be large, and, at a given power setting on the approach, or on a glide approach, the **descent angle** will be steeper. **The steeper descent angle, together with the high drag during the ground run, will shorten the landing distance required.** The steeper **descent angle** will, of course, also improve **obstacle clearance performance**.

In addition, lowering **flap** will reduce the aircraft's straight flight **stalling speed**; so both V_{SO} and the **50 feet** airspeed V_{REF} will be lower, resulting in a decrease in the aircraft's **momentum** and a consequent further shortening of the **landing run**.

It follows, then, that the smaller the angle of **flap** deployed, the lower will be the **drag** acting on the aircraft, the better the **lift/drag ratio**, the shallower the **descent angle**, the lower the **obstacle clearance performance**, the higher the **airspeeds** V_{SO} and V_{REF}, and, consequently, the longer the **landing distance required**.

Figures 5.7, 5.8 and *5.9* depict the different **angles of descent** on the **approach** and the differences in the **landing distance required** for an **approach** flown with a **large angle of flap**, a **small angle of flap**, and **no flap**, respectively. In each case, we have assumed that the aircraft achieves the **50 feet screen height** correctly. You can see, however, that if an approach into a field were necessary, following an engine failure, the use of **flap** would increase the aircraft's **obstacle clearance capability**.

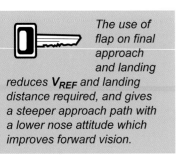

The use of flap on final approach and landing reduces V_{REF} and landing distance required, and gives a steeper approach path with a lower nose attitude which improves forward vision.

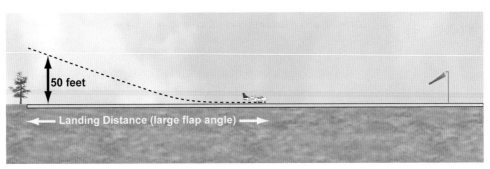

Figure 5.7 A landing with a large angle of flap selected.

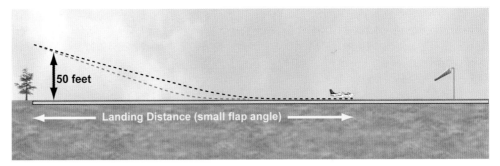

Figure 5.8 A landing with a small angle of flap selected.

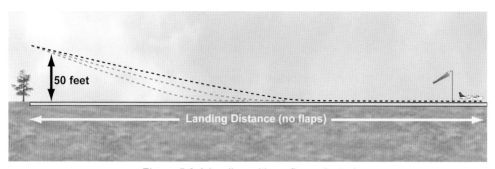

Figure 5.9 A landing with no flap selected.

It is always advisable for the pilot to land using the manufacturer's recommended **landing flap** setting for the aircraft.

The extension of **flap**, generally, requires a **lower nose attitude** for a given speed, which has the added advantage of giving the pilot a better view of the landing area during the approach. However, the effect of **flap** may vary significantly from one aircraft to another.

Calculations of Landing Distance Required.

Landing performance data may be presented in the form of **tables** or **graphs**. **Tables** are straight forward to interpret and if you have followed the examples we have used in the previous sections, you will have no trouble extracting data from a **landing distance required** table.

The most common form in which **landing performance data** is to be found, in an aircraft's **Flight Manual** or **Pilot's Operating Handbook**, is the **landing distance graph**, such as the one for the **PA-28-161 Warrior** depicted in *Figure 15.10, overleaf*.

Figure 5.9a An airfield with a grass runway. By kind permission of David Henson

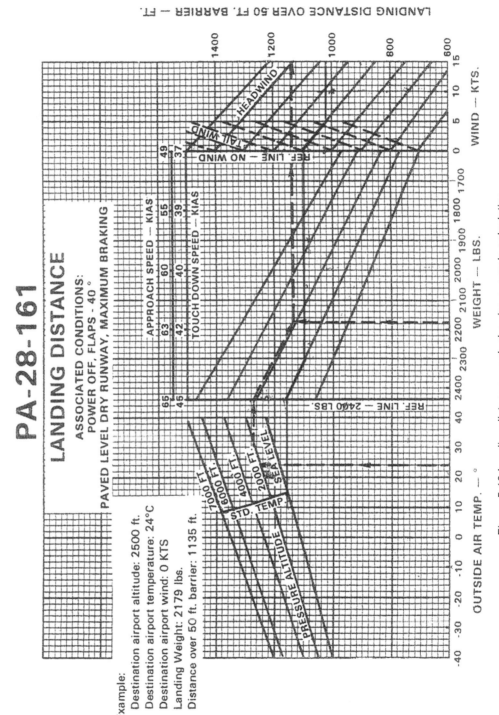

Figure 5.10 Landing distance graph showing example calculation.

You can read from the **associated conditions** box at the head of the graph (also shown at *Figure 5.11*) that the parameters which must be assumed when using the **graph** to calculate **landing distance required** are that the **approach** will be flown with **power off** (from the **50 feet** reference point) and with **40⁰ of flap**. It is further assumed that the landing will be on a **dry, level, paved runway** and that the pilot will use **maximum braking** during the **landing run**.

PA-28-161
LANDING DISTANCE
ASSOCIATED CONDITIONS: **POWER OFF, FLAPS - 40°** **PAVED LEVEL DRY RUNWAY, MAXIMUM BRAKING**

Figure 5.11 Associated Conditions to be assumed when using the Landing Distance Graph.

If the **associated conditions** are not present at the airfield at which the landing is to be made, or if the pilot selects a different **angle of flap**, or does not select **idle power** at the **50 feet** point, the figures extracted from the **graph** will have to be modified to allow for those deviations from these assumed conditions.

The graph at *Figure 15.10* allows the pilot to calculate the **landing distance required** for approaches flown in accordance with the stated **associated conditions**, for different **pressure altitudes, outside air temperatures, approach and touchdown speeds, aircraft weights** and **wind conditions**.

Example of Calculations of Landing Distance Required.
Let us now carry out an example calculation, as a pilot might wish to do before landing at an airfield with which he is unfamiliar and for which he wishes to compare the **landing performance** of his aircraft against the **landing distance available**.

After checking all the information available from official publications or flight guides concerning his destination aerodrome and obtaining a **weather forecast** for the estimated time of arrival (ETA), the pilot discovers that the following conditions will prevail.

Pressure Altitude of Destination Aerodrome:	500 feet
Surface Air Temperature at ETA:	10° Celsius
Expected Headwind Component at ETA on Runway-In-Use:	5 knots

With the above information and, with the knowledge that the **weight** of our aircraft on landing will be **2 300 lb**, we are now ready to begin our calculation of the **landing distance we will require** on arrival at our destination.

Examining the **landing distance graph**, we see that an example calculation has already been carried out, and that there are dotted vertical and horizontal lines on the graph, which illustrate the manufacturer's example. If we are unsure about how to use the graph, we can work through the manufacturer's sample example, but let us assume that we are already happy about the method to apply, and so we begin. In *Figure 5.10*, our use of the graph is marked by red lines.

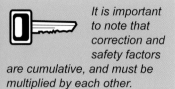

It is important to note that correction and safety factors are cumulative, and must be multiplied by each other.

On the left-hand side of the graph, we locate the horizontal **temperature scale** at the foot of the graph and draw a vertical line from the **10⁰ C** mark until it meets a point among the **pressure altitude lines** corresponding to **500 feet**: the **pressure altitude** of our destination airfield. There is no **500 feet line**, so we have to interpolate, choosing a suitable point between the **sea-level** and **2 000 feet** lines.

We then draw a horizontal line from the **500 feet** point to the next **vertical reference line** which marks the beginning of the **weight/approach/touchdown speed** section of the graph. From that reference line, we extend our line parallel to the slope of the nearest **weight-line** down to a point which corresponds to our expected **landing weight of 2 300 lbs**, read from the horizontal scale at the foot of the graph.

We note, reading vertically upwards to the **approach and touchdown speed scales**, that the speed at which we should fly our approach, at our landing weight of **2 300 lb**, is **64 knots**, as near as makes no difference, and that out touchdown speed should be **43 knots**.

Drawing, now, a further horizontal line towards the **vertical reference line** which marks the beginning of the **wind section of the graph**, we extend our line parallel to the nearest **downwards-sloping headwind line** to a point which corresponds to **5 knots** on the horizontal scale at the foot of the graph.

From that point we conclude the graph part of our calculation by drawing a horizontal line to meet the vertical scale at the extreme right-hand side of the graph which gives the **landing distance required**. We read from that scale that the **landing distance that we require is 1020 feet**. We note that this distance is the **horizontal distance** from the **50 feet screen height**, assuming a V_{REF} of **64 knots** at that height, to the point on the landing strip where, after applying brakes, we should come to a stop, provided all of the **associated conditions** apply.

Finally, we complete the calculation for our particular flight by applying any **correction factors** which must be applied to allow for any deviation from the **associated conditions**. For instance, if the surface of the landing strip was **short dry grass**, we would need to multiply **1 020 feet** by **1.15** to give us **1 173 feet**, and if the strip also had a **2% down slope in the landing direction**, we would have to multiply **1 265 feet** by **1.10** to give **1 290 feet**. (Note that when more than one correction factor applies, each new factor requires a further multiplication.) If other conditions prevailed, for instance, if the landing surface were wet, further factors would have to be applied.

The last action of all which should be taken is to multiply whatever answer we have arrived at by the **recommended overall safety factor of 1.43 for the landing**, to account for the fact that the graph's data assumes ideal conditions, a new and perfectly maintained aircraft, flown by an expert pilot. So, if we were landing on a **dry, short-grass strip with a 2% down-slope**, we would multiply **1290 feet** by **1.43** to give us a net **landing distance required** of **1 845 feet**.

This is the distance we must compare with the Landing Distance Available at our destination airfield.

If the **landing distance available** does not provide a generous safety margin over and above the calculated **landing distance required**, make sure that you set your

aiming point appropriately for the **approach**, that you maintain your **aiming point** correctly throughout the **approach**, and that you keep to the recommended **approach speed**. If you misjudge your **approach** make an early decision to go around.

Conclusion.

Whatever the phase of flight, but especially on **take-off** and **landing**, it is of crucial importance that pilots be aware of the **performance capabilities and limitations** of their aircraft. Many performance-related accidents have occurred where aircraft fail to get airborne on take-off, collide with obstacles on the climb-out, or overrun the runway on landing. Inevitably, such accidents are most likely to occur at small, grass airfields, especially if the strip in use is wet and/or soft, with a pronounced slope, and on a day when there is zero headwind component, or a tailwind component, on the runway-in-use.

Unless the dimensions of an airstrip, the prevailing conditions and the nature of the terrain surrounding the airfield are such that there is absolutely no doubt whatsoever that you can take-off and/or land with a healthy margin for error, you must carry out the **appropriate performance calculation** using the graphs in the **Pilot's Operating Handbook (POH)**, applying all the **correction and safety factors** that you have learnt about in this and the preceding chapters.

Remember that, when several correction factors apply to the performance data extracted from graphs, every applicable factor involves a further multiplication being made to your landing distance required.

Always apply the **overall safety factors**, **1.33 for take-off and 1.43 for landing**, which are mandatory for public transport flights and strongly recommended for general aviation flights. These **overall safety factors** are designed to take into account **a pilot's inexperience** or **lack of currency**, **the age and condition of the aircraft**, and **less than favourable ambient conditions**.

Finally, before using the performance figures contained in the **POH**, always check whether any **CAA Change Sheets and/or Supplements** instruct that modifications of the **POH performance data** apply.

Representative PPL - type questions to test your theoretical knowledge of Landing Performance.

1.   What effect would a 2% down-slope have on the landing distance required?

        a.   Increase it by 5%
        b.   Decrease it by 5%
        c.   Increase it by 10%
        d.   Decrease it by 10%

2.   Compared to a level runway, what would be the effect of landing on a downward sloping runway?

        a.   The landing performance will improve
        b.   The landing distance will be decreased
        c.   The landing distance will be increased
        d.   The landing distance will be unaffected

3.   Landings are carried out into wind because:

        a.   it increases the ground speed and reduces the landing distance required
        b.   it decreases the ground speed and reduces the landing distance available
        c.   it gives the pilot greater control over the aircraft at lower speeds..
        d.   it will reduce the ground speed and reduce the landing distance required

4.   If the stalling speed in the landing configuration is 55 knots, V_{REF} would be approximately:

        a.   65 knots
        b.   75 knots
        c.   71 knots
        d.   69 knots

5.   If the aircraft mass is increased by 15%, the landing distance required will increase by approximately:

        a.   15%, or a factor of 1.15
        b.   33%, or a factor of 1.33
        c.   10%, or a factor of 1.1
        d.   20%, or a factor of 1.2

6.   Why is flap used for landing?

      a.   The approach speed is increased and a flatter approach path is flown which improves forward vision

      b.   The approach speed is reduced and a steeper approach path is flown which improves forward vision

      c.   The approach speed is reduced and a flatter approach path is flown which improves forward vision

      d.   The approach speed is increased and a steeper approach path is flown which improves forward vision

7.   If the approach and landing speeds flown in an actual landing are higher than the speeds recommended in the aircraft manual, the effect will be that:

      a.   the landing distance will be increased

      b.   the landing distance will be decreased

      c.   the landing performance will improve

      d.   the landing distance will be unaffected

8.   The V_{REF} to be achieved by the landing screen height of 50 feet must be:

      a.   1.15 times the stalling speed in the take off configuration

      b.   1.3 times the stalling speed in the landing configuration

      c.   1.43 times the stalling speed in the landing configuration

      d.   33% of the stalling speed

9.   When landing, if an aircraft's indicated airspeed is lower than its true ground speed, then the aircraft is experiencing:

      a.   a tailwind

      b.   a headwind

      c.   increased atmospheric pressure

      d.   a 90° cross wind

10 .   What is the effect of an increase in mass on the stalling speed and landing distance required?

      a.   Increased stalling speed and decreased landing distance

      b.   Decreased stalling speed and decreased landing distance

      c.   Increased stalling speed and increased landing speed

      d.   Decreased stalling speed and increased landing distance

Question	1	2	3	4	5	6	7	8	9	10
Answer										

The answers to these questions can be found at the end of this book.

JAR-FCL PPL THEORETICAL KNOWLEDGE SYLLABUS
FLIGHT PERFORMANCE AND PLANNING.

The table below contains the principal topics and subtopics from the current outline syllabus for the theoretical examination in **Flight Performance and Planning** for the **Private Pilot's Licence**, as published in **JAR-FCL 1**. In this book, **Flight Performance and Planning** is covered in the section **Aeroplane Performance**. Syllabuses may be modified, so always check the latest examination documentation from your **national civil aviation authority**, or from **JAR-FCL/EASA**.

In the United Kingdom, **Flight Performace and Planning** is examined in the same paper as **Mass & Balance**.

FLIGHT PERFORMANCE AND PLANNING	
PERFORMANCE	
Take-off:	take-off run and distance available; take-off and initial climb; effects of mass, wind and density altitude; effects of ground surface and gradient; use of flaps.
Landing:	effects of mass, wind, density altitude and approach speed; use of flaps; ground surface and gradient.
In flight:	relationship between power required and power available; performance diagram; maximum rate and maximum angle of climb; range and endurance; effects of configuration, mass, temperature and altitude; reduction of performance during climbing turns; gliding; adverse effects (icing, rain; condition of the airframe; effect of flap).

ANSWERS TO THE AEROPLANE PERFORMANCE QUESTIONS

Chapter 1   *Introduction*

No Questions

Chapter 2   *Take-Off*

Question	1	2	3	4	5	6	7	8	9	10	11	12
Answer	a	c	a	c	d	b	b	c	d	d	a	b

Chapter 3   *Climb*

Question	1	2	3	4	5	6	7	8	9	10	11	12
Answer	b	b	d	c	d	c	d	a	b	c	a	d

Question	13
Answer	a

Chapter 4   *En-Route Performance*

Question	1	2	3	4	5	6	7	8	9	10	11	12
Answer	c	c	b	c	c	b	a	d	b	a	b	b

Question	13	14	15	16	17	18
Answer	a	d	d	c	a	a

Chapter 5   *Landing*

Question	1	2	3	4	5	6	7	8	9	10
Answer	c	c	d	c	a	b	a	b	a	c

Index

AERPOLANE PERFORMANCE INDEX